CHEMICAL RELAXATION

CHEMICAL RELAXATION

An Introduction to Theory and
Application of Stepwise Perturbation

GEORGE H. CZERLINSKI

UNIVERSITY OF PENNSYLVANIA
PHILADELPHIA, PENNSYLVANIA

1966

MARCEL DEKKER Inc., New York

MARCEL DEKKER, INC.

95 Madison Avenue, New York, New York 10016

LIBRARY OF CONGRESS CATALOG CARD NUMBER 66–16501

PRINTED IN THE UNITED STATES OF AMERICA

PREFACE

Since chemical relaxation is still a new area and very much in a state of flux, it is rather difficult to write a comprehensive book on this subject. The scope of this monograph, therefore, is limited to an introductory treatment. Such limitations lead to some arbitrariness in the selection of material, and it is unavoidable that different people will have different opinions as to the material that should be incorporated into an introductory text. This book was written with the intention of being not only reasonably elementary but also rather thorough in its treatment. I certainly feel I have selected the most appropriate material for such an introductory text. I have attempted to make the treatment correct as far as it goes and to avoid any falsehoods or outright errors; I shall be grateful for any constructive criticisms in this regard. This book requires some prior knowledge of chemical thermodynamics and kinetics as well as calculus; some knowledge of differential equations would also be helpful, although most of the text deals with algebraic operations.

I am very much indebted to the originator of chemical relaxation methods, Manfred Eigen, who introduced me to this field very early in its development; it would probably never have been developed without him. I also must thank him, as well as Gerhard Schwarz, Robert Berger, Quentin Gibson, and Britton Chance, for valuable comments on various parts of the manuscript. I would like to thank also the active participants of a seminar series based upon the contents of this book; George Hess, Karl Brandt, Donald Duffey, and Paul Parks. Finally, I am indebted to several secretaries who worked patiently on the various phases of this book.

Philadelphia, Pennsylvania   G. H. CZERLINSKI
June, 1966

v

TABLE OF CONTENTS

INTRODUCTION

The concept of chemical relaxation was originally introduced by Eigen (*1*). Up to 1954 it was practically impossible to follow chemical reactions that proceeded faster than about 1 millisecond. This limit was reached with rapid-flow methods, originally introduced by Hartridge and Roughton (*2*).

The various techniques to follow chemical reactions with half-lives below 1 millisecond were treated recently (*3*). The methods were divided into the (indirect) "competition methods" and the (direct) "perturbation methods." In competition methods the chemical system is steadily disturbed by some physical process competing with the chemical transformation. The sound-absorption technique is a typical example of a competition method and was originally employed by Eigen (*1*). A rather extensive review on these sound-absorption techniques appeared recently (*4*). Competition methods will not be dealt with in this book. In relaxation methods the term "competition methods" is narrowed to "stationary methods" (*5*).

In perturbation methods a system is in equilibrium or in a steady state and then rapidly perturbed; the resulting equilibration process is observed directly. A typical example of such a method is the temperature-jump method; the temperature is quickly increased and the response of the chemical system is observed (*6*). In relaxation methods the term "transient methods" is generally used instead of "perturbation methods" (*5*).

This book will deal primarily with transient methods. As the temperature-jump method is quite representative of transient methods and most applicable to more complex systems, derivations will primarily relate to data obtainable with the temperature-jump method. But the principles are applicable to any of the transient methods.

The treatment in this book will be different from prior derivations, insofar as *analytical* concentrations are considered as independent variables throughout. Such a treatment was first given early in 1964 for a very simple system (*7*). A rather extensive treatment was given later that year (*8*). Much of the material of this book is based on the second publication.

A rather general introduction to the methods used to investigate fast reactions in solutions was recently given by Caldin (*9*). A recent abstract on this subject was given by Hammes (*10*), who also gave, together with Eigen, a general introduction to chemical relaxation for biochemists (*11*). A quite recent review on fast reactions in solution was presented by Strehlow (*12*), but he remains somewhat restricted in his treatment on chemical relaxation by omitting enzyme reactions.

The book is divided into two parts; the more theoretical chapters are in the first half of the book, those dealing with experimentation are in the second half. Chemical relaxation will be derived on the grounds of classical kinetics. Such a derivation should be most instructive of the way in which chemical relaxation differs from classical kinetics. The theory of chemical relaxation is then progressively developed, finally relating all observables to analytical concentrations.

The terminology used will be one already developed (*8*). The indexed chemical components Y_i allow a more general treatment of the derivations. In specific experimental cases one may simply relate the generalized components to specific ones in the reaction system. Unspecified intermediates may keep their Y_i terminology. The glossary of terms should facilitate use of this book. Only the concepts developed in the first eight chapters will be listed in the glossary, as the concepts derived in later chapters are generally restricted to specific chapters.

Problems will be given at the end of each chapter. Some ask for further evaluations of presented equations, others for their full derivations, whereby extensive derivations in the text itself are diminished. Nevertheless, many derivations have been presented extensively to demonstrate clearly the various ways of their handling. At other places derivations are requested which are not treated in the text at all but consider special aspects. It is believed that one who wants to become highly creative in chemical relaxation should work on these problems to obtain greater understanding. The text, on the other hand, will not rely on any results obtained in the problems.

Kustin *et al.* (*13*) treated the theory of relaxation spectra quite recently. They deal with the general case of multiply coupled chemical relaxations, which can only be handled with matrix algebra. Such general treatment is certainly quite valuable from a theoretical point of view, but is not necessary for the many practical cases with reasonably separated relaxation times. For such cases the treatment in this monograph is most suitable, considering somewhat exhaustively up to three consecutive relaxation processes, and more-complex systems may easily be built up from the derived equations.

However, any more-complex systems require a quite elaborate fitting of parameter values to experimental data. Computer techniques are then more appropriate. Such techniques can practically not be avoided, whenever relaxation times are no longer " reasonably " separated, or even if more than three relaxation processes are measured; evaluations " by hand " would simply become too voluminous. To handle the complexity of multiply coupled reactions, digital computers seem more appropriate, operating on programs which actually employ matrix algebra.

The mathematical tool of matrix algebra was previously applied to the resolution of chemical relaxation time spectra by Castellan in 1963 (*14*) and by Eigen as early as 1960 (*15*). Similar mathematical techniques had previously been applied to problems in chemical kinetics, for example, by Berman and Schoenfeld (*16*). It might be mentioned again that the use of such mathematical techniques becomes valuable if incorporated into programs for modern high-speed computers. As such programs are still in a rather developmental stage, this whole area of handling the kinetics of multiply coupled reactions will not be treated in this monograph. At a later stage, when an elaborate computer program has been developed and tested thoroughly, the handling of such complex systems with high-speed computers may be treated, perhaps even in a future edition of this monograph. The equations derived here already provide an important basis for a generalized computer program.

For a first reading, the sections that are in smaller print and set off by horizontal rules may be omitted. Such sections are contained in the latter parts of Chapters 3 to 6. For an advanced future treatment of chemical relaxation see (*17*).

REFERENCES

1. M. Eigen, *Discussions Faraday Soc.*, **17**, 194 (1954).
2. H. Hartridge and F. J. W. Roughton, *Proc. Royal Soc.* (*London*), **A104**, 376 (1923).
3. M. Eigen, *in* A. Weissberger (ed.), *Technique of Organic Chemistry*, Vol. VIII, Pt. 2, p. 793, Wiley (Interscience), New York, 1963.

4. D. Sette (ed.), *Dispersion and Absorption of Sound by Molecular Processes* (Course XXVII of Proceedings of the International School of Physics, Enrico Fermi), Academic Press, New York, 1963.

5. M. Eigen and L. DeMaeyer, *in* A. Weissberger (ed.), *Technique of Organic Chemistry*, Vol. VIII, Pt. 2, p. 895, Wiley (Interscience), New York, 1963.

6. G. Czerlinski and M. Eigen, *Z. Elektrochem.*, **63**, 652 (1959).

7. G. Czerlinski and F. Hommes, *Biochim. Biophys. Acta*, **79**, 46 (1964).

8. G. Czerlinski, *J. Theoret. Biol.*, **7**, 435 (1964).

9. E. F. Caldin, *Fast Reactions in Solution*, Wiley, New York, 1964.

10. G. G. Hammes, *Ann. Rev. Phys. Chem.*, **15**, 13 (1964).

11. M. Eigen and G. G. Hammes, *in* F. F. Nord (ed.), *Advances in Enzymology*, Vol. XXV, p. 1, Wiley (Interscience), New York, 1963.

12. H. Strehlow, *Ann. Rev. Phys. Chem.*, **16**, 167 (1965).

13. K. Kustin, D. Shear, and D. Kleitman, *J. Theoret. Biol.*, **9**, 186 (1965).

14. G. W. Castellan, *Ber. Bunsenges.*, **67**, 898 (1963).

15. M. Eigen, *Z. Elektrochem.*, **64**, 115 (1960).

16. M. Berman and R. Schoenfeld, *J. Appl. Phys.*, **27**, 1361 (1956).

17. M. Eigen, *Chemische Relaxation*, Verlag Dr. D. Steinkopf, Darmstadt. An advanced treatise in three volumes, in preparation.

CHAPTER 1

CLASSICAL KINETICS

I–I. THE TWO-COMPONENT SYSTEM

The chemical system is defined by the equation

$$Y_1 \underset{k_2}{\overset{k_1}{\longrightarrow}} Y_2 \tag{1-1}$$

where Y_1 and Y_2 are the two components, which convert into each other. k_1 is the velocity constant of the conversion from Y_1 to Y_2 (in the direction of the upper arrow), whereas k_2 is the velocity constant for the reaction from Y_2 to Y_1 (in the direction of the lower arrow). These velocity constants are quantitatively defined by the differential equation

$$\frac{dc_1}{dt} = -k_1 c_1 + k_2 c_2 \tag{1-2}$$

In this equation c_i is the (instantaneous and thus time-dependent) concentration of component Y_i. Equation (1-2) describes appearance and disappearance of the individual components. The equation in this form is very rarely used. But as this reaction could become a very important step in a reaction sequence, it will be treated here.

At equilibrium it is

$$\frac{d\bar{c}_1}{dt} = 0 \tag{1-3}$$

The equilibrium is then derived from (1-2), giving

$$K_{2,1} \equiv \frac{k_2}{k_1} = \frac{\bar{c}_1}{\bar{c}_2} \tag{1-4}$$

The equilibrium concentrations are indicated by a bar over the concentration symbols.

Any change according to (1-2) can be observed, if the following relationship holds among the initial concentrations c_1^0 and c_2^0:

$$c_1^0 \neq K_{2,1} c_2^0 \qquad (1\text{-}5)$$

Y_1 and Y_2 may then be mixed and the temperature may be elevated suitably, to initiate the reaction (that is, equilibration).

Stoichiometry and the law of mass action demand the following relationships [one of the c_i^0 should always vanish, as one of them is no longer free, owing to the independent equation for the equilibrium constant; see the discussion after (5-6)]:

$$c_1 = c_1^0 + x \qquad (1\text{-}6)$$

$$c_2 = c_2^0 - x \qquad (1\text{-}7)$$

These equations may be combined and c_2 in (1-2) may be expressed in terms of c_1, leading to

$$\frac{c_1}{c_1^0 + c_2^0} = k_2 \tau - A \exp\left(-\frac{t}{\tau}\right) \qquad (1\text{-}8)$$

with

$$A = \frac{\bar{c}_1 - c_1^0}{c_1^0 + c_2^0} \qquad (1\text{-}9)$$

$$\tau^{-1} = k_1 + k_2 \qquad (1\text{-}10)$$

$$k_2 \tau = \bar{c}_1 (c_1^0 + c_2^0)^{-1} \qquad (1\text{-}11)$$

Insertion of (1-11) in (1-8) facilitates the visualization of the limits of (1-8) for $t \to 0$ and $t \to \infty$.

As (1-8) is of relatively little practical importance as such (and at this time), it will not be discussed further here. It will be taken up again in Section 1-4.

I-2. THE THREE-COMPONENT SYSTEM

Although three components could be connected together by two monomolecular reactions, such a system will not be considered here. The other possible three-component system is represented by

$$Y_1 + Y_2 \xrightarrow[k_2]{k_1} Y_3 \qquad (1\text{-}12)$$

The differential equation for the description of the kinetics of this system is given by

$$\frac{dc_1}{dt} = -k_1 c_1 c_2 + k_2 c_3 \qquad (1\text{-}13)$$

At equilibrium, (1-3) is again valid, and one obtains the dissociation constant

$$K_{2,1} \equiv \frac{k_2}{k_1} = \frac{\bar{c}_1 \bar{c}_2}{\bar{c}_3} \qquad (1\text{-}14)$$

If kinetics is to be followed, one has to establish, as the initial condition,

$$c_1^0 c_2^0 \neq K_{2,1} c_3^0 \qquad (1\text{-}15)$$

It is relatively easily possible to establish experimentally that one of the $c_i^0 = 0$, which is actually quite desirable, as the system would otherwise be "overdetermined" [see the discussion after (5-6)]. The simple process of mixing the two remaining components would then initiate the reaction. This initiation by mixing is in contrast to the initiation of reaction (1-1), requiring for its initiation a change of some *external* parameter (such as temperature).

Stoichiometry and the law of mass action lead to

$$c_1 = c_1^0 + x \qquad (1\text{-}16)$$

$$c_2 = c_2^0 + x \qquad (1\text{-}17)$$

$$c_3 = c_3^0 - x \qquad (1\text{-}18)$$

Here simple elimination of the reaction variable x is only possible if

$$c_1^0 = c_2^0 \qquad (1\text{-}19)$$

or

$$c_2^0 \gg c_1^0 \qquad (1\text{-}20)$$

or

$$c_1^0 \gg c_2^0 \qquad (1\text{-}21)$$

The concentration c_3^0 is then frequently zero. As conditions (1-20) and (1-21) are interchangeable, one of them is sufficient for further consideration. Condition (1-21) is here chosen to be omitted on the grounds that c_1 had previously been selected as the system-dependent variable. If the elimination of the reaction variable is not desired, one is referred to the textbook by Benson for further consideration (1).

Condition (1-19): $c_1^0 = c_2^0$, the latter being substituted. Employing this condition and equations (1-14) and (1-16) to (1-18), one may solve (1-13) in terms of the initial concentrations. Although the integration is relatively simple (substitution method), it will not be given here, owing to the large number of terms and the fact that the book deals primarily with chemical relaxation. One finally obtains

$$\frac{c_1}{c_1^0 + c_3^0} = \frac{1 - A \exp(-t/\tau)}{1 + A \exp(-t/\tau)} \frac{1}{2\tau k_1(c_1^0 + c_3^0)} - \frac{\frac{1}{2}K_{2,1}}{c_1^0 + c_3^0} \qquad (1\text{-}22)$$

with

$$A = \frac{1 - 2\tau k_1(c_1^0 + \frac{1}{2}K_{2,1})}{1 + 2\tau k_1(c_1^0 + \frac{1}{2}K_{2,1})} \qquad (1\text{-}23)$$

and

$$\tau^{-2} = 4k_1 k_2(c_1^0 + c_3^0) + k_2^2 \qquad (1\text{-}24)$$

The equations are for the more general case with $c_3^0 \neq 0$. Experimentally, one might frequently establish the condition $c_3^0 = 0$. But c_3^0 is carried in the equations, as one may also use the condition $c_1^0 = c_2^0 = 0 < c_3^0$ with initiation of the reaction by some *external* parameter (which is only possible if such conditions can be found for the particular system investigated). While the limit in c_1 for $t \to 0$ is easily obtained, the limit for $t \to \infty$ results in

$$[c_1]_{t \to \infty} = (2\tau k_1)^{-1} - \frac{1}{2}K_{2,1} \qquad (1\text{-}25)$$

One obtains the equilibrium concentration, as can later be derived (in Chapter 4).

Condition (1-20) allows a much simpler solution. Y_2 is buffering the system, so that $c_2 = c_2^0$ at all times. Equations (1-16) and (1-18) are then used and the kinetic equation can be linearized. The final solution is

$$\frac{c_1}{c_1^0 + c_3^0} = A \exp\left(-\frac{t}{\tau}\right) + k_2\tau \qquad (1\text{-}26)$$

with

$$A = \frac{c_1^0}{c_1^0 + c_3^0} - k_2\tau \qquad (1\text{-}27)$$

and

$$\tau^{-1} = k_1 c_2^0 + k_2 \qquad (1\text{-}28)$$

Again, it is preferable to have $c_3^0 = 0$. Any final equilibrium value can then be established by proper choice of c_1^0. But it is important to realize that the initial concentrations c_1^0 and c_2^0 must fulfill certain relations to the dissociation constant $K_{2,1}$ to allow detection of the changes. This is most easily visible for (1-26), if properly rewritten:

$$\frac{c_1}{c_1^0} = \frac{c_2^0}{c_2^0 + K_{2,1}} \exp\left(-\frac{t}{\tau}\right) + \frac{\bar{c}_1}{c_1^0} \qquad (1\text{-}29)$$

The concentration of Y_1 is completely unimportant. The principal condition for good detection is $c_2^0 > K_{2,1}$. The total kinetic change is down to $\frac{1}{2}$ of its possible maximum value at $c_2^0 = K_{2,1}$. Which one of the two conditions (1-19) or (1-20) should be established experimentally depends largely upon the magnitude of $K_{2,1}$ in relation to concentrations, which are used in the indication process (preferably the smallest ones!).

I-3. THE FOUR-COMPONENT SYSTEM

A. One Reaction Step

The first one to be considered is represented by

$$Y_1 + Y_2 \underset{k_2}{\overset{k_1}{\rightleftharpoons}} Y_3 + Y_4 \qquad (1\text{-}30)$$

The differential equation for this system is

$$\frac{dc_1}{dt} = -k_1 c_1 c_2 + k_2 c_3 c_4 \qquad (1\text{-}31)$$

Equation (1-3) is valid at equilibrium, giving

$$K_{2,1} \equiv \frac{k_2}{k_1} = \frac{\bar{c}_1 \bar{c}_2}{\bar{c}_3 \bar{c}_4} \qquad (1\text{-}32)$$

This equilibrium should *not* already be established by the initial concentrations. The following initial conditions may then be discussed:

$$c_1^0 = c_2^0 \qquad (1\text{-}33)$$

$$c_1^0, c_4^0 \ll c_2^0, c_3^0 \qquad (1\text{-}34)$$

For simplicity, one may select $c_4^0 = 0$ for the *first* condition. [One of these four c_i^0 always should be zero; see the discussion after (5-6)]. It is then

$$c_2 = c_1 = c_1^0 - x \qquad (1\text{-}35)$$

$$c_3 = c_3^0 + x \qquad (1\text{-}36)$$

$$c_4 = x \qquad (1\text{-}37)$$

One may now solve (1-31) in the same way as outlined before. It is most appropriate to solve for the relative change $c_1(c_1^0 + c_3^0)^{-1}$. The final result is (for $k_1 \neq k_2$)

$$\frac{c_1}{c_1^0 + c_3^0} = \frac{1 - A \exp(-t/\tau)}{1 + A \exp(-t/\tau)} \frac{1}{2\tau(k_1 - k_2)(c_1^0 + c_3^0)} - \frac{k_2(2c_1^0 + c_3^0)}{2(k_1 - k_2)(c_1^0 + c_3^0)} \tag{1-38}$$

with

$$A = \frac{1 - 2\tau(k_1 - k_2)\{c_1^0 + k_2(2c_1^0 + c_3^0)/[2(k_1 - k_2)]\}}{1 + 2\tau(k_1 - k_2)\{c_1^0 + k_2(c_1^0 + c_3^0)/[2(k_1 - k_2)]\}} \tag{1-39}$$

and

$$\tau^{-2} = 4k_1 k_2 c_1^0 (c_1^0 + c_3^0) + k_2^2 (c_3^0)^2 \tag{1-40}$$

These expressions are quite complex, in spite of the simplification by condition (1-33). Some further simplification is possible by keeping $c_3^0 = 0$ experimentally. But if $K_{2,1}$ is far away from unity, the concentration c_3^0 might have to be kept different from zero, to detect any change. It is much more convenient to use condition (1-34). This case has actually been treated recently in conjunction with chemical relaxation (2). For this case it is

$$c_2 = c_2^0 \qquad \text{and} \qquad c_3 = c_3^0 \tag{1-41}$$

$$c_1^0 - c_1 = c_4 - c_4^0 \tag{1-42}$$

Inserting these conditions, one obtains, upon integration of (1-31), for the relative concentration

$$\frac{c_1}{c_1^0 + c_4^0} = A \exp\left(-\frac{t}{\tau}\right) + k_2 c_3^0 \tau \tag{1-43}$$

where

$$A = \frac{k_1 c_1^0 c_2^0 - k_2 c_3^0 c_4^0}{c_1^0 + c_4^0} \tau \tag{1-44}$$

$$\tau^{-1} = k_1 c_2^0 + k_2 c_3^0 \tag{1-45}$$

Equation (1-43) practically agrees with (2-10) of Ref. 2. It may be considerably simplified if either $c_1^0 = 0$ or $c_4^0 = 0$ (either one actually should vanish).

B. Two Reaction Steps

The only other system with four components, to be considered, is represented by

$$Y_1 + Y_2 \underset{k_2}{\overset{k_1}{\rightleftharpoons}} Y_3 \underset{k_4}{\overset{k_3}{\rightleftharpoons}} Y_4 \qquad (1\text{-}46)$$

It is assumed that the first step is fast, the second step slow. For the investigation of the fast step one has to apply the equations derived for (1-12). The fast step may eventually be too fast for measurement by rapid-flow methods. Only the *slow* step will be investigated here.

There are two possible experimental conditions,

$$c_1^0 = c_2^0 \qquad (1\text{-}47)$$

$$c_1^0 \ll c_2^0 \qquad (1\text{-}48)$$

It is assumed that detection can only occur via component Y_4. It is in the time range of the slow process,

$$\frac{dc_4}{dt} = -k_4 c_4 + k_3 c_3 \qquad (1\text{-}49)$$

$$\frac{dc_1}{dt} = -k_1 c_1 c_2 + k_2 c_3 = 0 \qquad (1\text{-}50)$$

These equations are still valid for both experimental conditions. Now only condition (1-48) will be considered. The concentration c_2^0 is not changing and

$$c_3 + c_4 = c_1^0 - c_1 \qquad (1\text{-}51)$$

Employing (1-50) then leads to

$$c_3 = \frac{c_1^0 - c_4}{1 + K_{2,1}/c_2^0} \qquad (1\text{-}52)$$

Combining (1-52) with (1-49) gives

$$\frac{dc_4}{dt} = -\left(k_4 + \frac{k_3}{1 + K_{2,1}/c_2^0}\right)c_4 + k_3 c_1^0 \qquad (1\text{-}53)$$

Solving this differential equation gives

$$\frac{c_4}{c_1^0} = k_3 \tau [1 - \exp(-t/\tau)] \qquad (1\text{-}54)$$

with

$$\tau^{-1} = k_4 + k_3 (1 + K_{2,1}/c_2^0)^{-1} \qquad (1\text{-}55)$$

The time constant looks very much like that of a monomolecular reaction. The similarity to (1-10) is especially large for $c_2^0 \gg K_{2,1}$. But even then should k_4 not be too large, as the change in c_4 would otherwise become too small [(1-54) and (1-55)]. Time constants such as those in (1-55) belong to pseudo-monomolecular reactions.

PROBLEMS

1. Derive (1-8) and establish the limits for $t \to 0$.
2. Plot (1-8) with $k_2 = 5 \ \text{sec}^{-1}$, $k_1 = 1 \ \text{sec}^{-1}$, $c_2^0 = c_1^0 = 1 \ mM$.
3. Derive (1-22).
4. Show the limit of (1-22) for $t \to 0$.
5. Derive (1-26).
6. Show the limits of (1-26) for $t \to 0$ and $t \to \infty$.
7. Derive (1-38) and show that $c_1 \to c_1^0$, for $t \to \infty$.
8. Derive (1-43) and determine the limit in c_1 for $t \to 0$ and $t \to \infty$.
9. Derive (1-54) and determine the limits for $t \to 0$ and $t \to \infty$.

REFERENCES

1. S. W. Benson, *The Foundations of Chemical Kinetics*, McGraw-Hill, New York, 1960.
2. G. Czerlinski, *J. Theoret. Biol.*, **7**, 435 (1964).

CHAPTER 2

BASIS OF CHEMICAL RELAXATION

2–1. DEDUCTION FROM CLASSICAL KINETICS

To make the concept of chemical relaxation as instructive as possible, the conditions for (1-43) may be chosen: $c_1^0, c_4^0 \ll c_2^0, c_3^0$. This buffering leads to a time constant given by (1-45). The second term in (1-43) may be factored out, leading to

$$\frac{c_1}{c_1^0 + c_4^0} = k_2 c_3^0 \tau \left[1 + \frac{k_1 c_1^0 c_2^0 - k_2 c_3^0 c_4^0}{(c_1^0 + c_4^0) k_2 c_3^0} \exp\left(-\frac{t}{\tau}\right) \right] \tag{2-1}$$

No decision has as yet been made as to the magnitude of c_1^0 and c_4^0. Two limiting cases are possible, representing mixing from one side or the other. As they are of particular interest for this deduction, they will now be considered in more detail.

A. $c_4^0 = 0$, $c_1^0 > 0$

The reaction proceeds from left to right [according to the definition of (1-30)] with no amount of Y_4 initially present. Equation (2-1) then simplifies to

$$\frac{c_1}{c_1^0} = k_2 c_3^0 \tau \left[1 + \frac{k_1 c_2^0}{k_2 c_3^0} \exp\left(-\frac{t}{\tau}\right) \right] \tag{2-2}$$

The limits of (2-2) for $t \to 0$ and $t \to \infty$ can be derived directly. In the limit for $t \to \infty$, equilibrium is reached, giving

$$\frac{\bar{c}_1}{c_1^0} = k_2 c_3^0 \tau \tag{2-3}$$

13

Differentiation of (2-2) with respect to t at $t = 0$ gives

$$\frac{d}{dt}\left(\frac{c_1}{c_1^0}\right)_{t=0} = -k_1 c_2^0 \tag{2-4}$$

This result represents the first (negative) term of τ_1^{-1} in (1-45). The equation of the slope at $t = 0$ is then given by

$$\left(\frac{c_1}{c_1^0}\right)_{sl} = 1 - k_1 c_2^0 t \tag{2-5}$$

B. $c_1^0 = 0,\ c_4^0 > 0$

The reaction proceeds from right to left [according to the definition of (1-30)] with no amount of Y_1 initially present. Equation (2-1) then simplifies to

$$\frac{c_1}{c_4^0} = k_2 c_3^0 \tau[1 - \exp(-t/\tau)] \tag{2-6}$$

Equilibrium is reached for $t \to \infty$, leading to the same result (2-3) as before. Differentiation of (2-6) with respect to t at $t = 0$ gives the (positive) second term in the expression for τ^{-1} according to (1-45). The equation for the slope at $t = 0$ is then given by

$$\left(\frac{c_1}{c_4^0}\right)_{sl} = k_2 c_3^0 t \tag{2-7}$$

C. Discussion

The slopes according to (2-5) and (2-7) are generally determined experimentally. Knowledge of the initial concentrations c_2^0 and c_3^0 permits the computation of the two bimolecular rate constants k_1 and k_2. In ordinary kinetics, the rate data are frequently derived from the initial part of the reaction, where the effects of the backward reaction can be neglected. If the order of a reaction is not known, one would need to collect more from the curve than only the initial slope.

Chemical relaxation, on the other hand, operates near equilibrium. To demonstrate this clearly, (2-1) is plotted in Figure 2-1. As only the extremes **A** and **B** are used, the upper curve actually represents (2-2), the lower one (2-6). The dashed curves represent the approach to a different equilibrium value. This difference is obtained by maintaining $k_2 c_3^0$ constant in every case, namely, 2 sec^{-1}. For the full curves it is $k_1 c_2^0 = 1$ sec^{-1}, whereas $k_1 c_2^0 = 2$ sec^{-1} has been chosen for the dashed curves. These values give then two different equilibrium positions: $\frac{2}{3}$ for the full curves and $\frac{1}{2}$ for the dashed curves.

Chemical relaxation operates the following way. Equilibrium has been established for the solid curves; $\bar{c}_1/c_1^0$ is at $\frac{2}{3}$. The product $k_1 c_2^0$ is then " instantaneously " changed from 1 sec^{-1} to 2 sec^{-1}. This brings c_1/c_1^0 " instantaneously " onto the dashed curve at the ordinate $\frac{2}{3}$. As the equilibrium ordinate is now $\frac{1}{2}$, the relative concentration c_1/c_1^0 approaches this new value according to the kinetic properties of the system—that is, according to the dashed line. This process, following the initial " perturbation," is called *chemical relaxation*.

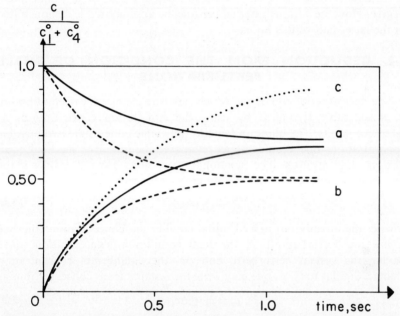

Figure 2-1. $c_1(c_1^0 + c_4^0)^{-1}$ versus time according to the general equation (2-1) with $k_2 c_3^0 = 2$ sec^{-1} in all three cases; $k_1 c_2^0$ is 1 sec^{-1} for the full curves a, 2 sec^{-1} for the dashed curves b, and zero for the dotted curve c (irreversible, with $c_1^0 = c_2^0 = 0$).

One realizes from Figure 2-1 that three observables are obtainable from chemical-relaxation experiments: the signal associated with the initial equilibrium concentration $\bar{c}_1$; the signal change derived from the equilibrium change $(\bar{c}_1)_{\text{initial}} \to (\bar{c}_1)_{\text{final}}$; and the time constant, associated with the relaxation process. The first observable is treated in "statics" of chemical relaxation, the second one in "thermodynamics," and the third one in "kinetics." These concepts—as applied to chemical relaxation—will be treated extensively in later chapters.

In explaining the operation of chemical relaxation, the product $k_1 c_2^0$ was changed. The change can certainly be accomplished in two ways, either by changing the buffering concentration c_2^0, or by changing the velocity constant k_1. In the former one adds Δc_2^0 to the initial concentration c_2^0. If the changes are fast, one would have to use rapid mixing techniques (down to about 1-ms resolution). The velocity constant itself could also be changed, but only by external parameters, such as temperature, field strength, and pressure. If X denotes the external parameter, effective perturbation only becomes possible if $dk_1/dX \neq 0$ to a "sufficient" degree. How the various external parameters are imposed is demonstrated in the latter half of this book.

2-2. DEDUCTION FROM THE CONDITION OF SMALL PERTURBATIONS

The derivation of equations, which describe changes near equilibrium, is considerably simplified by using the equilibrium concentrations as reference points. The question remains only which one of the two possible concentrations one should use as reference: the initial or the final equilibrium concentration. The functional expressions become simpler if the final equilibrium concentrations are used. It is then

$$\bar{c}_i = \bar{c}_i' + \Delta \bar{c}_i \tag{2-8}$$

with $\bar{c}_i$ the already introduced initial equilibrium concentration (the one *before* the perturbation), $\bar{c}_i'$ the final equilibrium concentration (*after* having the system perturbed), and $\Delta \bar{c}_i$ the equilibrium concentration change. Similar to (2-8), one may write the instantaneous concentrations as

$$c_i = \bar{c}_i' + \Delta c_i \tag{2-9}$$

The change Δc_i is then the instantaneous (time-dependent) concentration change.

A. Derivation

The chemical system (1-30) was treated in Section 2-1. This system will now also be used to demonstrate the basic conditions for this treatment of chemical relaxation. The differential equation of this system was given by (1-31). Substituting the various c_i by the expressions of (2-9), one obtains with equilibrium condition (1-3) and the important condition of small perturbations,

$$\bar{c}_i' \gg \Delta c_i \tag{2-10}$$

Initially,

$$\frac{d\,\Delta c_1}{dt} = -k_1\bar{c}_1'\,\Delta c_2 - k_1\bar{c}_2'\,\Delta c_1 + k_2\bar{c}_3'\,\Delta c_4 + k_2\bar{c}_4'\,\Delta c_3 \qquad (2\text{-}11)$$

Condition (2-10) allows us to omit the terms containing products of Δc_i, namely, $k_1\,\Delta c_1\,\Delta c_2$ and $k_2\,\Delta c_3\,\Delta c_4$. The laws of conservation of mass and stoichiometry allow us to establish three additional independent relationships among the Δc_i; for the system under consideration,

$$\Delta c_1 = \Delta c_2 \qquad (2\text{-}12)$$

$$\Delta c_3 = \Delta c_4 \qquad (2\text{-}13)$$

$$\Delta c_1 = -\Delta c_3 \qquad (2\text{-}14)$$

As Y_1 was chosen as the indicating component, the differential equation should be fully expressed in terms of Δc_1 as the only variable. Combining (2-11) to (2-14) accordingly, one obtains from (2-11),

$$\frac{d}{dt}\Delta c_1 = -[k_1(\bar{c}_1' + \bar{c}_2') + k_2(\bar{c}_3' + \bar{c}_4')]\Delta c_1 \qquad (2\text{-}15)$$

As the proper labeling in the integration is rather important, the integration variable x will now be introduced for Δc_1, leading with the definition

$$\tau^{-1} = k_1(\bar{c}_1' + \bar{c}_2') + k_2(\bar{c}_3' + \bar{c}_4') \qquad (2\text{-}16)$$

to

$$\frac{dx}{x} = -\frac{dt'}{\tau} \qquad (2\text{-}17)$$

The variable t' is used to denote *generally* the integration variable for time. The final concentration $\bar{c}_1'$ is considered as a reference value, so that at $t' \to 0$ it is $x = \bar{c}_1 - \bar{c}_1' = \Delta\bar{c}_1$ [Eq. (2-8)], at time $t' = t$ it is $x = c_1 - \bar{c}_1' = \Delta c_1$, and at $t' \to \infty$ it is $x = \bar{c}_1' - \bar{c}_1' = 0$. Integration should proceed from $t' = 0$ to $t' = t$, leading to

$$-\frac{t}{\tau} = \ln x \Big]_{\Delta\bar{c}_1}^{\Delta c_1} \qquad (2\text{-}18)$$

Inserting the limits and forming the antilog gives

$$\Delta c_1 = \Delta\bar{c}_1 \exp\left(-t/\tau\right) \qquad (2\text{-}19)$$

This equation is then the fundamental equation, describing the relaxation process.

B. Discussion

If the conditions of Section 2-1 prevail, it is $\bar{c}'_1 \ll \bar{c}'_2 = c^0_2$ (becoming eventually $c^0_2 + \Delta c^0_2$, as the final equilibrium is set as reference zero) and $\bar{c}'_4 \ll \bar{c}'_3 = c^0_3$. Inserting these conditions in (2-16) results directly in a time constant which was already derived in Chapter 1 [Eq. (1-45)]. It is the same constant appearing also in (2-1). One may then use the values employed in the construction of the curves of Figure 2-1, leading to Figure 2-2 for the relative concentration change $\Delta c_1/\Delta \bar{c}_1$.

The dashed line in Figure 2-2 is given by the equation for the tangents at $t = 0$. It is easily derived from (2-19) by differentiation, leading finally to

$$(\Delta c_1)_{sl} = \Delta \bar{c}_1(1 - t/\tau) \qquad (2\text{-}20)$$

It is immediately apparent that the slope of the relaxation curve at $t = 0$ intersects the abscissa at $t = \tau$. This slope can therefore be used to evaluate relaxation curves. But this slope can only be obtained with reasonably small error, if the traces are free of noise (statistical fluctuations of the trace; see the experimental section in the second half of the book).

If the noise level prevents a determination of τ and $\Delta \bar{c}_1$ with only small error according to the method just described, one may diminish the error by employing a set of theoretical curves on transparent paper. Each transparent "master" has a fixed τ [in millimeters of oscilloscope deflection, see also (1)] and $\Delta \bar{c}_1$ (as the measured signal change in millimeters) as parameter. Tektronix oscilloscopes have a total horizontal deflection of 100 mm. One then employs about 26 masters between 5 mm $\leqslant$ "τ" $\leqslant$ 40 mm and obtains the error width in the determination directly by approaching the actual curve with the transparent masters from "both sides": If τ denotes the *true* value, one approaches it from the side $\tau < \tau$ and from the side $\tau > \tau$. The constant τ is actually given in millimeters and has to be converted into time with the deflection factor of the time base of the oscilloscope. With this procedure one obtains two "best fits" to the noise curve, leading to two values in τ and $\Delta \bar{c}_1$ (as ΔS, see below), which represent the error limits of evaluation.

Modern mathematical machines may also be employed to obtain a value for τ and $\Delta \bar{c}_1$, representing the "best fit." Such a machine may be an analogue or digital computer (with analogue-to-digital converter for the latter). A digital computer is more suitable if later evaluations are also to be performed by mathematical machines.

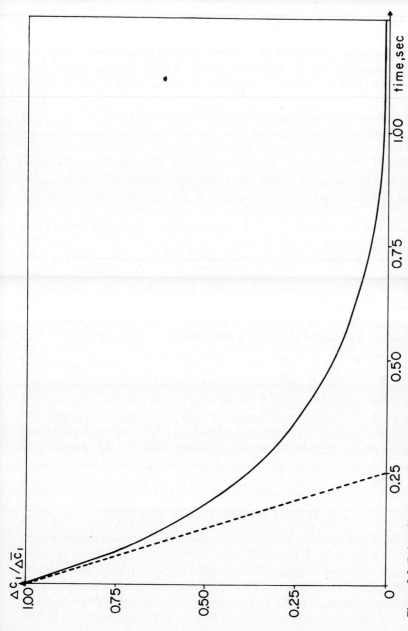

Figure 2-2. Relaxation process, normalized. The full curve is a representation of (2-19), the dashed line a representation of the slope, given by (2-20). The time constants for both equations are given by $\tau = 0.25$ sec; see discussion on page 18.

C. Consecutive Relaxation Processes

In Section 1-3B, a system was considered in (1-46) which consisted of two reaction steps. It was mentioned there that the first step is fast, the second one slow. As a relaxation process can be attributed to each step, one would obtain two time constants. The condition that one reaction is much faster than the other is then equivalent to saying that the two chemical relaxation time constants are widely separated along the time axis. This separation is expressed in general terms by the equation

$$\tau_j \ll \tau_{j+1} \tag{2-21}$$

Equation (2-21) is actually set as the basic postulate for any consecutive relaxation process and is important for two reasons. Condition (2-21) allows simplifications in the derivations of the individual expressions for τ_j, but also for ΔS_j (the signal change associated with the jth relaxation process, treated extensively in later chapters on thermodynamics). Condition (2-21) allows to determine the *true* values of τ_j and ΔS_j directly from the experimental curves; the overlap of consecutive processes is negligible.

So far, $\bar{c}_i$ has been distinguished from $\bar{c}_i'$. This was done primarily to demonstrate clearly the limits in the integration process. But condition (2-10) would allow the same simplification for (2-8) as it allowed for (2-11). This would lead to the practical approximation

$$\bar{c}_i = \bar{c}_i' \tag{2-22}$$

This approximation was written as a separate equation, as it will be employed throughout hereafter. This equation can be used as long as terms such as $(\bar{c}_i - \bar{c}_{i+1})$ do not appear. If such differences do appear, one would have to check the relative magnitude of the two concentrations and compare their differences. Quite generally one should prevent the appearance of differences of concentration terms in expressions for relaxation times.

2–3. THE CONCEPT OF "STATICS"

In Section 2-1, the concept of chemical relaxation was deduced from classical kinetics to demonstrate most instructively the region in which chemical relaxation operates. In Section 2-2 a separate derivation of chemical relaxation was given, based on the condition of small perturbations, Eq. (2-10). The solution for a four-component system was given by (2-19) with the chemical-relaxation time constant τ expressed by (2-16) for the special chemical system. Equation (2-19) has $\Delta \bar{c}_i$ as reference value. This equilibrium concentration change should be expressed in terms of the actually accessible initial (analytical) concentrations together with the system-characteristic parameters. These parameters are the enthalpy and the equilibrium constant of the reaction for the most widely used technique, the temperature-jump method. Expressions for such equilibrium concentration changes will be extensively given in Chapter 6. In these expressions, as well as in the expressions initially derived for the relaxation times [such as (2-16)], equilibrium concentrations appear and therefore should be substituted by the analytically accessible concentrations. This replacement is especially desirable in more complex systems. And analytical concentrations can only be used if chemical relaxation is to reveal intermediates, which are not accessible via equilibrium measurements. "Statics" then gives the relation between all the equilibrium concentrations and their initial analytical values.

In deriving the equations for statics, quadratic equations appear frequently, leading to two possible roots. The question is: Which one of the roots is valid?

A. Specific Example

The simplest chemical system, where such roots appear, is given by (1-12). If $\bar{x}$ is the equilibrium-concentration variable of the system, stoichiometry and conservation laws lead for the most general case [that is, every initial concentration $c_i^0 > 0$, although at least one of them should be zero, imposed by the law of mass action; see later discussion and after (5-6)!] to

$$c_1^0 + \bar{x} = \bar{c}_1 \tag{2-23}$$

$$c_2^0 + \bar{x} = \bar{c}_2 \tag{2-24}$$

$$c_3^0 - \bar{x} = \bar{c}_3 \tag{2-25}$$

To solve for any one equilibrium concentration, one would have to eliminate the concentration variable $\bar{x}$. This leaves two equations with three unknowns. The necessary (independent) fourth equation is obtained from (1-14), which becomes after substitution,

$$K_{2,1} = \frac{\bar{c}_1(c_2^0 - c_1^0 + \bar{c}_1)}{c_3^0 + c_1^0 - \bar{c}_1} \tag{2-26}$$

This form of the equilibrium constant anticipates a solution for $\bar{c}_1$. The expression with $\bar{c}_2$ as variable could be obtained by interchanging the indices 1 and 2. This interchange is then also valid for the final result. One may also solve for $\bar{c}_3$, leading to a somewhat different expression, which will not be considered here (see Chapter 4). From (2-26) one obtains easily the quadratic equation

$$(\bar{c}_1)^2 + (K_{2,1} + c_2^0 - c_1^0)\bar{c}_1 - K_{2,1}(c_1^0 + c_3) = 0 \qquad (2\text{-}27)$$

which has the two roots

$$(\bar{c}_1)_{1,2} = -\frac{1}{2}(K_{2,1} + c_2^0 - c_1^0)\left\{1 \pm \left[1 + \frac{4K_{2,1}(c_1^0 + c_3^0)}{(K_{2,1} + c_2^0 - c_1^0)^2}\right]^{1/2}\right\} \qquad (2\text{-}28)$$

In this equation three analytical concentrations appear. The system, on the other hand, is already fully determined with two analytical concentrations. Generally it is set $c_3^0 \equiv 0$. Equation (2-28)—and some former equations in a similar manner—still contains c_3^0 as nonvanishing for the simple reason that equilibrium may also be established by the condition $c_3^0 > 0 = c_1^0 = c_2^0$. If one wants to maintain $c_3^0 \equiv 0$, one has to take care of this latter condition by setting $c_1^0 = c_2^0$ and equal to the initial concentration of c_3^0. With this interpretation in mind, one may then quite generally omit c_3^0 in (2-28). In addition, one may normalize (2-28) by dividing both sides by $K_{2,1}$:

$$\frac{(\bar{c}_1)_{1,2}}{K_{2,1}} = -\frac{1}{2}\left(1 + \frac{c_2^0 - c_1^0}{K_{2,1}}\right)\left[1 \pm \left\langle 1 + \frac{4c_1^0/K_{2,1}}{(1 + [c_2^0 - c_1^0]/K_{2,1})^2}\right\rangle^{1/2}\right] \qquad (2\text{-}29)$$

It is quite apparent that this equation suffers a sign inversion whenever $K_{2,1} + c_2^0 \to c_1^0$. Equation (2-29) actually becomes indeterminate at this point, when used in the way written. Because of the importance of (2-29) and its roots for statics of chemical relaxation, it is quite advisable to plot (2-29) logarithmically, as shown in Figure 2-3 for $c_2^0 = K_{2,1}$.

The point at which the two curves cross is not accessible via (2-29). However, the denominator of the second term under the root becomes much smaller than unity for $K_{2,1} + c_2^0 \to c_1^0$. The second term under the root then becomes large in comparison with unity, leading to the considerably simplified relation

$$\frac{(\bar{c}_1)_{1,2}}{K_{2,1}} = \pm\left(\frac{c_2^0}{K_{2,1}}\right)^{1/2} \qquad (2\text{-}30)$$

This equation is only exactly true for $K_{2,1} + c_2^0 = c_1^0$. This equality is reached for the data of Figure 2-3, when $c_1^0/K_{2,1} = 2$. And as can be seen from the point of crossing of the dashed with the full curve, $\bar{c}_1/K_{2,1}$ is exactly where it should be according to (2-30) and its point of exact validity.

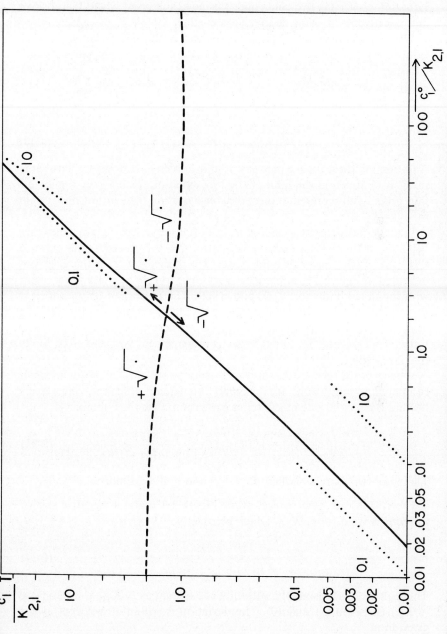

Figure 2-3. $\bar{c}_1/K_{2,1}$ versus $c_1^0/K_{2,1}$, according to (2-29) with $c_2^0/K_{2,1} = 1.0$. The full curve gives the (real) positive values, the dashed curve the (nonreal) negative values. $\pm\sqrt{}$ indicates which root has been used. The short strips labeled 0.1 and 10 refer to curves with these values for $c_2^0/K_{2,1}$.

Equation (2-30) has two roots and thus gives the point where the positive and negative roots coincide in absolute value.

The physical meaning of the dashed curve is that of a (relative) concentration, which has to be considered to be on the "disappearing side." Considering the dashed curve and its *negative* value only, one realizes easily the two relations

$$-(1 + \bar{c}_1/K_{2,1}) = \bar{c}_2/K_{2,1} \tag{2-31}$$

$$1 + c_2^0/K_{2,1} + \bar{c}_1/K_{2,1} = \bar{c}_3/K_{2,1} \tag{2-32}$$

Addition of these two equations results directly in $c_2^0/K_{2,1}$. This same result is obtained in the limit of the first equation for $c_1^0 \to \infty$. Figure 2-3 thus gives a full representation of the concentration behavior of this system for $c_2^0 = K_{2,1}$.

Figure 2-3 also shows some sections of dotted curves belonging to the cases $c_2^0/K_{2,1} = 0.1$ and 10. The curve with $c_2^0/K_{2,1} = 0.1$ proceeds very close to $\bar{c}_1/K_{2,1} = c_1^0/K_{2,1}$, as one would expect. The dashed curve for this case (not indicated in Figure 2-3) approaches very close to $\bar{c}_1/K_{2,1} = 1$, in agreement with the stated limits for (2-31) and (2-32). The indication of the (dotted) curve with $c_2^0/K_{2,1} = 10$ shows a shift to the right, especially at low $c_1^0/K_{2,1}$. The dashed curve (not shown for this case) now proceeds over a whole order of magnitude. Its total change is in agreement with the given limits for (2-31) and (2-32).

Whenever the second term under the square root of (2-29) becomes small compared to unity, one may expand this square root and omit terms beyond the second one in the series expansion. One thus obtains

$$\frac{\bar{c}_1}{K_{2,1}} = -\frac{1}{2}\left(1 + \frac{c_2^0 - c_1^0}{K_{2,1}}\right)\left\{1 \pm \left\langle 1 + \frac{2c_1^0/K_{2,1}}{[1 + (c_2^0 - c_1^0)/K_{2,1}]^2}\right\rangle\right\} \tag{2-33}$$

There are two extremes where this equation may be applied:

1. $c_1^0 \ll K_{2,1}$. One realizes from Figure 2-3 that the negative sign of the root is valid for $\bar{c}_1/K_{2,1}$, which becomes

$$\frac{\bar{c}_1}{K_{2,1}} \doteq \frac{c_1^0/K_{2,1}}{1 + c_2^0/K_{2,1}} \tag{2-34}$$

This equation is reasonably well fulfilled, as long as $\bar{c}_1/K_{2,1} \leqslant 0.1$ for any $c_2^0/K_{2,1}$ (between 0.1 and 10). The deviation is within 10 per cent at the given limit.

2. $c_1^0 \gg K_{2,1} + c_2^0$. The positive sign of the root is now valid and (2-33) becomes

$$\frac{\bar{c}_1}{K_{2,1}} \doteq \frac{c_1^0}{K_{2,1}} \tag{2-35}$$

This equation is reasonably well fulfilled for $\bar{c}_1/K_{2,1} > 10$ with the deviation near 10 per cent at the given limit.

Largest sensitivity to concentration changes in an equilibrium system is present where the equilibrium concentrations change strongest with reference to analytical concentrations. One may visualize this largest sensitivity most easily from Figure 2-3. As has been mentioned, (2-30) gives the condition for the inflection point of *both* curves. Both curves are steepest at this point (this steepness is most pronounced for curves with $c_2^0/K_{2,1} = 10$—for the range discussed herein), which is,

$$c_1^0 = c_2^0 + K_{2,1} \tag{2-36}$$

Although the equilibrium has highest sensitivity according to (2-36), condition (2-36) is certainly not ideal for the simplification of equations, especially for more complex systems. Much more suitable are the relations among analytical concentrations, already given by (1-19) and (1-20) or (1-21): equality or strong unequality among c_1^0 and c_2^0.

As $\bar{c}_1/K_{2,1}$ was considered the (continuous) dependent variable in Figure 2-3, one may consider strong unequality first, obtained by $c_2^0/K_{2,1} = 0.1$ in zero approximation. Detection is then most easily obtained via the smallest concentrations, $\bar{c}_2$ and $\bar{c}_3$, contained in the change represented by the dashed curve. For this pronounced unequality the dashed curve changes most strongly near $c_1^0/K_{2,1} = 1$. To cover a reasonable concentration range (and thus a range of concentration dependence of relaxation parameters), one should cover two orders of magnitude in c_1^0 and with $K_{2,1}$ as the "center of variation":

$$0.1K_{2,1} \leqslant c_1^0 \leqslant 10K_{2,1} \tag{2-37}$$

The necessity of this wide range can be seen directly from Figure 2-3 with $c_1^0 = 2K_{2,1}$ as the "center of variation." As one attempts quite frequently to attain ratios c_1^0/c_2^0, which are much different from unity, (2-37) becomes a rather important practical relation.

B. Simplifications

The normalized equation (2-29) may be considerably simplified for $c_1^0 = c_2^0$, resulting in

$$\frac{\bar{c}_1}{K_{2,1}} = -\frac{1}{2}\left(1 \pm \left\langle 1 + \frac{4c_1^0}{K_{2,1}} \right\rangle^{1/2}\right) \tag{2-38}$$

Only the negative root is applicable here. Equation (2-38) shows no inflection point, but demonstrates a change in slope. One obtains for $c_1^0 \ll K_{2,1}$;

$$\bar{c}_1/K_{2,1} \doteq c_1^0/K_{2,1} \qquad (2\text{-}39)$$

and for $c_1^0 \gg K_{2,1}$,

$$\bar{c}_1/K_{2,1} \doteq (c_1^0/K_{2,1})^{1/2} \qquad (2\text{-}40)$$

The (smooth) change in slope occurs at $c_1^0 = 2K_{2,1}$, where $\bar{c}_1 = \bar{c}_2 = \bar{c}_3$ and any small changes distribute equally among the three concentrations.

Another simplification of the normalized equation (2-29) is obtained for $c_2^0 \gg c_1^0$. The negative root is again valid and one obtains

$$\frac{(\bar{c}_1)}{K_{2,1}} = -\frac{1}{2}\left(1 + \frac{c_2^0}{K_{2,1}}\right)\left(1 - \left\langle 1 + \frac{4c_1^0/K_{2,1}}{(1 + c_2^0/K_{2,1})^2} \right\rangle^{1/2}\right) \qquad (2\text{-}41)$$

To scan c_2^0 around $K_{2,1}$, one also has to maintain $K_{2,1} \gg c_1^0$, which allows simplification of (2-41) to

$$\frac{\bar{c}_1}{K_{2,1}} = \frac{c_1^0/K_{2,1}}{1 + c_2^0/K_{2,1}} \qquad (2\text{-}42)$$

If $\bar{c}_1/K_{2,1}$ is plotted versus $c_1^0/K_{2,1}$ according to (2-42), an S-shaped curve is obtained with inflection point at $c_2^0 = K_{2,1}$. Variation of the concentration c_2^0 should therefore proceed according to (2-37) with $c_1^0 \rightarrow c_2^0$. Equation (2-37) or equivalent relations will be employed quite frequently in later chapters.

C. Sign of Root

Before proceeding to thermodynamics, the main result from the discussion of (2-28) should be summarized with reference to the sign of the root:

$$+\sqrt{\cdot} \qquad \text{for } c_1^0 > c_2^0 + K_{2,1} \qquad (2\text{-}43)$$

$$-\sqrt{\cdot} \qquad \text{for } c_1^0 < c_2^0 + K_{2,1} \qquad (2\text{-}44)$$

or, for more complex systems,

$+\sqrt{\cdot}$, if the sum of all terms, which have the same sign as the $K_{2,1}$ term, is *smaller* than the sum of all terms, having opposite signs compared to the $K_{2,1}$ term.

$-\sqrt{\cdot}$, if the sum of all terms with the same sign as the $K_{2,1}$ term is *larger* than the sum of all terms with the opposite sign compared to the $K_{2,1}$ term.

This rule concerning the choice of the sign is only valid as long as the terms are arranged as shown in (2-28). How equations are handled, when there is no sum such as in (2-28), will be shown in Chapter 4.

2-4. THE CONCEPT OF "THERMODYNAMICS"

In Section 2-2 it was stated that $dk_1/dX \neq 0$ to a "sufficient" degree [with X = external (perturbing) parameter]. More generally, one may write for a change in the equilibrium constant $K_{2,1}$,

$$\frac{\partial K_{2,1}}{\partial X} \neq 0 \tag{2-45}$$

The driving parameter X may for instance be the temperature T, leading to van't Hoff's equation ($\Delta H_{2,1}$ = enthalpy of the reaction),

$$\frac{\partial \ln K_{2,1}}{\partial T} = \frac{\Delta H_{2,1}}{RT^2} \tag{2-46}$$

The external driving parameter X will not be considered further here, to keep the derivation more general. The relations between X and the equilibrium constants will be considered in the second half of the book. Here only the relative changes in the equilibrium constants will be considered.

For linearizations of the equations one has to require

$$1 \gg \left| \frac{\Delta K_{2,1}}{K_{2,1}} \right| > 0 \tag{2-47}$$

Nonvanishing $\Delta K_{2,1}$ follows from (2-45). This relation (2-47) is quite generally valid for any equilibrium constant. The relations between the individual concentration changes and the relative changes in the equilibrium constants have been called "thermodynamics of chemical relaxation" (2).

The actually measured observables are the over-all signal changes ΔS_T. They have then to be related to the concentration changes $\Delta \bar{c}_i$ by

$$\Delta S_T = \sum_i \eta_i \, \Delta \bar{c}_i \tag{2-48}$$

The "characteristic signal" η_i is defined later [by (4.4)]. Any equilibrium concentrations $\bar{c}_i$ appearing in these equations have to be expressed in terms of initial concentrations c_i^0. These latter substitutions are treated in Chapter 7.

Here only a very simple example will be given, represented by (1-1) with the equilibrium constant given by (1-4). Employing (2-47) for this reaction gives

$$\frac{\Delta K_{2,1}}{K_{2,1}} = \frac{\Delta \bar{c}_1}{\bar{c}_1} - \frac{\Delta \bar{c}_2}{\bar{c}_2} \tag{2-49}$$

Stoichiometry and the law of mass action give

$$\Delta \bar{c}_1 = -\Delta \bar{c}_2 \tag{2-50}$$

Inserting (2-50) and (1-4) in (2-49) leads to

$$\frac{\Delta \bar{c}_1}{\bar{c}_1} = \frac{\Delta K_{2,1}}{K_{2,1}} (1 + K_{2,1})^{-1} \tag{2-51}$$

Equations (1-4), (1-6), and (1-7) (with equilibrium concentrations and with $c_2^0 = 0$) give the equation for $\bar{c}_1$, namely,

$$\bar{c}_1 = c_1^0 \frac{K_{2,1}}{1 + K_{2,1}} \tag{2.52}$$

Combining equations (2-51) and (2-52) gives

$$\Delta \bar{c}_1 = \frac{K_{2,1} c_1^0}{(1 + K_{2,1})^2} \frac{\Delta K_{2,1}}{K_{2,1}} \tag{2-53}$$

Equation (2-48) simplifies with (2-50) to

$$\Delta S_T = (\eta_1 - \eta_2) \Delta \bar{c}_1 \tag{2-54}$$

One may then easily combine (2-53) with (2-54) to give a closed expression for $\Delta S_T = f(c_1^0)$.

To detect any ΔS_T, one realizes from (2-54) that $\eta_1 \neq \eta_2$. But (2-53) also shows that one cannot measure anything if either $K_{2,1} \ll 1$ or $K_{2,1} \gg 1$. $\Delta \bar{c}_1$ shows up optimally, if $K_{2,1} = 1$. For detectability the "thermodynamic requirement" is therefore

$$0.1 \leqslant K_{2,1} \leqslant 10 \tag{2-55}$$

If $\eta_1 \gg \eta_2$, one may write the relative change $\Delta S_T/S_T$, which becomes equal to $\Delta \bar{c}_1/\bar{c}_1$ and thus is given by (2-51): The relative signal change is independent of c_i^0 for isolated monomolecular interconversions, and only for such reactions.

Only monomolecular interconversions give such a short derivation. Any nonmonomolecular reactions require quite elaborate derivations and discussions, as will be shown in Chapter 6.

PROBLEMS

1. Derive (2-5) and (2-7) in detail.
2. Insert intermediate steps in the derivation of (2-11) and (2-15).
3. Repeat the whole derivation following (2-10) with $\bar{c}_1$ as reference zero. What is the form of the final equation $\Delta c_1 = f(t)$?
4. Derive (2-20).
5. Derive the expression for $(\bar{c}_3)_{1,2}$ from (2-23) to (2-25) and (1-14).
6. Plot $\bar{c}_1/K_{2,1}$ versus $c_1^0/K_{2,1}$ according to (2-29) with $c_2^0/K_{2,1} = 0.5$ and 2.0. Also employ (2-34) and (2-35), and establish the deviations from the exact curve.

REFERENCES

1. G. Czerlinski and G. Schreck, *J. Biol. Chem.*, **239**, 913 (1964).
2. G. Czerlinski and G. Schreck, *Biochemistry*, **3**, 89 (1964).

CHAPTER 3

KINETICS OF CHEMICAL RELAXATION

3-1. ONE-STEP MECHANISMS

A. The Monomolecular Interconversion

The monomolecular interconversion is represented in Chapter 1 by the initial equation (1-1). The differential equation (1-2) becomes, with (1-3),

$$\Delta c_2 = -\Delta c_1 \tag{3-1}$$

(2-9), (2-10), and (2-22) for the equilibrium concentrations,

$$\frac{d\,\Delta c_1}{dt} = -(k_1 + k_2)\,\Delta c_1 \tag{3-2}$$

Integration with the proper limits leads to (2-19), with

$$\tau^{-1} = k_1 + k_2 \tag{3-3}$$

The relaxation time of monomolecular interconversions is thus independent of concentrations and actually identical with the time constant defined in (1-10).

B. Dissociation–Association

Dissociation–association is represented by (1-12) with the differential equation (1-13). With (1-3), (2-9) [plus (2-22)], (2-10), and

$$\Delta c_2 = \Delta c_1 \tag{3-4}$$

$$\Delta c_3 = -c_1 \tag{3-5}$$

differential equation (1-13) becomes

$$\frac{d\,\Delta c_1}{dt} = -\frac{1}{\tau}\,\Delta c_1 \tag{3-6}$$

with

$$\tau^{-1} = k_1(\bar{c}_1 + \bar{c}_2) + k_2 \qquad (3\text{-}7)$$

Integration again gives (2-19), with τ from (3-7). Now the relaxation time is concentration-dependent, and (1-28) results for the conditions $\bar{c}_1 \ll \bar{c}_2 \doteq c_2^0$.

C. The Four-Component System

The four-component system is represented by (1-30). The differential equation (1-31) becomes with (1-3), (2-19) [plus (2-22)], (2-10), (3-4), (3-5), and

$$\Delta c_4 = \Delta c_3 \qquad (3\text{-}8)$$

the same as (3-6), however with the reciprocal time constant

$$\tau^{-1} = k_1(\bar{c}_1 + \bar{c}_2) + k_2(\bar{c}_3 + \bar{c}_4) \qquad (3\text{-}9)$$

Condition (1-34) represents buffering by the components Y_2 and Y_3; that is, $\bar{c}_1 \ll \bar{c}_2 \doteq c_2^0$, $\bar{c}_4 \ll \bar{c}_3 \doteq c_3^0$. These conditions simplify (3-9) to an expression which is identical with (1-45).

D. Dimerization

An explicit expression for dimerization is not given here. It is referred to a derivation following (3-87). The relaxation time of dimerization is then given by (3-90).

3–2. TWO-STEP MECHANISMS

A. Three Components in Equilibration

Only one two-step mechanism can be set up with three components, namely,

$$Y_1 \underset{k_2}{\overset{k_1}{\rightleftarrows}} Y_2 \underset{k_4}{\overset{k_3}{\rightleftarrows}} Y_3 \qquad (3\text{-}10)$$

The three possible differential equations are

$$\frac{dc_1}{dt} = -k_1 c_1 + k_2 c_2 \qquad (3\text{-}11)$$

$$\frac{dc_2}{dt} = k_1 c_1 - k_2 c_2 - k_3 c_2 + k_4 c_3 \qquad (3\text{-}12)$$

$$\frac{dc_3}{dt} = k_3 c_2 - k_4 c_3 \qquad (3\text{-}13)$$

Only two of the three differential equations are independent. One may select *any two* to be the independent ones. Because of their shortness, (3-11) and (3-13) are preferable. Employing (2-9) together with (2-22) and remembering (1-3) gives for (3-11) and (3-13),

$$\frac{d \, \Delta c_1}{dt} = -k_1 \, \Delta c_1 + k_2 \, \Delta c_2 \qquad (3\text{-}14)$$

$$\frac{d \, \Delta c_3}{dt} = k_3 \, \Delta c_2 - k_4 \, \Delta c_3 \qquad (3\text{-}15)$$

The laws of conservation of mass and stoichiometry give the third independent relation among the Δc_i,

$$-\Delta c_2 = \Delta c_1 + \Delta c_3 \qquad (3\text{-}16)$$

Substituting for Δc_2 leads to two differential equations with only two unknowns:

$$\frac{d \, \Delta c_1}{dt} = -(k_1 + k_2)\Delta c_1 - k_2 \, \Delta c_3 \qquad (3\text{-}17)$$

$$\frac{d \, \Delta c_3}{dt} = -k_3 \, \Delta c_1 - (k_3 + k_4)\Delta c_3 \qquad (3\text{-}18)$$

The (negative!) coefficients of the Δc_i terms are *generally* expressed as a_{ij} such that

$a_{11} =$ the negative coefficient of the first term in the first row
$a_{12} =$ the negative coefficient of the second term in the first row
$a_{21} =$ the negative coefficient of the first term in the second row
$a_{22} =$ the negative coefficient of the second term in the second row

It certainly does not matter which equation is selected for the first row and which one for the second. But the concentration contained in the differential of the first row (the term on the left side of the equal sign) *must* also appear in the *first* term of *both* rows (even if one of the terms should vanish). The concentration contained in the differential of the second row will then always appear as the *second* term in *both* rows. Employing the above definitions of the a_{ij} upon the system consisting of (3-17) as "first row" and (3-18) as "second row" gives

$$a_{11} = k_1 + k_2 \qquad (3\text{-}19)$$

$$a_{12} = k_2 \qquad (3\text{-}20)$$

$$a_{21} = k_3 \qquad (3\text{-}21)$$

$$a_{22} = k_3 + k_4 \qquad (3\text{-}22)$$

The general solution of the two homogeneous linear differential equations of first order is then given by [the *final* equilibrium state being "reference zero," in expansion of the definition around (2-8), but maintaining (2-22)!]

$$\Delta c_1 = A_{11} \exp(-t/\tau_1) + A_{12} \exp(-t/\tau_2) \qquad (3\text{-}23)$$

$$\Delta c_3 = A_{31} \exp(-t/\tau_1) + A_{32} \exp(-t/\tau_2) \qquad (3\text{-}24)$$

The A_{ij} are concentration coefficients which will not be considered further in this chapter, where only the time constants τ_1 and τ_2 are of interest. It is defined at the onset:

$$\tau_1 < \tau_2 \qquad (3\text{-}25)$$

The expression for these two time constants in terms of the (generalized) coefficients a_{ij} is then

$$\frac{1}{\tau_1} = \frac{a_{11} + a_{22}}{2} [1 + (1 - b)^{1/2}] \qquad (3\text{-}26)$$

$$\frac{1}{\tau_2} = \frac{a_{11} + a_{22}}{2} [1 - (1 - b)^{1/2}] \qquad (3\text{-}27)$$

with

$$b = \frac{4(a_{11}a_{22} - a_{12}a_{21})}{(a_{11} + a_{22})^2} \qquad (3\text{-}28)$$

The structure of (3-26) and (3-27) indicates that the reciprocal relaxation times are the solution of a quadratic equation, derived from a determinant.† It has been indicated formerly (Section 2-2C) that condition (3-25) is not sufficient for the empirical evaluation of τ_1 and τ_2 under ordinary experimental signal-to-noise ratios (see also the instrumental chapters later on); the condition must be more restrictive, namely,

$$\tau_i \ll \tau_{i+1} \qquad (2\text{-}21)$$

This relationship applied to (3-26) and (3-27) means

$$1 \gg \frac{\tau_1}{\tau_2} = \frac{1 - (1 - b)^{1/2}}{1 + (1 - b)^{1/2}} \qquad (3\text{-}29)$$

† The quadratic equation may be expressed as
$$(a_{11} - \tau^{-1})(a_{22} - \tau^{-1}) - a_{21}a_{12} = 0$$
As determinants will not be used later on, they are already avoided here. A quite similar derivation was recently given by the author in *J. Theoret. Biol.*, **7**, 463 (1964).

Solving (3-29) for *any* b gives

$$b = \frac{4\tau_1}{\tau_2 + 2\tau_1 + \tau_1^2/\tau_2} \tag{3-30}$$

This equation may easily be simplified for condition (2-21). Equation (2-21) thus leads to

$$1 \gg b \tag{3-31}$$

It is also $b > 0$, owing to the fact that $a_{11} > a_{12}$ and $a_{22} > a_{21}$; see (3-28). Condition (3-31) allows one to expand the square root in (3-26) and (3-27) and to omit higher than linear terms:

$$(1 - b)^{1/2} = 1 - \tfrac{1}{2}b \tag{3-32}$$

If $k_2 \gg k_1$ and $k_3 \gg k_4$, Eq. (3-31) is even fulfilled, if $a_{11} \approx a_{22}$, according to (3-28). But this means that Y_2 is only present in very small concentrations, Eq. (3-10). One *must* then observe the concentration of Y_2 to see both relaxation processes. Actually, if $k_2 = k_3$, it is practically $\tau_2^{-1} = k_1 + k_4$, while $\tau_1^{-1} = 2k_2$. If, on the other hand, one observes two different relaxation processes at Y_1 or at Y_3, this result means that either

$$a_{11} \gg a_{22} \tag{3-33}$$

or

$$a_{22} \gg a_{11} \tag{3-34}$$

Either one of these two conditions allows always (see Chapter 6) detection of both relaxation process via component Y_2. Later, only conditions (3-33) and (3-34) will be considered, as the case $k_2 k_3 \gg k_1 k_4$ is considered somewhat rare and generally not detectable as two separate steps.

Equation (3-28) becomes, with (3-33),

$$b = \frac{4}{a_{11}} \left(a_{22} - \frac{a_{12}}{a_{11}} a_{21} \right) \tag{3-35}$$

This gives for the reciprocal short relaxation time, according to (3-26) and (3-31),

$$\tau_1^{-1} = a_{11} \tag{3-36}$$

Equation (3-35) has to be employed to obtain the slow reciprocal relaxation time, giving, together with (3-27) and (3-32),

$$\tau_2^{-1} = a_{22} - \frac{a_{12}}{a_{11}} a_{21} \tag{3-37}$$

This last equation can, for actual mechanisms, generally be further simplified (see below in this chapter). If condition (3-34) prevails, (3-28) becomes

$$b = \frac{4}{a_{22}} \left(a_{11} - \frac{a_{21}}{a_{22}} a_{12} \right) \tag{3-38}$$

τ_1^{-1} is immediately obtainable, giving

$$\tau_1^{-1} = a_{22} \tag{3-39}$$

Equation (3-27) becomes, with (3-32) and (3-38),

$$\tau_2^{-1} = a_{11} - \frac{a_{21}}{a_{22}} a_{12} \tag{3-40}$$

Equation (3-40) is the expression in the parentheses of (3-38). It is only natural that the equations of this section could have been derived from the corresponding ones of the previous section simply by index exchange.

In spite of the extreme similarity in the equations of the above two paragraphs, they have been written out separately, as actual mechanisms may not be as symmetric as (3-10). Then relations (3-33) and (3-34) would actually lead to different results. For system (3-10) one obtains for τ_1^{-1} [employing (3-19) to (3-22) together with (3-33) and (3-36)]

$$\tau_1^{-1} = k_1 + k_2 \tag{3-41}$$

Replacing (3-36) by (3-37) leads after simplification to

$$\tau_2^{-1} = k_3 \frac{1}{1 + K_{2,1}} + k_4 \tag{3-42}$$

By proper index exchange one could easily obtain the expressions for conditions (3-34). But symmetry of (3-10) allows always one to set Y_1 equal to the actual component of a system, which converts rapidly (which is directly connected to the rapid relaxation process).

No equilibrium concentrations appear in (3-41) and (3-42), which permits us to neglect "statics" for this system; both relaxation processes are independent of the analytical concentrations. Factor 10 is the minimum separation for (2-21), (3-33), and (3-34), if one permits about a 10 per cent error in the results. But actual experimental conditions generally demand a wider separation limit for (2-21). The above simplification may then be associated with an even smaller error than 10 per cent and fully acceptable. Condition (3-31) is not very extreme; b can easily be larger than 1/10. Fulfillment of (2-21) is far more important.

The experimentally very rare case of a two-step system with only three components was treated here quite extensively, as many of the basic equations will later be used and not derived again. Only the last two equations of this treatment actually deal with system (3-10).

B. Four Components

1. The association reaction with monomolecular interconversion in the associate is illustrated by

$$Y_1 + Y_2 \underset{k_2}{\overset{k_1}{\rightleftarrows}} Y_3 \underset{k_4}{\overset{k_3}{\rightleftarrows}} Y_4 \tag{3-43}$$

The differential equation is written for the first and the last component:

$$\frac{dc_1}{dt} = -k_1 c_1 c_2 + k_2 c_3 \tag{3-44}$$

$$\frac{dc_4}{dt} = k_3 c_3 - k_4 c_4 \tag{3-45}$$

The relations among the Δc_i are

$$\Delta c_1 = \Delta c_2 \tag{3-46}$$

$$-\Delta c_3 = \Delta c_1 + \Delta c_4 \tag{3-47}$$

Introducing (2-9) [together with (2-22)], the two differential equations become, with (3-46) and (3-47),

$$\frac{d\,\Delta c_1}{dt} = -[k_1(\bar{c}_1 + \bar{c}_2) + k_2]\Delta c_1 - k_2\,\Delta c_4 \tag{3-48}$$

$$\frac{d\,\Delta c_4}{dt} = -k_3\,\Delta c_1 - (k_3 + k_4)\Delta c_4 \tag{3-49}$$

According to the definition under (3-18), one may immediately write down the a_{ij} coefficients. If condition (3-33) prevails, one has to use (3-36) and (3-37), leading to

$$\tau_1^{-1} = k_1(\bar{c}_1 + \bar{c}_2) + k_2 \tag{3-50}$$

$$\tau_2^{-1} = k_3 \frac{\bar{c}_1 + \bar{c}_2}{K_{2,1} + \bar{c}_1 + \bar{c}_2} + k_4 \tag{3-51}$$

If, on the other hand, (3-34) prevails, one has to employ (3-39) and (3-40), giving

$$\tau_1^{-1} = k_3 + k_4 \tag{3-52}$$

$$\tau_2^{-1} = k_1(\bar{c}_1 + \bar{c}_2) + k_2 \frac{1}{1 + K_{3,4}} \tag{3-53}$$

It is immediately apparent that conditions (3-33) and (3-34) lead to completely different results.

2. The association reaction with monomolecular interconversion in one of the dissociation products is illustrated by

$$Y_4 \underset{k_4}{\overset{k_3}{\rightleftharpoons}} Y_2 \underset{k_2}{\overset{k_1}{\rightleftharpoons}} Y_3 \qquad (3\text{-}54)$$
$$Y_1$$

The differential equations are easily written down. But it is advisable for better comparison to start with the same concentrations as differentials as in (3-44) and (3-45). The relations among the Δc_i are now given by

$$\Delta c_1 = -\Delta c_3 \qquad (3\text{-}55)$$

$$-\Delta c_2 = \Delta c_3 + \Delta c_4 \qquad (3\text{-}56)$$

Employing these relations in the differential equations leads to coefficients a_{ii}, which are identical with those belonging to system (3-43), as derived. Furthermore, it is $a_{12} = k_1 \bar{c}_1$ and $a_{21} = k_4$. Relation (3-33) leads then to (3-50) and

$$\tau_2^{-1} = k_3 + k_4 \frac{K_{2,1} + \bar{c}_2}{K_{2,1} + \bar{c}_1 + \bar{c}_2} \qquad (3\text{-}57)$$

This last equation is distinctly different from (3-51). Relation (3-34) leads to (3-52) and

$$\tau_2^{-1} = k_1 \left(\frac{1}{1 + K_{4,3}} \bar{c}_1 + \bar{c}_2 \right) + k_2 \qquad (3\text{-}58)$$

Equation (3-58) is distinctly different from both (3-50) and (3-53).

3. A modification of the above derivation is possible, if it is established in advance which one of the two steps is much faster than the other one. Assuming mechanism (3-43) and the establishment of a fast bimolecular step followed by a slow monomolecular step, one may immediately write down (3-44) for the fast step. While the fast step proceeds, the slow step has not even started, and (3-45) may be omitted for the time range of the fast step. But during the observation time of the fast step, relations exist among the Δc_i which are in part different from the ones given above. Valid then are only conditions (3-4) and (3-5). Although (3-4) is identical with (3-46), Eq. (3-5) is certainly quite different from (3-47). It is $\Delta c_4 \equiv 0$ for the time range of measuring the fast step. The solution is then immediately given by (3-7)—or (3-50), if one prefers.

After the fast change has equilibrated, (1-3) holds. The differential equation becomes zero, which does *not* mean that it is *negligible* for the second step. For the time range of the slow step, (3-45) has to be considered, and in conjunction with (3-46) and (3-47). The differential equation is then only (3-49), while (3-48) becomes an equation with the left side being *zero*. One may then easily substitute Δc_4 for Δc_1, leading to

$$\frac{d\,\Delta c_4}{dt} = \left[\frac{k_2 k_3}{k_1(\bar{c}_1 + \bar{c}_2) + k_2} - (k_3 + k_4)\right]\Delta c_4 \qquad (3\text{-}59)$$

Rearrangement of (3-59) demonstrates that the relaxation time of the slow process is given by (3-51).

If, on the other hand, it has been established that the monomolecular interconversion in system (3-43) is much faster than the bimolecular reaction, (3-45) is valid during the fast step with (3-44) not yet appearing. This also leads for the fast step to (3-52), which is equivalent to (3-3) for one-step mechanisms. Equation (3-45) then goes with $\Delta c_3 = -\Delta c_4$ as relation among the Δc_i. If one considers the slow step, the left side of (3-45) becomes zero and (3-44) is fully valid in conjunction with (3-46) and (3-47). One again obtains (3-53) as a result for the slow relaxation process.

This modified derivation is possible for any system of consecutive reactions of any length if relation (2-21) is fulfilled and if the sequence of the rapidity of the individual steps follows the natural sequence. A number of such consecutive reactions will now be considered further, employing this modified derivation, based on the "stationary condition" [Czerlinski and Eigen (*1*)].

C. Five Components

1. Association from two sides is illustrated by

$$Y_1 + Y_2 \underset{k_2}{\overset{k_1}{\rightleftarrows}} Y_3 \underset{k_4}{\overset{k_3}{\rightleftarrows}} Y_4 + Y_5 \qquad (3\text{-}60)$$

If the left reaction step is much faster than the right one, (3-7) is valid for the fast step. The relaxation time for the slow step is then given by

$$\frac{1}{\tau_2} = k_3\left(\frac{\bar{c}_1 + \bar{c}_2}{K_{2,1} + \bar{c}_1 + \bar{c}_2}\right) + k_4(\bar{c}_4 + \bar{c}_5) \qquad (3\text{-}61)$$

If the right reaction step is much faster than the left one, the resulting equations are identical in structure to the previous ones, owing to the symmetry of (3-60).

2. Association toward two sides is illustrated by

$$Y_3 \underset{k_1}{\overset{k_2}{\longrightarrow}} Y_2 \overset{Y_1 \quad Y_4}{\underset{k_4}{\overset{k_3}{\longrightarrow}}} Y_5 \tag{3-62}$$

As this system is also symmetric, only one case needs to be considered. If the left reaction step is much faster than the right one, (3-7) gives the time constant for this fast step. The time constant for the slow step is then given by

$$\frac{1}{\tau_2} = k_3\left(\bar{c}_2 + \bar{c}_4 \frac{K_{2,1} + \bar{c}_2}{K_{2,1} + \bar{c}_1 + \bar{c}_2}\right) + k_4 \tag{3-63}$$

3. Two consecutive associations are illustrated by

$$Y_1 + Y_2 \underset{k_2}{\overset{k_1}{\longrightarrow}} Y_3 \underset{k_4}{\overset{k_3}{\longrightarrow}} Y_5 \tag{3-64}$$
$$Y_4$$

This system is no longer symmetric, leading to two distinguishable possibilities (3-33) and (3-34). The two differential equations are (3-44) and

$$\frac{dc_4}{dt} = -k_3 c_3 c_4 + k_4 c_5 \tag{3-65}$$

a. The left step is very fast. Equation (3-7) gives its relaxation time. For the slow step, the left side of (3-44) is zero and one obtains for the slow relaxation time

$$\frac{1}{\tau_2} = k_3\left(\bar{c}_3 + \bar{c}_4 \frac{\bar{c}_1 + \bar{c}_2}{K_{2,1} + \bar{c}_1 + \bar{c}_2}\right) + k_4 \tag{3-66}$$

b. The right step is very fast. One then obtains from (3-65),

$$\frac{1}{\tau_1} = k_3(\bar{c}_3 + \bar{c}_4) + k_4 \tag{3-67}$$

For the slow step, one again has to employ the "steady-state treatment," where the left side of (3-65) is now zero. One obtains

$$\frac{1}{\tau_2} = k_1(\bar{c}_1 + \bar{c}_2) + k_2\left(\frac{K_{4,3} + \bar{c}_3}{K_{4,3} + \bar{c}_3 + \bar{c}_4}\right) \tag{3-68}$$

Equations (3-66) and (3-68) are certainly quite different, although they derive from the same system (3-64).

4. Monomolecular interconversion connected to a four-component reaction step is illustrated by

$$Y_1 \underset{k_2}{\overset{k_1}{\rightleftharpoons}} Y_3 \underset{k_4}{\overset{k_3}{\longrightarrow}} Y_5 \qquad (3\text{-}69)$$
$$\qquad Y_2 \quad Y_4$$

This system is again quite unsymmetric.

a. The left reaction step is much faster than the right one. The fast relaxation time is then determined by (3-9). For the slow step the left side of the differential equation (1-31) is zero, while the nonzero differential equation is given by

$$\frac{dc_5}{dt} = k_3 c_3 - k_4 c_5 \qquad (3\text{-}70)$$

The relations among the Δc_i are

$$\Delta c_1 = \Delta c_2 = -\Delta c_4 \qquad (3\text{-}71)$$

$$\Delta c_3 = -\Delta c_1 - \Delta c_5 \qquad (3\text{-}72)$$

Solving for the slow relaxation time gives

$$\frac{1}{\tau_2} = k_3 \left\{ \frac{1 + K_{2,1}\bar{c}_3/(\bar{c}_1 + \bar{c}_2)}{1 + K_{2,1}(\bar{c}_3 + \bar{c}_4)/(\bar{c}_1 + \bar{c}_2)} \right\} + k_4 \qquad (3\text{-}73)$$

The time constant τ_2 becomes thus a rather complex function of the individual equilibrium concentrations.

b. The right reaction step is much faster than the left one. Equation (3-52) is then valid for the fast step. One obtains for the slow step the chemical time constant

$$\frac{1}{\tau_2} = k_1(\bar{c}_1 + \bar{c}_2) + k_2 \left(\bar{c}_3 + \bar{c}_4 \frac{1}{1 + K_{3,4}} \right) \qquad (3\text{-}74)$$

Equations (3-73) and (3-74) show completely different concentration dependencies.

D. Six Components

1. One of the two asymmetric alternatives is given by

$$Y_1 \underset{k_2}{\overset{k_1}{\rightleftharpoons}} Y_3 \underset{k_4}{\overset{k_3}{\rightleftharpoons}} Y_5 \qquad (3\text{-}75)$$
$$\qquad Y_2 \quad Y_4 \qquad Y_6$$

a. If the left reaction step is much faster than the right one, the fast chemical relaxation time constant is determined by (3-9). For the slow step, the left side of the differential equation (1-31) is zero, whereas the "nonzero" differential equation is given by

$$\frac{dc_5}{dt} = k_3 c_3 - k_4 c_5 c_6 \qquad (3\text{-}76)$$

With the easily derivable relations among the Δc_i, one obtains as slow relaxation time

$$\frac{1}{\tau_2} = k_3 \left\{ \frac{1 + K_{2,1}\bar{c}_3/(\bar{c}_1 + \bar{c}_2)}{1 + K_{2,1}(\bar{c}_3 + \bar{c}_4)/(\bar{c}_1 + \bar{c}_2)} \right\} + k_4(\bar{c}_5 + \bar{c}_6) \qquad (3\text{-}77)$$

The first term in this expression shows the same complexity as the first term of (3-73).

b. If the right reaction step is much faster than the left one, the fast chemical relaxation time constant is given by

$$\tau_1^{-1} = k_3 + k_4(\bar{c}_5 + \bar{c}_6) \qquad (3\text{-}78)$$

The slow relaxation process is with its time constant determined by

$$\frac{1}{\tau_2} = k_1(\bar{c}_1 + \bar{c}_2) + k_2\left(\bar{c}_3 + \bar{c}_4 \frac{\bar{c}_5 + \bar{c}_6}{K_{3,4} + \bar{c}_5 + \bar{c}_6}\right) \qquad (3\text{-}79)$$

The second term in (3-79) is identical in structure with the first term in (3-66).

2. The other one of the asymmetric alternatives of consecutive two-step reactions with six components is given by

$$Y_1 \underset{k_2}{\overset{k_1}{\rightleftarrows}} Y_3 \underset{k_4}{\overset{k_3}{\rightleftarrows}} Y_5 \qquad (3\text{-}80)$$
$$\quad Y_2 \quad Y_4 \quad Y_6$$

a. The left reaction step proceeds much faster than the right one. The τ_1^{-1} is again given by (3-9). To derive τ_2^{-1}, it is chosen as the second differential equation

$$\frac{dc_6}{dt} = -k_3 c_3 c_6 + k_4 c_5 \qquad (3\text{-}81)$$

With the vanishing differential equation (1-31) and the relation among the Δc_i, one obtains

$$\frac{1}{\tau_2} = k_3 \left(\bar{c}_3 + \bar{c}_6 \frac{1 + K_{2,1}\bar{c}_3/(\bar{c}_1 + \bar{c}_2)}{1 + K_{2,1}(\bar{c}_3 + \bar{c}_4)/(\bar{c}_1 + \bar{c}_2)}\right) + k_4 \qquad (3\text{-}82)$$

The rather complex factor of (3-73) and (3-77) is now appearing in conjunction with an equilibrium concentration.

b. The right reaction step proceeds much faster than the left one. The time constant of the fast step is then determined by

$$\tau_1^{-1} = k_3(\bar{c}_3 + \bar{c}_6) + k_4 \tag{3-83}$$

The slow time constant is given by

$$\frac{1}{\tau_2} = k_1(\bar{c}_1 + \bar{c}_2) + k_2\left(\bar{c}_3 + \bar{c}_4 \frac{K_{4,3} + \bar{c}_3}{K_{4,3} + \bar{c}_3 + \bar{c}_6}\right) \tag{3-84}$$

Again a relatively complex expression is obtained with the second term identical in structure with the first term in (3-63).

E. Seven Components

Only one completely symmetric system can be written down:

$$Y_1 \underset{k_2}{\overset{k_1}{\rightleftharpoons}} Y_3 \underset{k_4}{\overset{k_3}{\rightleftharpoons}} Y_5 \tag{3-85}$$
$$Y_2 \qquad Y_4 \qquad Y_6 \qquad Y_7$$

The time constant of the fast relaxation process is given by (3-9). The time constant of the much slower relaxation process is given by

$$\frac{1}{\tau_2} = k_3\left\{\bar{c}_3 + \bar{c}_6 \frac{1 + K_{2,1}\bar{c}_3/(\bar{c}_1 + \bar{c}_2)}{1 + K_{2,1}(\bar{c}_3 + \bar{c}_4)/(\bar{c}_1 + \bar{c}_2)}\right\} + k_4(\bar{c}_5 + \bar{c}_7) \tag{3-86}$$

The first term of this equation agrees with the first term of (3-82).

F. Threefold Identity among Components

So far it was not considered that some Y_i may be identical with some Y_j. Such identity would lead to a whole group of "loop-containing" systems. One could imagine that the relaxation times of such systems are simply obtained by setting the appropriate $\bar{c}_i = \bar{c}_j$ in the equations describing the relaxation times with $\bar{c}_i \neq \bar{c}_j$. To verify this idea, a very familiar two-step mechanism is investigated first:

$$2Y_1 \underset{k_2}{\overset{k_1}{\rightleftharpoons}} Y_2 \underset{k_4}{\overset{k_3}{\rightleftharpoons}} Y_3 \tag{3-87}$$
$$Y_1$$

This system is somewhat more complicated than previous ones, owing to the multiple appearance of Y_1. The system will therefore be treated in more detail than the previous ones.

1. If the left reaction step is much faster than the right one, the differential equation for the fast step *only* is given by

$$\frac{dc_2}{dt} = k_1 c_1^2 - k_2 c_2 \tag{3-88}$$

One has to employ as the condition among the two Δc_i,

$$\Delta c_1 = -2\Delta c_2 \tag{3-89}$$

If there are n molecules of Y_2 produced, $2n$ molecules of Y_1 had to be consumed. Equality exists therefore only if the number of n molecules of Y_2 is multiplied with the stoichiometric factor 2. This same course of thinking leads for concentration changes to (3-89). Substituting $\bar{c}_i + \Delta c_i$ for c_i in (3-88) and employing (3-89) leads, with the introduced simplifications, to

$$\tau_1^{-1} = 4k_1\bar{c}_1 + k_2 \tag{3-90}$$

This equation is identical with (4) of Ref. 2. The slow step requires two new differential equations, as (3-88) can no longer be used. Equation (3-88) has to be replaced by

$$\frac{dc_2}{dt} = k_1 c_1^2 - k_2 c_2 - k_3 c_1 c_2 + k_4 c_3 \tag{3-91}$$

In addition one may use as the second differential equation,

$$\frac{dc_3}{dt} = k_3 c_1 c_2 - k_4 c_3 \tag{3-92}$$

Because of the pre-equilibrium, the first two terms of (3-91) combine to zero. This gives one equation. Equation (3-92) is the differential equation, changing during the measurement of τ_2. As there are three unknown concentration parameters, a third equation is necessary, which is derived from stoichiometry and the conservation of mass:

$$-\Delta c_1 = 2\Delta c_2 + 3\Delta c_3 \tag{3-93}$$

The validity of this equation is best recognized by writing down the analytical concentration of the monomer:

$$c_1^0 = \bar{c}_1 + 2\bar{c}_2 + 3\bar{c}_3 \tag{3-94}$$

Differentiation of (3-94) and a change of differentials to differences leads directly to (3-93). There is no relation between the Δc_i other than (3-93).

Substitution of (3-93) in the equilibrium equation among Δc_1 and Δc_2 gives

$$\Delta c_2 = -\frac{6\bar{c}_1}{K_{2,1} + 4\bar{c}_1}\Delta c_3 \qquad (3\text{-}95)$$

Equation (3-92) becomes, near equilibrium,

$$\frac{d\,\Delta c_3}{dt} = k_3(\bar{c}_1\,\Delta c_2 + \bar{c}_2\,\Delta c_1) - k_4\,\Delta c_3 \qquad (3\text{-}96)$$

Substitution of (3-93) and (3-95) in (3-96) gives a differential equation with Δc_3 as the only variable; the slow time constant is then given by

$$\tau_2^{-1} = k_4 + 9k_3\bar{c}_2(1 + 4\bar{c}_1/K_{2,1})^{-1} \qquad (3\text{-}97)$$

The appearance of numbers from stoichiometry is expected in polymerization reactions.

2. The right reaction step is much faster than the left one. Equation (3-92) is valid for the fast step, leading to

$$\tau_1^{-1} = k_3(\bar{c}_1 + \bar{c}_2) + k_4 \qquad (3\text{-}98)$$

In the derivation of this equation, use has been made of the relation

$$\Delta c_1 = \Delta c_2 = -\Delta c_3 \qquad (3\text{-}99)$$

This relation is valid for the fast step. For the slow step, (3-93) is valid again, (3-96) is zero, and $d\,\Delta c_2/dt \neq 0$. In a similar manner, as just shown for the derivation of (3-97), one arrives for the slow relaxation time at the equation

$$\tau_2^{-1} = k_2 + 2k_1\bar{c}_1\,\frac{2 + 3\bar{c}_1/K_{2,1}}{1 + 3\bar{c}_2/K_{2,1}} \qquad (3\text{-}100)$$

Again, stoichiometric numbers appear in the expression.

At the beginning of this section, it was mentioned that one might perhaps derive the equations of τ_j for systems with some $Y_i = Y_l$ simply by equalizing the corresponding $c_i = c_l$ and using otherwise the previously derived equation. But the derivations thereafter show clearly that this cannot be done. One has to rederive the relations completely.

There exist only very few biological systems, following the trimerization reaction (3-87). But there is one important example: the trimerization of a polypeptide chain. The tertiary (and secondary) structures of Y_1 may then be quite different from that of Y_2, and both of them again quite different from the tertiary (and secondary) structure of Y_3. The trimerization reaction has here been reported first, because its slow relaxation times are so radically different from those of former systems. Hereafter, only twofold identity among components will be considered—in Section 3-2G all those associated with dimerization, in Section 3-2H the double dissociations, and in Section 3-2I the most elementary complete enzyme reaction.

The text below will be written in smaller type, to indicate its subordinate importance.

G. Two-Step Reactions with One Dimerization

1. The first reaction system is quite similar to (3-87):

$$2Y_1 \underset{k_2}{\overset{k_1}{\rightleftharpoons}} Y_2 \underset{k_4}{\overset{k_3}{\rightleftharpoons}} Y_3 \qquad (3\text{-}101)$$
$$Y_4$$

a. The left reaction step is much faster than the right one, leading for τ_1^{-1} directly to (3-90). For the slow relaxation process, one has as equations among the Δc_i,

$$\Delta c_4 = -\Delta c_3 \qquad (3\text{-}102)$$

$$\Delta c_2 = -\tfrac{1}{2}\Delta c_1 - \Delta c_3 \qquad (3\text{-}103)$$

One may select as differential equations

$$\frac{dc_1}{dt} = k_1 c_1^2 + k_2 c_2 \qquad (3\text{-}104)$$

$$\frac{dc_3}{dt} = k_3 c_2 c_4 - k_4 c_3 \qquad (3\text{-}105)$$

As the first one is zero by the condition of wide separation of relaxation times and being at equilibrium during observation of the slow relaxation process, one may easily solve for the slow relaxation process. But in doing so, one may use the differential equation given by (3-104) twice. The result is

$$\tau_2^{-1} = k_3 \left(\bar{c}_2 + \bar{c}_4 \frac{4\bar{c}_1}{K_{2,1} + 4\bar{c}_1} \right) + k_4 \qquad (3\text{-}106)$$

This result may be compared with (3-66). Equation (3-106) cannot be derived from (3-66) by simply setting $\bar{c}_1 = \bar{c}_2$. Another factor of 2 is associated with the concentration, originating from stoichiometry.

b. The right step is now considered much faster than the left one. The fast relaxation time is given by

$$\tau_1^{-1} = k_3(\bar{c}_2 + \bar{c}_4) + k_4 \qquad (3\text{-}107)$$

For the slow relaxation process, (3-102) to (3-104) are valid, while (3-105) becomes zero. One doubles (3-104) and obtains for the slow relaxation process,

$$\tau_2^{-1} = 4k_1\bar{c}_1 + k_2 \frac{K_{4,3} + \bar{c}_2}{K_{4,3} + \bar{c}_2 + \bar{c}_4} \tag{3-108}$$

The second term is identical with (3-68), as one would expect.

  2. A simple modification of (3-101) is given by

$$2Y_1 \xrightleftharpoons[k_2]{k_1} Y_2 \overset{k_3}{\underset{k_4}{\rightleftharpoons}} Y_3 \tag{3-109}$$
$$Y_4$$

This system is related to (3-60), but (3-109) becomes unsymmetric, which is not the case with (3-60).

  a. The left reaction step is much faster than the right one, leading, for τ_1^{-1}, again to (3-90). For the slow relaxation process one has as equations among the Δc_i,

$$\Delta c_4 = \Delta c_3 \tag{3-110}$$

and (3-103). As differential equations one now has (3-104) and

$$\frac{dc_3}{dt} = k_3 c_2 - k_4 c_3 c_4 \tag{3-111}$$

The left side of (3-104) is again zero. Proceeding then as before, one obtains

$$\tau_2^{-1} = k_3 \frac{4\bar{c}_1}{K_{2,1} + 4\bar{c}_1} + k_4(\bar{c}_3 + \bar{c}_4) \tag{3-112}$$

This result may be compared with (3-61). In addition to $\bar{c}_1 = \bar{c}_2$, one has to add a factor 2 to $\bar{c}_1$ to obtain (3-112) from (3-61).

  b. The right reaction step is much faster than the left one, leading to a fast relaxation time of

$$\tau_1^{-1} = k_3 + k_4(\bar{c}_3 + \bar{c}_4) \tag{3-113}$$

The slow relaxation time, on the other hand, is now given by

$$\tau_2^{-1} = 4k_1\bar{c}_1 + k_2 \frac{\bar{c}_3 + \bar{c}_4}{K_{3,4} + \bar{c}_3 + \bar{c}_4} \tag{3-114}$$

Also, this equation would have to be compared with (3-61).

  3. Certainly, also, the following combination might be present:

$$2Y_1 \xrightleftharpoons[k_2]{k_1} Y_2 \overset{k_3}{\underset{k_4}{\rightleftharpoons}} Y_3 \tag{3-115}$$
$$Y_4 \quad Y_5$$

This system is related to (3-75).

a. The left reaction step is much faster than the right one, leading to a time constant for the fast relaxation process, which is given by (3-90); that for the slow step is obtained from

$$\frac{dc_3}{dt} = k_3 c_2 c_4 - k_4 c_3 c_5 \tag{3-116}$$

The relations among the Δc_i for the slow process are

$$\Delta c_3 = \Delta c_5 = -\Delta c_4 \tag{3-117}$$

and (3-103). Solving for the long time constant gives

$$\tau_2^{-1} = k_3 \left(\bar{c}_2 + \bar{c}_4 \frac{4\bar{c}_1}{K_{2,1} + 4\bar{c}_1} \right) + k_4 (\bar{c}_3 + \bar{c}_5) \tag{3-118}$$

The difference in structure compared to (3-79) is apparent.

b. The right reaction step is much faster than the left one. The short relaxation time becomes

$$\tau_1^{-1} = k_3 (\bar{c}_2 + \bar{c}_4) + k_4 (\bar{c}_3 + \bar{c}_5) \tag{3-119}$$

Solving for the long relaxation time results in

$$\tau_2^{-1} = 4k_1 \bar{c}_1 + k_2 \frac{1 + K_{3,4} \bar{c}_2 / (\bar{c}_3 + \bar{c}_5)}{1 + K_{3,4} (\bar{c}_2 + \bar{c}_4) / (\bar{c}_3 + \bar{c}_5)} \tag{3-120}$$

Similarities and differences between (3-120) and the former (3-77) are easily recognized.

4. Another change in the number of components is represented by

$$2Y_1 \underset{k_2}{\overset{k_1}{\rightleftharpoons}} Y_2 \underset{k_4}{\overset{k_3}{\rightleftharpoons}} Y_3 \tag{3-121}$$

a. If the left step is much faster than the right one, τ_1^{-1} is given by (3-90) and τ_2^{-1} by

$$\tau_2^{-1} = k_3 \frac{4\bar{c}_1}{K_{2,1} + 4\bar{c}_1} + k_4 \tag{3-122}$$

Only (3-103) is available for the relationship among the Δc_i.

b. If the right step is much faster than the left one, τ_1^{-1} becomes concentration-independent (the sum of the two rate constants in the fast reaction step.) It is now, for the slow relaxation process,

$$\tau_2^{-1} = 4k_1 \bar{c}_1 + k_2 \frac{1}{1 + K_{3,4}} \tag{3-123}$$

One may compare this equation with (3-53).

5. A similar system with only three different types of components is given by

$$Y_3 \underset{k_4}{\overset{k_3}{\rightleftarrows}} Y_1 \underset{k_2}{\overset{k_1}{\rightleftarrows}} \tfrac{1}{2}Y_2 \tag{3-124}$$

The right reaction step is the well-known dimerization step. But the monomolecular interconversion is now associated with the monomer.

a. The left reaction step being by far the fastest one makes τ_1 again concentration-independent. To derive τ_2, the following two differential equations may be considered:

$$\frac{dc_2}{dt} = k_1 c_1^2 - k_2 c_2 \tag{3-125}$$

$$\frac{dc_3}{dt} = -k_3 c_3 + k_4 c_3 \tag{3-126}$$

Among the Δc_i there now exists the relationship

$$\Delta c_1 = -\Delta c_3 - 2\Delta c_2 \tag{3-127}$$

One finally arrives at

$$\tau_2^{-1} = 4k_1 \bar{c}_1 \frac{1}{1 + K_{4,3}} + k_2 \tag{3-128}$$

This result may be compared with (3-123).

b. A relatively very fast right reaction step leads for τ_1^{-1} to (3-90), whereas one obtains for the slow step,

$$\tau_2^{-1} = k_3 + k_4 \frac{1}{1 + 4\bar{c}_1 K_{1,2}} \tag{3-129}$$

This last equation is quite distinguishable in general structure from (3-122).

6. A system, similar to the previous one, but with one more component, is given by

$$Y_3 + Y_4 \underset{k_4}{\overset{k_3}{\rightleftarrows}} Y_1 \underset{k_2}{\overset{k_1}{\rightleftarrows}} \tfrac{1}{2}Y_2 \tag{3-130}$$

Aside from (3-125), the differential equation

$$\frac{dc_3}{dt} = -k_3 c_3 c_4 + k_3 c_1 \tag{3-131}$$

is relevant. Equations (3-127) and (3-110) hold for the slow concentration changes.

a. If the left reaction step is much faster than the right one, one obtains

$$\tau_1^{-1} = k_3 (\bar{c}_3 + \bar{c}_4) + k_4 \tag{3-132}$$

and

$$\tau_2^{-1} = 4k_1 \bar{c}_1 \frac{\bar{c}_3 + \bar{c}_4}{K_{4,3} + \bar{c}_3 + \bar{c}_4} + k_2 \tag{3-133}$$

b. If the right reaction step is much more rapid than the left, τ_1^{-1} is given by (3-90) and τ_2^{-1} by

$$\tau_2^{-1} = k_3(\bar{c}_3 + \bar{c}_4) + k_4 \frac{1}{1 + 4\bar{c}_1 K_{1,2}} \tag{3-134}$$

The second term of this equation is identical with the second term of (3-129)— as is to be expected.

7. A system quite similar to (3-130) is represented by

$$Y_3 \xrightleftharpoons[k_4]{k_3} Y_1 \xrightleftharpoons[k_2]{k_1} \tfrac{1}{2}Y_2 \\ \searrow Y_4 \tag{3-135}$$

The second differential equation is now given by

$$\frac{dc_3}{dt} = -k_3 c_3 + k_4 c_1 c_4 \tag{3-136}$$

For the relations among the Δc_i, there are (slow process) (3-127) and (3-102).

a. If the left side of the reaction is much faster than the right one, one obtains

$$\tau_1^{-1} = k_3 + k_4(\bar{c}_1 + \bar{c}_4) \tag{3-137}$$

$$\tau_2^{-1} = 4k_1 c_1 \frac{1 + K_{4,3}\bar{c}_4}{1 + K_{4,3}(\bar{c}_1 + \bar{c}_4)} + k_2 \tag{3-138}$$

b. If the right reaction step proceeds much faster than the left one, τ_1^{-1} results from (3-90), while

$$\tau_2^{-1} = k_3 + k_4\left(\bar{c}_1 + \bar{c}_4 \frac{1}{1 + 4K_{1,2}\bar{c}_1}\right) \tag{3-139}$$

The differences among these and preceding equations are clearly visible.

8. Finally, one has to consider the dimerization reaction, containing one more component compared to cases 6 and 7.

$$Y_3 \xrightleftharpoons[k_4]{k_3} Y_1 \xrightleftharpoons[k_1]{k_2} \tfrac{1}{2}Y_2 \\ \swarrow \quad \searrow \\ Y_4 \quad Y_5 \tag{3-140}$$

The differential equations are given by (3-125) and

$$\frac{dc_3}{dt} = -k_3 c_3 c_4 + k_4 c_1 c_5 \tag{3-141}$$

For any slow relaxation process the relations among the Δc_i are given by (3-127), (3-110), and

$$\Delta c_5 = -\Delta c_3 \tag{3-142}$$

a. If the left reaction step is much faster than the right one, one obtains

$$\tau_1^{-1} = k_3(\bar{c}_3 + \bar{c}_4) + k_4(\bar{c}_1 + \bar{c}_5) \tag{3-143}$$

$$\tau_2^{-1} = 4k_1\bar{c}_1 \frac{1 + K_{4,3}\bar{c}_1/(\bar{c}_3 + \bar{c}_4)}{1 + K_{4,3}(\bar{c}_1 + \bar{c}_5)/(\bar{c}_3 + \bar{c}_4)} + k_2 \tag{3-144}$$

The familiar factor of (3-120) is now associated with the first term, containing the forward rate constant for the dimerization step.

b. If the right reaction step is much faster than the left one, the result is (3-90) for τ_1^{-1} and

$$\tau_2^{-1} = k_3(\bar{c}_3 + \bar{c}_4) + k_4\left(\bar{c}_1 + \bar{c}_5 \frac{1}{1 + 4K_{1,2}\bar{c}_1}\right) \tag{3-145}$$

The differences in structure among (3-118) and (3-145) are quite evident: $\bar{c}_1$ appears twice in the former, but only once in the latter. This criterion actually distinguishes types 1 to 4 from types 5 to 8 for the slow step and the case that the dimerization is much faster than the other reaction.

H. Isomolecular Associations

1. One may consider as "typically representative,"

$$Y_1 \underset{k_2}{\overset{k_1}{\longrightleftharpoons}} Y_2 \underset{k_4}{\overset{k_3}{\longrightleftharpoons}} Y_3$$
$$Y_4 \qquad\qquad Y_4 \tag{3-146}$$

One may derive this reaction from system (3-87), by reducing the number of identical components by one in a different way than was done to arrive at system (3-101). For all reaction types to be considered, the isomolecular component will be labeled Y_4, and the differential equations will be written with c_1 and c_3 as independent variables.

a. If the left reaction step is faster than the right one, it is

$$\tau_1^{-1} = k_1(\bar{c}_1 + \bar{c}_4) + k_2 \tag{3-147}$$

$$\tau_2^{-1} = k_3 \frac{\bar{c}_4(\bar{c}_2 + \bar{c}_4 + 2[\bar{c}_1 + K_{2,1}])}{\bar{c}_1 + \bar{c}_4 + K_{2,1}} + k_4 \tag{3-148}$$

This equation is derived in conjunction with

$$\Delta c_2 = -\Delta c_1 - \Delta c_3 \tag{3-149}$$

and

$$\Delta c_4 = \Delta c_1 - \Delta c_3 \tag{3-150}$$

b. If the right reaction step is much faster than the left one, it becomes

$$\tau_1^{-1} = k_3(\bar{c}_2 + \bar{c}_4) + k_4 \tag{3-151}$$

$$\tau_2^{-1} = k_1\left(\bar{c}_1 \frac{2\bar{c}_4 + K_{4,3}}{\bar{c}_2 + \bar{c}_4 + K_{4,3}} + \bar{c}_4\right) + k_2 \frac{2\bar{c}_2 + K_{4,3}}{\bar{c}_2 + \bar{c}_4 + K_{4,3}} \tag{3-152}$$

These last two equations for τ_2^{-1} are much more complicated than anything before. Fortunately, they do belong to not very frequent cases.

2. Isomolecular association may also occur at two quite different (but mutually exclusive) sites, leading to

$$Y_1 \underset{k_2}{\overset{k_1}{\rightleftharpoons}} Y_2 \underset{k_4}{\overset{k_3}{\rightleftharpoons}} Y_3 \qquad (3\text{-}153)$$
$$Y_4 \qquad Y_4$$

Because of symmetry, only one case needs to be considered, giving

$$\tau_1^{-1} = k_1 + k_2(\bar{c}_2 + \bar{c}_4) \qquad (3\text{-}154)$$

To obtain the much longer second time constant, one has to employ (3-149) and

$$\Delta c_4 = -\Delta c_1 - \Delta c_3 \qquad (3\text{-}155)$$

Inserting the proper Δc_i into the differential equations leads to

$$\tau_2^{-1} = k_3 \frac{\bar{c}_2 + \bar{c}_4}{1 + K_{2,1}(\bar{c}_2 + \bar{c}_4)} + k_4 \qquad (3\text{-}156)$$

This expression for τ_2^{-1} is again quite simple.

I. Catalytic Reactions

1. The first example is actually the third alternative for isomolecular association:

$$Y_1 \overset{}{\underset{k_2 \; k_1}{\curvearrowright}} Y_4 \overset{}{\underset{k_3 \; k_4}{\curvearrowright}} Y_3 \qquad (3\text{-}157)$$
$$Y_2$$

It is also the first example of an enzymatic reaction as a more specific case. The reaction is symmetric, and again only one type needs to be considered. The fast step is given by (3-147), the slow step by

$$\tau_2^{-1} = \bar{c}_4 \left(k_4 + k_3 \frac{\bar{c}_3}{K_{2,1} + \bar{c}_1 + \bar{c}_4} \right) \qquad (3\text{-}158)$$

For the derivation of this last equation, one has to employ the relations among the Δc_i given by (3-149) and

$$\Delta c_4 = \Delta c_1 + \Delta c_3 \qquad (3\text{-}159)$$

The special property of (3-158) is that τ_2^{-1} is directly proportional to $\bar{c}_4$. The rate constant k_3 can be made somewhat dependent upon $\bar{c}_4$. But whether this would show up experimentally in a plot of τ_2^{-1} versus $\bar{c}_4$ depends very much upon the magnitude of the individual parameters.

2. Another rather common catalytic reaction is given by

$$Y_1 \overset{}{\underset{k_2 \; k_1}{\curvearrowright}} Y_4$$
$$Y_3 \qquad Y_2 \qquad (3\text{-}160)$$

For this system with four "unknowns" the following relations exist among the Δc_i for the slow process:

$$\Delta c_1 = -\Delta c_3 \tag{3-161}$$

$$\Delta c_2 = -\Delta c_4 = 0 \tag{3-162}$$

Thus there are three independent equations for four "unknowns," necessitating employment of only one differential equation.

a. The bimolecular reaction is much faster than the monomolecular one, leading to

$$\tau_1^{-1} = k_1(\bar{c}_1 + \bar{c}_4) + k_2(\bar{c}_2 + \bar{c}_3) \tag{3-163}$$

$$\tau_2^{-1} = k_3 + k_4 \tag{3-164}$$

The somewhat surprising result is that the second relaxation process becomes concentration-independent!

b. The monomolecular reaction is much faster than the bimolecular one. τ_1^{-1} has then the same value as τ_2^{-1} in (3-164). One obtains for the slow process,

$$\tau_2^{-1} = k_1\bar{c}_4 + k_2\bar{c}_2 \tag{3-165}$$

Also, this time constant is very uninvolved, but it is remarkable that $\bar{c}_1$ and $\bar{c}_3$ never do show up.

3. Addition of another component to system (3-160) gives

$$\tag{3-166}$$

The relation among the Δc_i for both reactions being effective (any slow step) is given by (3-149), (3-159), and (3-162).

a. The left reaction step is much faster than the right one. The short time constant is then determined by (3-163) with the *exception* that $\bar{c}_3$ there has to be replaced by $\bar{c}_5$. For the long time constant, one obtains for this case,

$$\tau_2^{-1} = k_4\bar{c}_4 + (k_3 + k_4\bar{c}_3)\left(1 + \frac{K_{2,1}\bar{c}_5 + \bar{c}_1}{K_{2,1}\bar{c}_2 + \bar{c}_4}\right)^{-1} \tag{3-167}$$

b. The *right* reaction step is much faster than the left one. The short time constant is now determined by (3-113) with the *exception* that $\bar{c}_4$ there has to be replaced by $\bar{c}_2$. For the long time constant one then obtains

$$\tau_2^{-1} = k_1\bar{c}_4 + k_2\bar{c}_5 + (k_1\bar{c}_1 + k_2\bar{c}_2)\left(1 + \frac{K_{3,4} + \bar{c}_3}{\bar{c}_4}\right)^{-1} \tag{3-168}$$

Both of these last two equations have the common feature that the concentration-dependent correction factor acts on *two* terms of the expression for the step-relaxation time.

4. Finally, the following symmetric case may be considered:

$$Y_1 \quad Y_4 \quad Y_6$$
$$\text{(diagram)} \quad k_2 \quad k_1 \quad k_3 \quad k_4 \qquad \text{(3-169)}$$
$$Y_3 \quad Y_2 \quad Y_5$$

Because of the high symmetry, only one slow process needs to be considered. If the fast relaxation process is determined by (3-163), the slow process is given by

$$\tau_2^{-1} = (k_3\bar{c}_5 + k_4\bar{c}_6)\left(1 + \frac{K_{2,1}\bar{c}_3 + \bar{c}_1}{K_{2,1}\bar{c}_2 + \bar{c}_4}\right)^{-1} + k_3\bar{c}_2 + k_4\bar{c}_4 \qquad (3\text{-}170)$$

This equation is quite similar in structure to (3-167), although it has one more term, as has (3-168) compared to (3-167).

3–3. MULTISTEP MECHANISMS

A. The Substitution Method

1. The most elementary system with more than two reaction steps is given by

$$Y_1 \underset{k_2}{\overset{k_1}{\rightleftharpoons}} Y_2 \underset{k_4}{\overset{k_3}{\rightleftharpoons}} Y_3 \underset{k_6}{\overset{k_5}{\rightleftharpoons}} Y_4 \qquad (3\text{-}171)$$

To make the "substitution method" as instructive as possible, system (3-171) will first be discussed in two parts. The first part contains the left two reaction steps only. The two relaxation times were discussed previously. The results are given by (3-41) and (3-42).

In the second part of the discussion it is assumed that the left step is "negligibly slow." The fast step is given by

$$\tau_1^{-1} = k_5 + k_6 \qquad (3\text{-}172)$$

The much slower middle step results then—analogous to the treatment for system (3-10)—in

$$\tau_2^{-1} = k_3 + k_4 \frac{1}{1 + K_{5,6}} \qquad (3\text{-}173)$$

One may now consider the case that the left *and* the right step in (3-171) are much faster than the middle reaction step. The relaxation times of these individual steps are then given by (3-41) and (3-172). But under "normal" conditions (that is, with only one indicating species present), only one of them will be expected to be measured (this aspect will be treated extensively in later chapters). As both steps are completely separated in time by the much slower middle step, their relative speed has no implication. The two relaxation times can even be identical. There is no interference in detection, if the left reaction step is followed by observing changes in c_1 (or c_2) and the right step is followed by observing changes in c_4 (or c_3).

The slowest relaxation time, τ_3, may be observed via any one of the four components of the system. Its expression is a combination of (3-42) and (3-173):

$$\tau_3^{-1} = \frac{1}{1 + K_{2,1}} k_3 + k_4 \frac{1}{1 + K_{5,6}} \qquad (3\text{-}174)$$

This expression can be thought of as being obtained by substituting in (3-42) an equilibrium factor which is quite similar to the equilibrium factor associated there already with k_3. $K_{i,j}$ in this equilibrium factor is then defined such that i is the index of the rate constant for the fast transition *away* from the slow step, and j (the second index) is the index of the rate constant for the fast transition *toward* the slow step.

This substitution method is quite generally applicable, but will not be treated here extensively, so as to keep the content of this chapter within limits. Later the substitution method will only be used as an example for any newly developed multistep system. There are still enough mechanisms, where the substitution method cannot directly be applied; one of them is directly derivable from (3-171).

The substitution method can so far only be applied to systems in which a slow step is bordered by two fast steps. A different solution has to be sought for a mechanism of type (3-171) with the left step being very fast, the right step very slow, and the middle step in between but sufficiently separated in time from either one of the neighboring reaction steps. This condition may be expressed quantitatively in terms of the "step-relaxation times":

$$k_1 + k_2 \gg k_3 + k_4 \gg k_5 + k_6 \qquad (3\text{-}175)$$

Considering now only the slowest relaxation time, the following conditions hold among the Δc_i:

$$\Delta c_3 = -\Delta c_1 - \Delta c_2 - \Delta c_4 \qquad (3\text{-}176)$$

This is the only derivable "stoichometric" relation among the four Δc_i. One thus has to use three differential equations in addition—(3-11), (3-12), and

$$\frac{dc_4}{dt} = k_5 c_3 - k_6 c_4 \qquad (3\text{-}177)$$

Proceeding for all three differential equations as shown earlier in this chapter leads to

$$\frac{d\Delta c_1}{dt} = -k_1 \Delta c_1 + k_2 \Delta c_2 \qquad (3\text{-}178)$$

$$\frac{d\Delta c_2}{dt} + \frac{d\Delta c_1}{dt} = -k_4 \Delta c_1 - (k_3 + k_4)\Delta c_2 - k_4 \Delta c_4 \qquad (3\text{-}179)$$

$$\frac{d\Delta c_4}{dt} = -k_5 \Delta c_1 - k_5 \Delta c_2 - (k_5 + k_6)\Delta c_4 \qquad (3\text{-}180)$$

First, only that derivation will be used, which employed (3-37) for the calculation of the slowest relaxation time (here τ_3). It is thereby indicated that one could also maintain condition (3-25), which is less stringent than the (equivalent) condition (3-175). It is now only assumed that the left step is much faster than anything else. Equation (3-179) and (3-180) then become [together with (3-178)]

$$\frac{d\,\Delta c_2}{dt} = -[k_3 + k_4(1 + K_{2,1})]\Delta c_2 - k_4\,\Delta c_4 \qquad (3\text{-}181)$$

$$\frac{d\,\Delta c_4}{dt} = -k_5(1 + K_{2,1})\Delta c_2 - (k_5 + k_6)\Delta c_4 \qquad (3\text{-}182)$$

Equation (3-37) may now be employed with the proper definitions of the a_{ij} and conditions, resulting after simplification in

$$\tau_3^{-1} = k_5 \left[\frac{1}{1 + K_{4,3}(1 + K_{2,1})} \right] + k_6 \qquad (3\text{-}183)$$

Equation (3-59) was obtained by a modified derivation, which may as well be employed for the system under consideration. To employ the modified derivation of the slowest relaxation time, it is only necessary that *during* occurrence of the slowest step [(3-180) nonvanishing], both (3-178) and (3-179) are zero. One arrives then at a differential equation, containing Δc_4 as the only variable, and (3-183) is the equation for the time constant. It is very important to realize the only condition for the modified derivation: The left and middle steps are quite fast with respect to the right step. There is no specific requirement with reference to the relative speed of the two fast relaxation processes.

If one compares the structure of (3-42) with (3-183), one immediately realizes a general law for the structure of slowest relaxation times in systems of consecutive monomolecular interconversions. If a system of n consecutive monomolecular interconversions is written,

$$Y_1 \underset{k_2}{\overset{k_1}{\rightleftharpoons}} Y_2 \underset{k_4}{\overset{k_3}{\rightleftharpoons}} \cdots \underset{k_{2(n-1)}}{\overset{k_{2n-3}}{\rightleftharpoons}} Y_n \underset{k_{2n}}{\overset{k_{2n-1}}{\rightleftharpoons}} Y_{n+1} \qquad (3\text{-}184)$$

and the slowest step is all the way to the right, the slowest relaxation process has a time constant of

$$\tau_n^{-1} = k_{2n} + k_{2n+1}\left(1 + \sum_{j=1}^{n-1} \prod_{i=j}^{n-1} K_{2i,2i-1}\right)^{-1} \qquad (3\text{-}185)$$

Although (3-185) represents a general expression for τ_n^{-1}, it is of little practical value, as will become quite apparent in later chapters.

Equation (3-185) is valid only for a very slow *terminal* interconversion. If some intermediary monomolecular step is much slower than any other, the smallest reciprocal relaxation time contains again the two smallest rate constants, but each one is associated with an equilibrium factor, similar to the one of (3-185).

One obtains then the generalized form of (3-174). Although consecutive mono-molecular reactions are of little value, the generalized equations for the slowest process may be considered the "backbone" equation for any other system of consecutive reaction steps.

2. If only one more component is added to the system given by (3-171), a number of possibilities arise.

a. One such possibility is given by

$$Y_1 \underset{k_2}{\overset{k_1}{\rightleftarrows}} Y_2 \underset{k_4}{\overset{k_3}{\rightleftarrows}} Y_3 \underset{k_6}{\overset{k_5}{\rightleftarrows}} Y_4 + Y_5 \tag{3-186}$$

To handle such three-step mechanisms more systematically, the formerly introduced coefficients a_{jj} will be used again. They are generally defined by

$$a_{jj} = k'_{2j} + k'_{2j-1} \tag{3-187}$$

with $k'_{2j} = k_{2j}$ for monomolecular transitions or $k'_{2j} = k_{2j}(\bar{c}_r + \bar{c}_s)$ for bimolecular transitions (with r and s representing the indices of the interacting components). Some examples of a_{jj} are given by (3-19) and (3-22). One may now distinguish:

$a_{22} \ll a_{11}, a_{33}$. The result for the slowest relaxation process is then immediately obtained by "substitution," employing the structures of (3-42) and (3-51). The result is

$$\tau_3^{-1} = k_3 \frac{1}{1 + K_{2,1}} + k_4 \frac{\bar{c}_4 + \bar{c}_5}{K_{5,6} + \bar{c}_4 + \bar{c}_5} \tag{3-188}$$

$a_{11} \ll a_{22}, a_{33}$. One has to write the differential equations for c_1, c_2, and c_4. Considering then only dc_1/dt as different from zero leads easily to the expression for the relaxation-time constant,

$$\tau_3^{-1} = k_1 + k_2 \frac{1}{1 + K_{3,4}[1 + K_{5,6}(\bar{c}_4 + \bar{c}_5)^{-1}]} \tag{3-189}$$

The equation was written in such a way that structural similarity to (3-183) is quite apparent. But the denominator may also be written

$$1 + k_3 \left(k_4 \frac{\bar{c}_4 + \bar{c}_5}{K_{5,6} + \bar{c}_4 + \bar{c}_5} \right)^{-1}$$

demonstrating strong similarity to the second term of (3-188). One could have obtained (3-189) also by proper substitution.

$a_{33} \ll a_{11}, a_{22}$. One obtains via the just-mentioned differential equations

$$\tau_3^{-1} = k_5 \frac{1}{1 + K_{4,3}(1 + K_{2,1})} + k_6(\bar{c}_4 + \bar{c}_5) \tag{3-190}$$

It is evident that (3-190) could have been obtained by employing the first term of (3-183) for the first term in this relaxation time, with its second term referring only to the bimolecular transition of (3-186).

b. Another possibility is given by

$$Y_1 \xrightleftharpoons[k_2]{k_1} Y_2 \xrightleftharpoons[k_4]{k_3} Y_3 \xrightleftharpoons[k_6]{k_5} Y_4 \atop Y_5 \qquad (3\text{-}191)$$

The following relations may then exist among the individual reciprocal step relaxation times:

$a_{22} \ll a_{11}, a_{33}$. Combining the structures of (3-42) and (3-57) gives

$$\tau_3^{-1} = k_3 \frac{1}{1 + K_{2,1}} + k_4 \frac{K_{6,5} + \bar{c}_3}{K_{6,5} + \bar{c}_3 + \bar{c}_5} \qquad (3\text{-}192)$$

Conversion of the second term in (3-192) results in

$$k_4 \frac{1}{1 + \bar{c}_5(K_{6,5} + \bar{c}_3)^{-1}}$$

while the second term in (3-188) converts to

$$k_4 \frac{1}{1 + K_{5,6}(\bar{c}_4 + \bar{c}_5)^{-1}}$$

If one considered the "backbone" of these two converted terms, one recognizes the second term of (3-174).

$a_{11} \ll a_{22}, a_{33}$. Solving the system of three differential equations with all simplifying conditions leads for the slowest relaxation process to

$$\tau_3^{-1} = k_1 + k_2 \frac{1}{1 + K_{3,4}[1 + \bar{c}_5(K_{6,5} + \bar{c}_3)^{-1}]} \qquad (3\text{-}193)$$

Similarity and difference between this equation and (3-189) is evident. Rewriting the denominator shows that the coefficient with k_4 is the same one which is present in (3-192).

$a_{33} \ll a_{22}, a_{11}$. Solving for these conditions gives

$$\tau_3^{-1} = k_5 \left(\bar{c}_3 + \bar{c}_5 \frac{1}{1 + K_{4,3}(1 + K_{2,1})} \right) + k_6 \qquad (3\text{-}194)$$

One realizes the expansion of this equation over the type of (3-58), where the fast step to the left of (3-191) is nonexistent.

c. The third possibility of five components in three consecutive reactions is given by

$$Y_1 \xrightleftharpoons[k_2]{k_1} Y_2 \xrightleftharpoons[k_4]{k_3} Y_3 \xrightleftharpoons[k_6]{k_5} Y_4 \atop Y_5 \qquad (3\text{-}195)$$

Again, three relations have to be considered.

$a_{22} \ll a_{11}, a_{33}$. Combination of the proper (and adapted) equations for systems (3-43) and (3-54) leads to

$$\tau_3^{-1} = k_3 \frac{1}{1 + K_{2,1}} + k_4 \left(\bar{c}_3 + \bar{c}_5 \frac{1}{1 + K_{5,6}} \right) \tag{3-196}$$

The correction factor is again associated with that concentration in the bimolecular step, which is not connected to two reaction steps, such as in (3-194) and previous comparable systems of two consecutive reactions.

$a_{11} \ll a_{22}, a_{33}$. One may write three relations among the Δc_i for the slowest process, two of them are independent, such as (3-176) and

$$\Delta c_5 = \Delta c_3 + \Delta c_4 \tag{3-197}$$

Employment of the differential equations for c_1, c_4, and c_5 leads with the applicable assumptions to

$$\tau_3^{-1} = k_1 + k_2 \frac{1}{1 + K_{3,4}\{\bar{c}_3 + \bar{c}_5[1 + (1 + K_{6,5})^{-1}]\}^{-1}} \tag{3-198}$$

It is apparent that the factor with $\bar{c}_5$ lies between 1 and 2 for any $K_{6,5}$.

$a_{33} \ll a_{11}, a_{22}$. For these conditions one arrives at

$$\tau_3^{-1} = k_6 + k_5 \frac{1}{1 + \bar{c}_5[\bar{c}_3 + K_{3,4}(1 + K_{2,1})^{-1}]^{-1}} \tag{3-199}$$

For $K_{2,1} \to 0$, one obtains, after rearrangement, an expression of the type (3-57).

3. Although systems with a slow monomolecular interconversion between two fast reactions of any type can now easily be derived by substitution, more complex systems with slowest bimolecular interconversions are still somewhat obscure. Necessary background material will therefore first be collected in the following sections. Here only some slowest relaxation times will be considered, employing the substitution method to some simpler systems. The criterion for selection is that the slowest step is monomolecular and $a_{22} \ll a_{11}, a_{33}$.

a.

$$Y_1 \underset{k_2}{\overset{k_1}{\longleftrightarrow}} Y_2 \underset{k_4}{\overset{k_3}{\longleftrightarrow}} Y_3 \underset{k_6}{\overset{k_5}{\longleftrightarrow}} Y_4 \tag{3-200}$$

$$Y_5 \qquad Y_6$$

The expression for the smallest reciprocal relaxation time may be gathered from the general structures of (3-42) and (3-73). One obtains

$$\tau_3^{-1} = k_3 \frac{1}{1 + K_{2,1}} + k_4 \frac{1 + K_{5,6}\bar{c}_3/(\bar{c}_4 + \bar{c}_6)}{1 + K_{5,6}(\bar{c}_3 + \bar{c}_5)/(\bar{c}_4 + \bar{c}_6)} \tag{3-201}$$

Certainly, one could also have converted the coefficient with k_4 to

$$\left[1 + \frac{\bar{c}_5}{\bar{c}_3 + (\bar{c}_4 + \bar{c}_6)K_{6,5}}\right]^{-1}$$

showing more similarity in structure to the coefficient immediately below (3-192).

b.

$$Y_1 \underset{k_2}{\overset{k_1}{\rightleftharpoons}} Y_2 \underset{k_4}{\overset{k_3}{\rightleftharpoons}} Y_3 \underset{k_6}{\overset{k_5}{\rightleftharpoons}} Y_4 \qquad (3\text{-}202)$$
$$Y_6 \qquad\qquad Y_5$$

This system is now "almost trivial," but has been selected to show the two different types of coefficients for association right next to each other in one equation. It is

$$\tau_3^{-1} = k_3 \frac{K_{1,2} + \bar{c}_2}{K_{1,2} + \bar{c}_2 + \bar{c}_6} + k_4 \frac{\bar{c}_4 + \bar{c}_5}{K_{5,6} + \bar{c}_4 + \bar{c}_5} \qquad (3\text{-}203)$$

One may convert the two coefficients into the ones written explicitly below (3-192) in conjunction with k_4 (the first one requiring reindexing).

c. Quite generally one may state that a small monomolecular rate constant in an equation for the slowest relaxation time carries the factor $(1 + K'_{i,j})^{-1}$, where i is the index of the fast velocity constant *away* from the slow step and j is the index of the fast velocity constant *toward* the slow step. The "prime" indicates additional involvement of equilibrium concentrations, where bimolecular steps are involved. If only k_i is a bimolecular rate constant, it is

$$K'_{i,j} = \frac{\bar{c} \text{ of component, not in chain}}{K_{j,i} + \bar{c} \text{ of component within chain}} \qquad (3\text{-}204)$$

If only k_j is a bimolecular rate constant, it is

$$K'_{i,j} = \frac{K_{i,j}}{\sum \bar{c} \text{ of both associating components}} \qquad (3\text{-}205)$$

If both k_i and k_j are bimolecular rate constants, it is

$$K'_{i,j} = \frac{\bar{c} \text{ of comp., associating with comp. in chain}}{\bar{c} \text{ of comp. in chain} + K_{j,i}\sum \bar{c} \text{ of both associating comps.}} \qquad (3\text{-}206)$$

This way the coefficients with the slow monomolecular rate constants are normalized.

B. Selected Consecutive Sequential Mechanisms

Only those mechanisms will be considered which show some resemblance to practical cases and cannot be obtained directly by substitution. They all have three steps and a terminal one is much slower than any other.

1. SYSTEMS WITH SIX COMPONENTS.

a. The first one under consideration was previously given as (3-200). $a_{33} \ll a_{11}, a_{22}$ can still easily be handled, since it is an expansion of (3-194) to

$$\tau_3^{-1} = k_5 \left[\bar{c}_3 + \bar{c}_5 \frac{1}{1 + K_{4,3}(1 + K_{2,1})} \right] + k_6(\bar{c}_4 + \bar{c}_6) \qquad (3\text{-}207)$$

$a_{11} \ll a_{22}, a_{33}$ requires its own derivation. One may employ the differential equations $d\,\Delta c_1/dt$, $d\,\Delta c_3/dt + d\,\Delta c_4/dt$, and $d\,\Delta c_4/dt$. Only the first one does not become zero for the slowest step. With the relations among the Δc_i one finally arrives at

$$\tau_3^{-1} = k_1 + k_2 \frac{1}{1 + K_{3,4}\{1 + \bar{c}_5[\bar{c}_3 + (\bar{c}_4 + \bar{c}_6)K_{6,5}]^{-1}\}} \qquad (3\text{-}208)$$

One realizes that (3-206) is also contained in (3-208), although at a more remote location than in (3-201).

b. Next, system (3-202) will be considered. $a_{11} \ll a_{22}, a_{33}$. The differential equations are $d\,\Delta c_1/dt$, $d\,\Delta c_4/dt$, and $d\,\Delta c_3/dt + d\,\Delta c_4/dt$. Only the first one becomes different from zero for the slowest process, the relaxation time of which is

$$\tau_3^{-1} = k_1 + k_2 \left\{ \bar{c}_2 + \bar{c}_6 \frac{1}{1 + K_{3,4}[1 + K_{5,6}(c_4 + c_5)^{-1}]} \right\} \qquad (3\text{-}209)$$

The structure of this equation is, as one would expect, on the ground of the above-mentioned "rules." $a_{33} \ll a_{11}, a_{22}$. The differential equations are $d\,\Delta c_1/dt$, $d\,\Delta c_2/dt + d\,\Delta c_1/dt$, and $d\,\Delta c_4/dt$, and only the last one becomes different from zero for the slowest relaxation process, the time constant of which is given by

$$\tau_3^{-1} = k_5 \frac{1}{1 + K_{4,3}[1 + \bar{c}_6(K_{1,2} + \bar{c}_2)^{-1}]} + k_6(\bar{c}_4 + \bar{c}_5) \qquad (3\text{-}210)$$

The equilibrium coefficient is here inverse in structure compared to the one in (3-209), as one should expect.

c. System (3-202) may be "modified" to give

$$Y_1 \underset{k_2}{\overset{k_1}{\rightleftarrows}} Y_2 \underset{k_4}{\overset{k_3}{\rightleftarrows}} Y_3 \underset{k_6}{\overset{k_5}{\rightleftarrows}} Y_4$$
$$\begin{array}{cc} & \\ Y_6 & Y_5 \end{array} \qquad (3\text{-}211)$$

All three limiting possibilities have to be considered. $a_{11} \ll a_{22}, a_{33}$ with $d\,\Delta c_1/dt \neq 0$ and $d\,\Delta c_6/dt = d\,\Delta c_5/dt = 0$. One obtains for this relaxation process

$$\tau_3^{-1} = k_1 + k_2 \left\{ 1 + K_{3,4} \frac{1}{[1 + K_{5,6}(\bar{c}_4 + \bar{c}_5)^{-1}]^{-1}\bar{c}_6 + \bar{c}_3} \right\}^{-1} \qquad (3\text{-}212)$$

If $K_{5,6} \equiv 0$, Eq. (3-212) becomes of the type (3-51). The "distant" equilibrium factor is again associated with that concentration (here $\bar{c}_6$) which is not within the chain, as in previous systems of coupled reactions.

$a_{22} \ll a_{11}$, a_{33} with $d\,\Delta c_6/dt \neq 0$, while the other two differential equations vanish. One obtains

$$\tau_3^{-1} = k_3 \frac{1}{1 + K_{2,1}} + k_4[\bar{c}_3 + \bar{c}_6(1 + [1 + K_{6,5}(\bar{c}_4 + \bar{c}_5)]^{-1})] \quad (3\text{-}213)$$

The equilibrium factor has here some resemblance to the one contained in (3-198) with the same properties of variability.

$a_{33} \ll a_{11}$, a_{22} with $d\,\Delta c_5/dt \neq 0$, while the remaining two differential equations become zero. It is then

$$\tau_3^{-1} = k_5 \frac{1}{1 + \bar{c}_6[\bar{c}_3 + K_{3,4}(1 + K_{2,1})^{-1}]^{-1}} + k_6(\bar{c}_4 + \bar{c}_5) \quad (3\text{-}214)$$

If $K_{2,1} \to 0$ (component Y_1 nonexistent), (3-214) can be converted to the structure of (3-68), which represents two consecutive associations. If, on the other hand, $\bar{c}_5 \to 0$ (component Y_5 nonexistent), (3-214) becomes practically identical with (3-199).

2. A SYSTEM WITH SEVEN DIFFERENT COMPONENTS.

a. A threefold association (or dissociation), is demonstrated by

$$Y_1 \underset{k_2}{\overset{k_1}{\rightleftharpoons}} Y_2 \underset{k_4}{\overset{k_3}{\rightleftharpoons}} Y_3 \underset{k_6}{\overset{k_5}{\rightleftharpoons}} Y_4$$
$$Y_7 \qquad\qquad Y_6 \qquad\qquad Y_5 \quad (3\text{-}215)$$

Another component is here added to the chain of system (3-211). Three possibilities are now considered, selecting the three differential equations $d\,\Delta c_6/dt$, $d\,\Delta c_5/dt$, and $d\,\Delta c_7/dt$.

$a_{11} \ll a_{22}$, a_{33} leads for the slowest relaxation process to

$$\tau_3^{-1} = k_1 + k_2\left(\bar{c}_2 + \bar{c}_7 \frac{1}{1 + K_{3,4}\{\bar{c}_3 + \bar{c}_6[1 + K_{5,6}(\bar{c}_4 + \bar{c}_5)^{-1}]^{-1}\}^{-1}}\right) \quad (3\text{-}216)$$

The structure of the factor with $\bar{c}_7$ is rather striking. One can directly imagine the next factor added to $\bar{c}_5$ for the case of another quite fast reaction step connecting to the right side of (3-215). If the right reaction step in (3-215) is omitted, (3-216) reduces to an equation which can easily be converted to the structure of (3-66).

$a_{22} \ll a_{11}$, a_{33}. One may write down the result for the slow step directly according to the substitution method:

$$\tau_3^{-1} = k_3 \frac{1}{1 + \bar{c}_7(\bar{c}_2 + K_{1,2})^{-1}} + k_4\left(\bar{c}_3 + \bar{c}_6 \frac{1}{1 + K_{5,6}(\bar{c}_4 + \bar{c}_5)^{-1}}\right) \quad (3\text{-}217)$$

Similarity to structural parts of (3-214) and (3-216) are quite evident. $a_{33} \ll a_{11}, a_{22}$ leads with the above differential equations to

$$\tau_3^{-1} = k_5 \frac{1}{1 + \bar{c}_6(\bar{c}_3 + K_{3,4}\{1 + \bar{c}_7/(K_{1,2} + \bar{c}_2)\}^{-1})^{-1}} + k_6(\bar{c}_4 + \bar{c}_5) \quad (3\text{-}218)$$

There is considerable similarity between (3-214) and (3-218). If $\bar{c}_2 = 0$ and $\bar{c}_7 = 1$ (and dimensionless), one may "formally" derive (3-214) from (3-218).

    b. Further combinations among seven (or more) different components in three-step reactions will not be considered now, although many of their equations could be derived by the previously mentioned substitution method or pure analogy. But these equations are generally quite complex, which makes their use less valuable. This is particularly the case, if isomolecular reactions are also incorporated. Under such conditions it is preferable to employ buffering conditions. How kinetic relations are modified upon buffering is shown in Chapter 5 [first in conjunction with (5-29)].

    There is one complex system, which is of particular interest for enzyme reactions; this system involves multiple feedback and is quite representative of the complexity of derivations. This same system also demonstrates very well what aspects have to be considered to obtain useful expressions for the relaxation times. Such a system will therefore be derived in detail next.

3–4. MULTIPLE FEEDBACK

A. The "Two-Step-Bimolecular Two-Path System"

    One component combines with two different components sequentially and in two different pathways. The alcohol-dehydrogenase system contains such a dual-path sequence. One cycle of a full dehydrogenase system can generally be isolated by selecting the pH range (3). As several new methods are employed for the elementary solution of the problem, the presentation will be given quite elaborately. The reaction system is presented in general terms to make it easily applicable to any similar multicyclic system:

$$
\begin{array}{ccc}
& Y_2 \xrightarrow[k_2]{k_1} Y_3 & \\
Y_5' \diagdown & & \diagup Y_5'' \\
& Y_6 & \\
k_6 \downarrow k_5 & & k_4 \downarrow k_3 \\
& Y_1 \xrightarrow[k_8]{k_7} Y_4 &
\end{array}
\qquad (3\text{-}219)
$$

All bimolecular rate constants have odd indices, all monomolecular ones even indices. Certainly, it is $Y_5' = Y_5''$; separation has only been introduced for computational reasons. The relations among the Δc_i for the slowest steps are

$$\Delta c_3 = -\Delta c_4 - \Delta c_6 \quad (3\text{-}220)$$

$$\Delta c_5 = -\Delta c_1 - \Delta c_4 \quad (3\text{-}221)$$

$$\Delta c_2 = \Delta c_6 - \Delta c_1 \quad (3\text{-}222)$$

By substitution one may select several other combinations of three equations. But only three equations can be found to be functionally independent, which is based on the fact that the system permits only three laws of conservation: Equation (3-220) represents the law of conservation of the mass of Y_6, (3-221) that of the conservation of the mass of Y_5, and (3-222) represents a combination of (3-220) and the law of conservation of the mass of Y_1 (comprising components Y_1, Y_2, Y_3, and Y_4). These conservation equations are a direct consequence of the definition of the analytical concentrations c_1^0, c_5^0, and c_6^0.

Looking now at the isolated step-relaxation times, it is here only assumed that the steps involving Y_6 are much slower than the steps involving Y_5. As for the consideration of this section, it does not matter how close or how far apart the steps with Y_5' and with Y_5'' are. The additional labeling of Y_5 is only introduced for purposes of theoretical differentiation. If these two fast step-relaxation times are sufficiently far apart, the first relaxation-time constant is given by an equation of the type of (3-7), the second one by an equation of the type (3-63).

For the derivation of the third relaxation-time constant one may then consider, as in equilibrium,

$$\frac{d \Delta c_5'}{dt} = k_6 \Delta c_1 - k_5 \bar{c}_2 \Delta c_5 - k_5 \bar{c}_5 \Delta c_2 \equiv 0 \qquad (3\text{-}223)$$

$$\frac{d \Delta c_5''}{dt} = k_4 \Delta c_4 - k_3 \bar{c}_3 \Delta c_5 - k_3 \bar{c}_5 \Delta c_3 \equiv 0 \qquad (3\text{-}224)$$

The differentiation between Y_5' and Y_5'' ceases with these two equations. Only one differential equation can be formed, in which neither equation (3-223) nor (3-224) appear:

$$\frac{d \Delta c_6}{dt} = k_2 \Delta c_3 + k_8 \Delta c_4 - k_1 \bar{c}_2 \Delta c_6 - k_1 \bar{c}_6 \Delta c_2 - k_7 \bar{c}_1 \Delta c_6 - k_7 \bar{c}_6 \Delta c_1$$

$$(3\text{-}225)$$

There are six unknowns; therefore, only six equations are necessary. If (3-223) and (3-224) are selected as separate equations, the sixth equation has to be selected such that it covers at least all remaining reaction steps. And (3-225) is the only one which fulfills this requirement. If $Y_6 \equiv 0$, this approach is not possible. The two slow monomolecular interconversions would have to be treated differently (see the next section!).

Equation (3-225) describes the third relaxation process and is nonvanishing in its time range, now under consideration. This equation contains *all* rate constants of the two slower steps, leading to the result that there is no fourth relaxation time. The physical meaning of this result will be discussed later [behind (3-268)]. To solve (3-225) one has to convert it so that Δc_6 is the only variable concentration change. There is a large number of possibilities in which this conversion can be accomplished, the question then being whether there is any preferable way.

The reactions involving Y_5 are considered quite rapid. This may simply be due to the fact that $\bar{c}_5$ is comparatively quite high, or buffered, which has the same effect. Δc_5 would then be relatively quite small (compared to $\bar{c}_5$). It is also always immediately equilibrating. It is also quite unlikely that Y_5 will be employed for indicating purposes. One may therefore eliminate Δc_5 first, which is also an advantage on the grounds that (3-225) contains no Δc_5. One may establish four independent equations, in which Δc_5 appears: (3-223), (3-224), (3-221), and

$$\Delta c_5 = \Delta c_2 + \Delta c_3 \qquad (3\text{-}226)$$

which may take the place of either (3-220) or (3-222). The concentration change Δc_5 could be eliminated by just employing equations (3-223) and (3-224). One should then also omit (3-221) and (3-226), whereas omission of only one of them is permissible. It seems thus more advisable to take both of these last two equations and insert them suitably into (3-223) and (3-224). Use of (3-226) seems to give functions which are quite similar in structure.

$$k_6\, \Delta c_1 = k_5(\bar{c}_2 + \bar{c}_5)\Delta c_2 + k_5\bar{c}_2\, \Delta c_3 \qquad (3\text{-}227)$$

$$k_4\, \Delta c_1 = k_3(\bar{c}_3 + \bar{c}_5)\Delta c_3 + k_3\bar{c}_3\, \Delta c_2 \qquad (3\text{-}228)$$

Using (3-221) instead results in the pair

$$(k_6 + k_5\bar{c}_2)\Delta c_1 + k_5\bar{c}_2\, \Delta c_4 = k_5\bar{c}_5\, \Delta c_2 \qquad (3\text{-}229)$$

$$(k_4 + k_3\bar{c}_3)\Delta c_4 + k_3\bar{c}_3\, \Delta c_1 = k_3\bar{c}_5\, \Delta c_3 \qquad (3\text{-}230)$$

Either Δc_1 or Δc_4 can be eliminated in these last two equations, but any one solution would be more complex than the elimination of Δc_1 from (3-227) and (3-228). Elimination of either Δc_1 or Δc_4 from the last two equations introduces immediately subtractive terms, which should be avoided in derivations, finally covering wide ranges in the individual parameters (and small experimental errors may become large ones in decisive differences). It is also apparent that while the former pair of equations carries only three unknown variables, the latter pair carries four of them.

Either the first pair [(3-227) and (3-228)] or the second pair [(3-229) and (3-230)] may then be combined with (3-220) *and* (3-222). At the end, every $\Delta c_{i \neq 6}$ has to be expressed in terms of Δc_6, so that insertion in (3-225) and its solution become possible. These possible solutions will now be derived and discussed, starting with the first pair.

Equations (3-227) and (3-228) lead to the following relation between Δc_2 and Δc_3:

$$[K_{5,6}(\bar{c}_2 + \bar{c}_5) - K_{3,4}\bar{c}_3]\Delta c_2 = [K_{3,4}(\bar{c}_3 + \bar{c}_5) - K_{5,6}\bar{c}_2]\Delta c_3 \qquad (3\text{-}231)$$

Although this equation gives a rather symmetric relation between Δc_2 and Δc_3, it seems not very helpful, as all concentration changes should be related to Δc_6. The change Δc_4 does not appear in (3-227) or (3-228) or (3-321). One therefore *has* to use (3-220) for its elimination. Δc_3 then may be derived from (3-227) and Δc_2 from (3-228)—where the exchange of the two equations is also possible. Δc_1 finally has to be derived from (3-222). One thus obtains in the first place,

$$K_{6,5}(\Delta c_6 - \Delta c_2) = (\bar{c}_2 + \bar{c}_5)\Delta c_2 + \bar{c}_2 \, \Delta c_3 \tag{3-232}$$

$$K_{4,3}(\Delta c_6 - \Delta c_2) = (\bar{c}_3 + \bar{c}_5)\Delta c_3 + \bar{c}_3 \, \Delta c_2 \tag{3-233}$$

Solving both equations for Δc_2 and eliminating Δc_2 leads to an equation for Δc_3; solving both equations for Δc_3 and eliminating Δc_3 leads to an equation for Δc_2. The resulting equations are

$$\Delta c_2 = \alpha \, \Delta c_6 \tag{3-234}$$

$$\Delta c_3 = \beta \, \Delta c_6 \tag{3-235}$$

with

$$\alpha = \left(\frac{K_{4,3}}{K_{4,3} + \bar{c}_3} - \frac{K_{6,5}}{K_{6,5} + \bar{c}_2 + \bar{c}_5} \right) \bigg/ \left(\frac{\bar{c}_3 + \bar{c}_5}{\bar{c}_3 + K_{4,3}} - \frac{\bar{c}_2}{\bar{c}_2 + \bar{c}_5 + K_{6,5}} \right) \tag{3-236}$$

and

$$\beta = \left(\frac{K_{4,3}}{\bar{c}_3 + \bar{c}_5} - \frac{K_{6,5}}{\bar{c}_2} \right) \bigg/ \left(\frac{K_{4,3} + \bar{c}_3}{\bar{c}_3 + \bar{c}_5} - \frac{K_{6,5} + \bar{c}_2 + \bar{c}_5}{\bar{c}_2} \right) \tag{3-237}$$

These last two equations could certainly be simplified further, but the magnitude of each term relative to unity would thereby be covered up. The appearance of subtractive terms makes it difficult to visualize the range of α and β, as long as no specific values for the parameters are given. One easily derives from (3-220), (3-222), (3-234), and (3-235) that

$$\Delta c_1 = (1 - \alpha)\Delta c_6 \tag{3-238}$$

$$\Delta c_4 = -(1 + \beta)\Delta c_6 \tag{3-239}$$

The various equations could now be inserted in (3-225), which is here postponed until after the comprehensive discussion.

The "second pair" consisted of (3-229) and (3-230). One may eliminate either Δc_1 or Δc_4, resulting in a combined equation, which still contains three different Δc_i in contrast to (3-231). Any simplification of this kind is therefore not worthwhile, and one may immediately proceed with the combination of these equations with (3-220) and (3-222).

Equation (3-229) offers itself as *the* equation for Δc_2, while (3-230) offers itself as *the* equation for Δc_3. Δc_1 and Δc_4 are then derived from (3-220) and (3-222). One obtains thus in the first place,

$$\bar{c}_5 \, \Delta c_2 = (K_{6,5} + \bar{c}_2)(\Delta c_6 - \Delta c_2) - \bar{c}_2(\Delta c_6 + \Delta c_3) \tag{3-240}$$

$$\bar{c}_5 \, \Delta c_3 = (K_{4,3} + \bar{c}_3)(-\Delta c_6 - \Delta c_3) + \bar{c}_3(\Delta c_6 - \Delta c_2) \tag{3-241}$$

One may now proceed as before to obtain the expressions for Δc_2 and Δc_3, which are now

$$\Delta c_2 = \alpha \, \Delta c_6 \tag{3-242}$$

$$\Delta c_3 = \beta \, \Delta c_6 \tag{3-243}$$

with

$$\alpha = \left(\frac{K_{4,3}}{K_{4,3} + \bar{c}_3 + \bar{c}_5} + \frac{K_{6,5}}{\bar{c}_2} \right) \Bigg/ \left(\frac{\bar{c}_2 + \bar{c}_5 + K_{6,5}}{\bar{c}_2} - \frac{\bar{c}_3}{\bar{c}_3 + \bar{c}_5 + K_{4,3}} \right) \tag{3-244}$$

and

$$\beta = \left(\frac{K_{4,3}}{\bar{c}_3} + \frac{K_{6,5}}{K_{6,5} + \bar{c}_2 + \bar{c}_5} \right) \Bigg/ \left(\frac{\bar{c}_3 + \bar{c}_5 + K_{4,3}}{\bar{c}_3} - \frac{\bar{c}_2}{\bar{c}_2 + \bar{c}_5 + K_{6,5}} \right) \tag{3-245}$$

There is no doubt that the denominator and both α and β are always positive. If the earlier assumption, $\bar{c}_5 \gg \bar{c}_2$, $\bar{c}_3$, is valid, the denominator will even be much larger than unity. The peculiar symmetry characteristics among these last two equations are also quite striking. The expressions for the remaining Δc_i are now easily obtained with (3-220) and (3-222), resulting in equations which are "slightly different" from (3-238) plus (3-239):

$$\Delta c_1 = (1 - \alpha)\Delta c_6 \tag{3-246}$$

$$\Delta c_4 = (\beta - 1)\Delta c_6 \tag{3-247}$$

Before these results are discussed further, one more derivation will be given.

There is one alternative approach, in which (3-229) and (3-230) may be used. In this approach, (3-222) is employed to eliminate Δc_2 in (3-229), and (3-220) is applied to replace Δc_3 in (3-230). The alternative approach leads in the first place to

$$(K_{6,5} + \bar{c}_2)\Delta c_1 + \bar{c}_2 \, \Delta c_4 = \bar{c}_5(\Delta c_6 - \Delta c_1) \tag{3-248}$$

$$(K_{4,3} + \bar{c}_3)\Delta c_4 + \bar{c}_3 \, \Delta c_1 = -\bar{c}_5(\Delta c_6 + \Delta c_4) \tag{3-249}$$

As already twice before, one may now solve both equations for Δc_4, eliminate Δc_4, and express Δc_1 in terms of Δc_6; on the other hand, one may solve both equations for Δc_1, eliminate Δc_1, and express Δc_4 in terms of Δc_6. The result is

$$\Delta c_1 = \alpha' \, \Delta c_6 \tag{3-250}$$

$$\Delta c_4 = -\beta' \, \Delta c_6 \tag{3-251}$$

with

$$\alpha' = \left(\frac{\bar{c}_5}{\bar{c}_5 + \bar{c}_3 + K_{4,3}} + \frac{\bar{c}_5}{\bar{c}_2} \right) \Bigg/ \left(\frac{\bar{c}_2 + \bar{c}_5 + K_{6,5}}{\bar{c}_2} - \frac{\bar{c}_3}{\bar{c}_3 + \bar{c}_5 + K_{4,3}} \right) \tag{3-252}$$

and

$$\beta' = \left(\frac{\bar{c}_5}{\bar{c}_3} + \frac{\bar{c}_5}{\bar{c}_5 + \bar{c}_2 + K_{6,5}} \right) \Bigg/ \left(\frac{\bar{c}_3 + \bar{c}_5 + K_{4,3}}{\bar{c}_3} - \frac{\bar{c}_2}{\bar{c}_2 + \bar{c}_5 + K_{6,5}} \right) \tag{3-253}$$

The denominators are identical with those of equations (3-244) and (3-245). One should expect that

$$\alpha' = 1 - \alpha \qquad (3\text{-}254)$$

$$\beta' = 1 - \beta \qquad (3\text{-}255)$$

One may expect this from comparison of (3-246) with (3-250) and of (3-247) with (3-251). One may prove (3-254) and (3-255) easily by employing the full expressions for α and β from (3-244) and (3-245); the final result can be shown to agree with the right sides of (3-252) and (3-253).

The concentration changes Δc_2 and Δc_3 are now expressed in terms of Δc_6 by employing equations (3-220) and (3-222), leading to

$$\Delta c_2 = (1 - \alpha')\Delta c_6 \qquad (3\text{-}256)$$

$$\Delta c_3 = (\beta' - 1)\Delta c_6 \qquad (3\text{-}257)$$

The structural similarity to (3-246) and (3-247) is quite evident, as one should expect from the previous two equations (3-254) and (3-255).

It is of interest now to compare the various expressions for α and β obtained thus far. As was already pointed out indirectly, α according to (3-244) and α' according to (3-252) are always positive, whatever the equilibrium constants and whatever the equilibrium concentrations. One might expect problems in the error to interfere severely, when $\bar{c}_2$, $\bar{c}_3 \gg \bar{c}_5$, $K_{4,3}$, $K_{6,5}$. But the denominator may easily be rewritten

$$\frac{\bar{c}_2 + \bar{c}_5 + K_{6,5}}{\bar{c}_2} - \frac{\bar{c}_3}{\bar{c}_3 + \bar{c}_5 + K_{4,3}}$$

$$= \frac{\bar{c}_3(\bar{c}_5 + K_{6,5}) + (\bar{c}_5 + K_{4,3})(\bar{c}_5 + K_{6,5}) + \bar{c}_2(\bar{c}_5 + K_{4,3})}{\bar{c}_2(\bar{c}_3 + \bar{c}_5 + K_{4,3})} \qquad (3\text{-}258)$$

The difference then disappears and no problems of error interference become visible at all. This consideration is valid for all four equations (3-244), (3-245), (3-252), and (3-253). But it is also apparent from inspection that none of the differences can be eliminated in (3-236) and (3-237). It is also quite apparent that any one of the differences may become close enough to zero that the error in the determinations becomes larger than the difference, making any further evaluation impossible. Equations (3-236) and (3-237) should therefore not be used further.

One finally has a choice of either using α and β from (3-244) and (3-245) or α' and β' from (3-252) and (3-253) for the further processing of (3-225). As there are four Δc_i to be substituted, one may also employ all four equations, thus avoiding the appearance of differences. Actually, all these now remaining coefficients α, α', β, and β' are positive. As (3-254) and (3-255) have also to be fulfilled, one realizes at once the fundamental relation

$$0 < \alpha, \alpha', \beta, \beta' < 1 \qquad (3\text{-}259)$$

All four coefficients will now be used in combination, employing thus (3-242), (3-243), (3-250), and (3-251) in the further processing of (3-225).

Equation (3-225) becomes, with the proper substitutions,

$$\frac{d\,\Delta c_6}{dt} = -\tau_3^{-1}\,\Delta c_6 \tag{3-260}$$

with

$$\tau_3^{-1} = k_2\beta + k_8\beta' + k_1(\bar{c}_2 + \alpha\bar{c}_6) + k_7(\bar{c}_1 + \alpha'\bar{c}_6) \tag{3-261}$$

By employing (3-254) and (3-255), one may write τ_3^{-1} in various other ways to demonstrate individual features. On the other hand, one may also look at the ratio α/β to learn more about their difference. One obtains

$$\frac{\alpha}{\beta} = \frac{(\bar{c}_2 K_{4,3} + \bar{c}_3 K_{6,5} + K_{4,3} K_{6,5}) + \bar{c}_5 K_{6,5}}{(\bar{c}_2 K_{4,3} + \bar{c}_3 K_{6,5} + K_{4,3} K_{6,5}) + \bar{c}_5 K_{4,3}} \tag{3-262}$$

One realizes that numerator and denominator are only different by the very last term. One may then give limits for the ratio α/β: If

$$\frac{K_{6,5}}{K_{4,3}} < 1 \qquad \text{then } 1 > \frac{\alpha}{\beta} > \frac{K_{6,5}}{K_{4,3}} \tag{3-263}$$

$$\frac{K_{6,5}}{K_{4,3}} > 1 \qquad \text{then } 1 < \frac{\alpha}{\beta} < \frac{K_{6,5}}{K_{4,3}} \tag{3-264}$$

These relationships may become important in the evaluation of results. Similarly, one may derive the ratio α'/β', which becomes

$$\frac{\alpha'}{\beta'} = \frac{\bar{c}_2 + \bar{c}_3 + \bar{c}_5 + K_{4,3}}{\bar{c}_2 + \bar{c}_3 + \bar{c}_5 + K_{6,5}} \tag{3-265}$$

The limits for α'/β' are given by

$$1 < \frac{\alpha'}{\beta'} < \frac{K_{4,3}}{K_{6,5}} \qquad \text{for } \frac{K_{4,3}}{K_{6,5}} > 1 \tag{3-226}$$

$$1 > \frac{\alpha'}{\beta'} > \frac{K_{4,3}}{K_{6,5}} \qquad \text{for } \frac{K_{4,3}}{K_{6,5}} < 1 \tag{3-267}$$

Whereas in (3-262) the limit $K_{6,5}/K_{4,3}$ could be approached simply by a relatively large $\bar{c}_5$, this is not possible at all in (3-265). To approach the limit $K_{4,3}/K_{6,5}$ in (3-265), one has to observe

$$\bar{c}_2, \bar{c}_3, \bar{c}_5 \ll K_{4,3}, K_{6,5} \tag{3-268}$$

This extreme condition (3-268) is unfortunately difficult to obtain experimentally. The easily accessible range places α/β and α'/β' generally near the middle between the indicated limits.

Equation (3-261) permits four (limiting) processes to occur, depending upon the size of the individual terms. For better visualization it is also referred to the reaction scheme of (3-219).

1. $k_2\beta \gg k_8\beta'$. Rate constant k_2 is involved in the relaxation process, described by (3-261) and k_8 is not.

a. $k_1(\bar{c}_2 + \alpha\bar{c}_6) \gg k_7(\bar{c}_1 + \alpha'\bar{c}_6)$. The reaction step between Y_1 and Y_4 is not operating at all. Chemical relaxation proceed only among the remaining three steps.

b. $k_1(\bar{c}_2 + \alpha\bar{c}_6) \ll k_7(\bar{c}_1 + \alpha'\bar{c}_6)$. Chemical relaxation proceeds counterclockwise; that is, mass transfer after perturbation occurs in the direction from Y_1 to Y_4 to Y_3 to Y_2 and back to Y_1.

2. $k_2\beta \ll k_8\beta'$. Rate constant k_8 involved in the relaxation process, described by (3-261) and k_2 is not.

a. $k_1(\bar{c}_2 + \alpha\bar{c}_6) \gg k_7(\bar{c}_1 + \alpha'\bar{c}_6)$. Chemical relaxation proceeds in a clockwise cycle (contrary to 1,b), which means that mass transfer after perturbation occurs in the direction from Y_1 to Y_2 to Y_3 to Y_4 and back to Y_1.

b. $k_1(\bar{c}_2 + \alpha\bar{c}_6) \ll k_7(\bar{c}_1 + \alpha'\bar{c}_6)$. The reaction step between Y_2 and Y_3 is not operating at all. Only the remaining three steps are involved in the chemical relaxation process. This case is the alternative case to 1,a.

Each term in (3-261) contains a rate constant and a concentration-containing factor. As the latter can be varied to some degree by the experimenter, he may be able to a certain extent to switch between limiting processes.

B. The "Reduced" Cycle

The "reduced" cycle consists of two pathways for bimolecular association coupled with monomolecular interconversion. Two bimolecular associations, and two monomolecular interconversions make up the four-step cycle. Such a system may be described in general terms by the scheme

$$(3\text{-}269)$$

The labeling in this scheme is quite similar to the one in (3-219), to facilitate later comparisons of the structures of equivalent solutions. Y_5' and Y_5'' have again been separated solely for computational reasons. It will soon become clear why scheme (3-269) was not treated before the apparently more complicated scheme (3-219).

Again, only the slowest relaxation process will be treated. For this process one may choose among several relations for the various Δc_i, which may be derived from only *two* conservation laws;

$$\Delta c_1 + \Delta c_2 + \Delta c_3 + \Delta c_4 = 0 \qquad (3\text{-}270)$$

$$\Delta c_1 + \Delta c_4 + \Delta c_5 = 0 \qquad (3\text{-}271)$$

Equations (3-223) and (3-224) are again fully valid; no reindexing is necessary. An equation such as (3-225) is unfortunately not directly available. On the other hand, a fifth equation *has* to be found. And this fifth equation has to contain all four rate constants of the slow monomolecular interconversions.

Initially, one may write the differential equations for Y_3 and Y_4:

$$\Delta \dot{c}_3 = k_1 \, \Delta c_2 + k_4 \, \Delta c_4 - k_2 \, \Delta c_3 - k_3 \bar{c}_3 \, \Delta c_5 - k_3 \bar{c}_5 \, \Delta c_3 \qquad (3\text{-}272)$$

$$\Delta \dot{c}_4 = k_7 \, \Delta c_1 + k_3 \bar{c}_3 \, \Delta c_5 + k_3 \bar{c}_5 \, \Delta c_3 - k_4 \, \Delta c_4 - k_8 \, \Delta c_4 \qquad (3\text{-}273)$$

The sum of these two differential equations results in one, which is quite similar to (3-225):

$$\Delta \dot{c}_3 + \Delta \dot{c}_4 = k_1 \, \Delta c_2 - k_2 \, \Delta c_3 + k_7 \, \Delta c_1 - k_8 \, \Delta c_4 \qquad (3\text{-}274)$$

To solve this last equation more conveniently, an "imaginary operator" is introduced such that

$$\Delta \dot{c}_3 + \Delta \dot{c}_4 \equiv -\Delta \dot{c}_6 \qquad (3\text{-}275)$$

Employing this "operator" also for concentration changes, one immediately realizes the validity of equations (3-220) and (3-222). One may then directly start on with the "second pair" of equations (3-229) and (3-230). As all original definitions are now valid, one may proceed directly to (3-242), (3-243), (3-250), and (3-251), together with the appropriate definition of coefficients. Equations (3-254) and (3-255) are again valid without restriction, as are (3-259), (3-262), and the equations thereafter up to (and including) (3-268).

The solution may temporarily be given in terms of the (imaginary) parameter Δc_6, which simply means validity of (3-260); *but* τ_3^{-1} here has a different meaning for reaction scheme (3-269). One derives from (3-274), upon proper substitution,

$$\tau_3^{-1} = \alpha k_1 + \beta k_2 + \alpha' k_7 + \beta' k_8 \qquad (3\text{-}276)$$

The coefficients to the rate constants are given by (3-244), (3-245), (3-250), and (3-251), respectively. The similarity between equations (3-261) and (3-276) is quite evident.

Equation (3-276) again permits four (limiting) processes to occur, depending upon the size of the individual terms. For better visualization, it is referred to the initial reaction scheme, represented by (3-269).

1. $k_2 \beta \gg k_8 \beta'$. Rate constant k_2 is involved in the relaxation process described by (3-276), k_8 is not.

a. $k_1 \alpha \gg k_7 \alpha'$. The reaction step between Y_1 and Y_4 is not at all involved in the relaxation process, which proceeds only within the remaining three steps.

b. $k_1\alpha \ll k_7\alpha'$. The chemical relaxation process moves essentially only in one direction, counterclockwise, with direction of mass flow after perturbation from Y_1 to Y_4 to Y_3 to Y_2 and back to Y_1.

2. $k_2\beta \ll k_8\beta'$. Rate constant k_8 is involved in the relaxation process described by (3-276), k_2 is not.

a. $k_1\alpha \gg k_7\alpha'$. Chemical relaxation proceeds essentially only in one direction, clockwise (in contrast to 1,b); mass flow upon perturbation proceeds in the general direction from Y_1 to Y_2 to Y_3 to Y_4 and back to Y_1.

b. $k_1\alpha \ll k_7\alpha'$. The reaction step between Y_2 and Y_3 is not operating at all. Only the remaining three steps are involved in the chemical relaxation process. This case is thus the alternative to case 1,a.

Each term in equation (3-276) contains a rate constant and a concentration-containing factor. As an investigator may vary the latter to some degree, he becomes able to choose among limiting processes, although the extent of such choice may be rather limited.

Such cyclic reactions may easily occur in biological systems. Actually, one might even expect the presence of systems of such cycles. Such more complex systems will not be considered in this introductory treatment. The same principles developed before would have to be applied.

So far, the monomolecular steps in the system of (3-269) were considered as being much slower than the bimolecular ones. But it is also possible that the monomolecular steps in this system proceed much faster than the bimolecular ones. Such a system should then lead to a relaxation time which is clearly different from (3-276). To employ the same slow rate constants as before, and to obtain an expression which is better comparable with both (3-261) and (3.276), the system is rewritten

$$\begin{array}{ccc} Y_2 & \underset{k_2}{\overset{k_1}{\rightleftarrows}} & Y_3 \\ {\scriptstyle k_6}\Big\uparrow{\scriptstyle k_5} & Y_6 & {\scriptstyle k_4}\Big\uparrow{\scriptstyle k_3} \\ Y_1 & \underset{k_8}{\overset{k_7}{\rightleftarrows}} & Y_4 \end{array} \qquad (3\text{-}277)$$

With reference to analytical concentrations one may write the two equations

$$c_1^0 = \bar{c}_1 + \bar{c}_1 + \bar{c}_3 + \bar{c}_4 \qquad (3\text{-}278)$$

$$c_6^0 = \bar{c}_6 + \bar{c}_3 + \bar{c}_4 \qquad (3\text{-}279)$$

The relations among the Δc_i for the slowest step are then given by (3-220), for instance, and (3-222). The two much faster equilibria are simply given by equations which are simplified compared to (3-223) and (3-224):

$$k_6\,\Delta c_1 = k_5\,\Delta c_2 \qquad (3\text{-}280)$$

$$k_3\,\Delta c_3 = k_4\,\Delta c_4 \qquad (3\text{-}281)$$

Four equations are now given and the fifth for the fifth (and last) unknown variable is given by the differential equation for Δc_6, which turns out to be identical to (3-225). Upon solving for τ_3^{-1} one realizes that (3-225) is again valid, but the parameters are highly simplified and become

$$\alpha = (1 + K_{5,6})^{-1} \tag{3-282}$$

$$\beta = (1 + K_{3,4})^{-1} \tag{3-283}$$

$$\alpha' = (1 + K_{6,5})^{-1} \tag{3-284}$$

$$\beta' = (1 + K_{4,3})^{-1} \tag{3-285}$$

One realizes almost instantly that relations (3-254) and (3-255) are again valid. One may write down the full equation for τ_3^{-1} and obtains, upon simplification,

$$\tau_3^{-1} = \frac{K_{4,3}k_2 + k_8}{K_{4,3} + 1} + (k_1 K_{6,5} + k_7)\bar{c}_1 + \frac{K_{6,5}k_1 + k_7}{K_{6,5} + 1}\bar{c}_6 \tag{3-286}$$

The first term is just a constant. The monomolecular rate constants k_2 and k_8 cannot be calculated separately, even if $K_{4,3}$ were known. The bimolecular rate constants could also not be calculated from the slopes of plots of τ_3^{-1} versus $\bar{c}_1$ or $\bar{c}_6$, respectively, even if $K_{6,5}$ were known. But any difference between these two slopes just mentioned would be the indication of system (3-277). As one may also have $K_{6,5} \ll 1$, any absence of a difference between the slopes does not exclude the presence of a system given by (3-277).

PROBLEMS

1. Derive (3-6).
2. Derive (3-9) in detail.
3. What is the expression of the relaxation time for the system $Y_1 + Y_2 + Y_3 \rightleftharpoons Y_4$?
4. Derive (3-30) and compute b for $\tau_2 = 10\tau_1$. If this value for b is used for (3-32), which is then employed in (3-26), (3-27), and (3-29), how large is the deviation from the exact value for these equations?
5. Derive (3-57) and (3-58) for the system (3-54), according to the "steady-state treatment."
6. Derive (3-63).
7. Write down the various relations among the Δc_i for the system (3-75) and both cases a and b; then derive (3-77) and (3-79).
8. Derive (3-82), (3-84), and (3-86).
9. Show that (3-106) can also be derived from the two differential equations *without* multiplying (3-104) by 2.
10. Derive (3-148) and (3-152) in detail.
11. Show how (3-164) and (3-165) are derived.

12. Derive (3-170) in detail.
13. Derive the longest relaxation time for four consecutive monomolecular inter-conversions using a system of four differential equations (one terminal inconversion is much slower than any other step). Compare the results with (3-185) for $n = 4$.
14. Derive (3-189) and (3-199) in detail, starting with the differential equations for c_1, c_4, and c_5.
15. Derive in detail (3-212), (3-213), and (3-214), employing the differential equations mentioned below (3-211).
16. Derive (3-216) to (3-218) employing the differential equations mentioned in the text below (3-215).
17. Derive (3-242) and (3-243) in detail from (3-229) and (3-230).
18. Derive (3-250) and (3-251) in detail from (3-229) and (3-230).
19. Prove (3-254) and (3-255) in the way indicated in the text below these equations.

REFERENCES

1. G. Czerlinski and M. Eigen, *Z. Elektrochem.*, **63**, 652 (1959), discussion following (28).
2. G. Czerlinski and F. Hommes, *Biochim. Biophys. Acta.*, **79**, 46 (1964).
3. G. Czerlinski, "The Mechanism of Action of the Pyridine Nucleotide Dependent Dehydrogenases," at a symposium, University of Kentucky, Lexington, Kentucky, March 16 to 18, 1965 (Proceedings in preparation).

CHAPTER 4

STATICS (EQUILIBRIUM CONCENTRATIONS AND SIGNALS)

4–1. ONE-STEP MECHANISMS

A. The Monomolecular Interconversion

The monomolecular interconversion is represented by (1-1), with the dissociation constant given by (1-4). In this system

$$c_1^0 - \bar{c}_1 = \bar{c}_2 - c_2^0 \tag{4-1}$$

Solving (1-4) and (4-1) for $\bar{c}_1$ gives the simple relationship (generally with $c_2^0 \equiv 0$, as the system would be "overdetermined" with $c_1^0, c_2^0 \neq 0$; see below):

$$\bar{c}_1 = \frac{K_{2,1}}{1 + K_{2,1}} (c_1^0 + c_2^0) \tag{4-2}$$

Equilibrium concentrations $\bar{c}_i$ are not generally directly measured, but by means of some signal S_T. In optical-detection systems, one generally has also to consider a reference signal S_0 (it is, for instance, the signal obtained without any absorbing or fluorescing component Y_i). One may then write

$$S_T - S_0 = \sum_i \eta_i \bar{c}_i \tag{4-3}$$

where η_i is the characteristic signal of the ith component, defined by

$$\eta_i = \frac{\partial S_T}{\partial \bar{c}_i} \tag{4-4}$$

η_i is not necessarily independent of $\bar{c}_i$, but it may be considered so under restricting conditions. Such restricting conditions prevail when the total light absorption of the solution is small. If these conditions are not fulfilled, one has to employ Beer-Lambert's law:

$$\frac{S_T - S_0}{S_0} = \exp\left[-l\sum \bar{c}_i \varepsilon_i\right] - 1 \tag{4-5}$$

With l the length of the light path in the solution and ε_i the (natural) molar extinction coefficient of the ith component, it is then

$$\frac{\eta_i}{S_0} = \frac{\partial}{\partial \bar{c}_i}\left(\frac{S_T - S_0}{S_0}\right) = -l\varepsilon_i \exp\left[-l\sum_i \bar{c}_i \varepsilon_i\right] \tag{4-6}$$

The sign in (4-6) gives the direction of the slope. It is negative for transmissions (as considered here) and positive for fluorescence (the *absorbed* light is partly converted into fluorescence). Equation (4-6) is simplified to a concentration-independent expression for sufficiently small $\sum \bar{c}_i \varepsilon_i$ (the exponent has to be small compared to unity). One realizes that for this condition

$$\eta_i = -l\varepsilon_i S_0 \tag{4-7}$$

Equation (4-3) becomes for system (1-1),

$$S_T - S_0 = \eta_1 \bar{c}_1 + \eta_2 \bar{c}_2 \tag{4-8}$$

$\bar{c}_2$ is expressed in terms of $\bar{c}_1$ by (4-1). Equation (4-8) becomes, with (4-2),

$$S_T - S_0 = \left[\eta_2 + (\eta_1 - \eta_2)\frac{K_{2,1}}{1 + K_{2,1}}\right](c_1^0 + c_2^0) \tag{4-9}$$

The signal varies with the sum of the initial concentrations, but no specific information about the three parameters in the proportionality factor can be derived; the values for η_1, η_2, and $K_{2,1}$ can therefore not be obtained from (4-9).

If elucidation of chemical relaxation processes from transmitted signals is not the major aim but evaluation from extinction-recording instrumentation, one may replace η_i by η_i', the characteristic extinction of the ith component defined by $\partial(\text{extinction})/\partial \bar{c}_i$. They differ in dimension and cannot be used interchangeably. A treatment employing the η_i' starts with (4-58).

B. Dissociation–Association

Dissociation–association, represented by (1-12) with the definition of the dissociation constant in (1-14). The initial concentrations "relax" to the equilibrium concentrations upon mixing and waiting a "sufficient" time.

One obtains from (2-23) to (2-25),

$$c_1^0 - \bar{c}_1 = c_2^0 - \bar{c}_2 \qquad (4\text{-}10)$$

$$c_1^0 - \bar{c}_1 = -(c_3^0 - \bar{c}_3) \qquad (4\text{-}11)$$

Equation (1-14) may now be solved for $\bar{c}_1$, employing (4-10) and (4-11). The result for $K_{2,1} + c_2^0 > c_1^0$ is given by [compare (2-28) and its extensive discussion; generally it is also $c_3^0 \equiv 0$; see below and following (5-6)]

$$\bar{c}_1 = \frac{K_{2,1} + c_2^0 - c_1^0}{2} \left\{ \left[1 + \frac{4K_{2,1}(c_1^0 + c_3^0)}{(K_{2,1} + c_2^0 - c_1^0)^2} \right]^{1/2} - 1 \right\} \qquad (4\text{-}12)$$

The concentration $\bar{c}_2$ is obtained from (4-12) by exchange of indices between $\bar{c}_1$ and $\bar{c}_2$. The general expression for $\bar{c}_3$ may be obtained by directly solving a square-root relationship or by combining (4-11) with (4-12). One obtains

$$\bar{c}_3 = \tfrac{1}{2}(c_1^0 + c_2^0 + 2c_3^0 + K_{2,1}) \left\{ 1 - \left[1 - \frac{4(c_1^0 + c_3^0)(c_2^0 + c_3^0)}{(c_1^0 + c_2^0 + 2c_3^0 + K_{2,1})^2} \right]^{1/2} \right\}$$

$$(4\text{-}13)$$

This equation is actually more applicable than (4-12), which shows an indefinite point at

$$c_1^0 = K_{2,1} + c_2^0 \qquad (4\text{-}14)$$

At this point one must employ (2-30) to obtain a meaningful value for $\bar{c}_1$. Equation (4-12) is very useful for the experimental condition $c_1^0 = c_2^0$, given previously as (1-19). Equation (4-13), on the other hand, is barely simplified by $c_1^0 = c_2^0$. Equation (4-12) simplifies for $c_1^0 = c_2^0$ to (with either $c_1^0 = 0$ or $c_3^0 = 0$)

$$\bar{c}_1 = \frac{K_{2,1}}{2} \left\{ \left[1 + \frac{4(c_1^0 + c_3^0)}{K_{2,1}} \right]^{1/2} - 1 \right\} \qquad (4\text{-}15)$$

The other condition under consideration is given by $c_1^0 \ll c_2^0$. Although this condition (1-20) leads to little simplification of (4-12) as such, considerable simplification is possible with the only additional condition $c_3^0 = 0$ [ordinarily (see below) established in an experiment]. The square root may then be expanded and nonlinear terms omitted, leading finally to [compare (2-35)]

$$\bar{c}_1 = \frac{K_{2,1}c_1^0}{K_{2,1} + c_2^0} \qquad (4\text{-}16)$$

Using the same conditions as just cited leads also to a very simple equation for $\bar{c}_3$ by combining (4-11) with (4-16):

$$\bar{c}_3 = \frac{c_1^0 c_2^0}{K_{2,1} + c_2^0} \tag{4-17}$$

For the expression of the signal, one has to combine (4-3), (4-10), and (4-11), resulting (for the linearized case) in

$$S_T - S_0 = \eta_2(c_2^0 - c_1^0) + \eta_3(c_1^0 + c_3^0) + (\eta_1 + \eta_2 - \eta_3)\bar{c}_1 \tag{4-18}$$

For $\bar{c}_1$ one may now use the general expression given by (4-12) or any one of the more specific equations. The condition for (4-13) causes one term in (4-18) to disappear. Most worthwhile, however, is to consider the conditions leading to (4-16). One obtains

$$S_T - S_0 = \eta_2 c_2^0 + \eta_3 c_1^0 + (\eta_1 + \eta_2 - \eta_3) \frac{K_{2,1} c_1^0}{K_{2,1} + c_2^0} \tag{4-19}$$

One may now consider the conditions among the η_i which permit the elucidation of the dissociation constant $K_{2,1}$. The characteristic signals η_1 and η_2 are derived from measurements on isolated components. η_3 is generally not accessible this way. It is easily obtained for the special case that $\eta_1 + \eta_2 = \eta_3$, but $K_{2,1}$ then remains inaccessible.

The initial condition $c_2^0 \gg c_1^0$ makes it quite desirable to keep $\eta_2 \ll \eta_3$ possibly so small that even its product with c_2^0 may be neglected in comparison with $\eta_3 c_1^0$. This actually is a quite common occurrence where an enzyme reacts with a colorless substrate (= component Y_2). Such an additional relationship leads, after rearrangement, to

$$\frac{S_T - S_0}{\eta_1 c_1^0} = \frac{\eta_3}{\eta_1} + \left(1 - \frac{\eta_3}{\eta_1}\right) \frac{K_{2,1}}{K_{2,1} + c_2^0} \tag{4-20}$$

The last term vanishes for $c_2^0 \gg K_{2,1}$, permitting the determination of η_3 (as long as η_3 is not much smaller than η_1). The last term is largest for $c_2^0 \ll K_{2,1}$; at half its height it is $c_2^0 = K_{2,1}$, a way of determining $K_{2,1}$.

C. The Four-Component System

The four-component system is represented by (1-30) with the definition for the equilibrium constant by (1-32). In addition to (4-10) and (4-11), a third condition holds [from (2-23) and (2-26)]:

$$c_1^0 - \bar{c}_1 = -(c_4^0 - \bar{c}_4) \tag{4-21}$$

Combining (1-32), (4-10), (4-11), and (4-21) and solving for $\bar{c}_1$ gives [one of the c_i^0 has to vanish, see (5-6); this equation is valid for the practical case $c_1^0 < c_2^0 + K_{2,1}(2c_1^0 + c_3^0 + c_4^0)$; see the discussion after (2-28)]

$$\bar{c}_1 = \frac{c_2^0 - c_1^0 + K_{2,1}(2c_1^0 + c_3^0 + c_4^0)}{2(K_{2,1} - 1)}$$

$$\times \left[1 - \left(1 - \frac{4K_{2,1}(K_{2,1} - 1)(c_1^0 + c_3^0)(c_1^0 + c_4^0)}{[c_2^0 - c_1^0 + K_{2,1}(2c_1^0 + c_3^0 + c_4^0)]^2} \right)^{1/2} \right] \qquad (4\text{-}22)$$

If $K_{2,1}$ approaches unity, the second term under the square root becomes small compared to 1. The square root may then be expanded and the non-linear terms omitted. After doing so, one realizes that the differences $(K_{2,1} - 1)$ cancel. A similar process has to be undertaken if

$$c_2^0 = c_1^0 + K_{2,1}(2c_1^0 + c_3^0 + c_4^0) \qquad (4\text{-}23)$$

This equality can either be avoided experimentally or one employs some mathematical operation. One may, for instance, use (4-10) and substitute for $\bar{c}_2$ an expression which is quite similar to (4-22), except that the indices for c_1^0 and c_2^0 are exchanged. Another more elegant way is to use the fact that the approach to condition (4-23) means that the second term under the square root of (4-22) becomes large compared to 1, which is then neglected. In the final result, these critical differences cancel out again. One obtains a very simple relationship, which is not considered here because of its rare occurrence (and its quite limited range of validity). Simplification of (4-22) is also accomplished if either $K_{2,1} \ll 1$ or $K_{2,1} \gg 1$.

Another simplification becomes possible if two equilibrium concentrations appear as sum, such as $(\bar{c}_1 + \bar{c}_2)$ or $(\bar{c}_3 + \bar{c}_4)$ in (3-9). Equation (5-8) considers their interrelationship. For further discussion on such sums of equilibrium concentrations and their use, the reader is referred to Chapter 5.

1. $c_1^0 = c_2^0 > 0$ represents condition (1-33), leading to

$$\bar{c}_1 = \frac{K_{2,1}}{2(K_{2,1} - 1)} (2c_1^0 + c_3^0 + c_4^0)$$

$$\times \left[1 - \left(1 - \frac{4(K_{2,1} - 1)(c_1^0 + c_3^0)(c_1^0 + c_4^0)}{K_{2,1}(2c_1^0 + c_3^0 + c_4^0)^2} \right)^{1/2} \right] \qquad (4\text{-}24)$$

In experiments, one can frequently arrange that $c_3^0 = c_4^0 = 0$. This condition would simplify the derivation very much and one obtains almost directly

$$\bar{c}_1 = \frac{c_1^0}{1 + (K_{1,2})^{1/2}} \qquad (4\text{-}25)$$

Unfortunately, these conditions for (4-25) are only of interest as long as $K_{2,1}$ is near unity.

2. $c_1^0, c_4^0 \ll c_2^0, c_3^0$ represents the case for "buffering," condition (1-34). Equation (4-22) is simplified to

$$\bar{c}_1 = \frac{c_2^0 + K_{2,1}c_3^0}{2(K_{2,1} - 1)} \left\{ 1 - \left[1 - \frac{4K_{2,1}(K_{2,1} - 1)c_3^0(c_1^0 + c_4^0)}{(c_2^0 + K_{2,1}c_3^0)^2} \right]^{1/2} \right\} \quad (4\text{-}26)$$

The second term under the root is small compared to unity for any value of $K_{2,1}$. The square root may therefore be expanded and higher terms omitted, giving

$$\bar{c}_1 = \frac{K_{2,1}c_3^0(c_1^0 + c_4^0)}{K_{2,1}c_3^0 + c_2^0} \quad (4\text{-}27)$$

Dividing by $(c_1^0 + c_4^0)$ and substituting (1-32) with the proper simplifications results in

$$\frac{\bar{c}_1}{c_1^0 + c_4^0} = \frac{k_2 c_3^0}{k_2 c_3^0 + k_1 c_2^0} \quad (4\text{-}28)$$

This equation becomes identical to (2-3) for $c_4^0 \to 0$, as one should expect.

3. $c_3^0 = c_4^0 = 0 < c_1^0 \ll c_2^0$ gives another buffering condition that might be established under certain conditions. The part equal to zero changes (4-22) to

$$\bar{c}_1 = \frac{c_2^0 - c_1^0 + 2K_{2,1}c_1^0}{2(K_{2,1} - 1)} \left\{ 1 - \left[1 - \frac{4K_{2,1}(K_{2,1} - 1)(c_1^0)^2}{(c_2^0 - c_1^0 + 2K_{2,1}c_1^0)^2} \right]^{1/2} \right\} \quad (4\text{-}29)$$

The full condition makes the second term under the root small compared to unity as long as $c_2^0 \gg 2K_{2,1}c_1^0$, allowing expansion of the root and omission of nonlinear terms, and giving

$$\bar{c}_1 = \frac{K_{2,1}(c_1^0)^2}{c_2^0} \quad (4\text{-}30)$$

The condition of $c_2^0 \approx 2K_{2,1}c_1^0$ with $K_{2,1} \gg 1$ is more practical than the one leading to (4-30) and is treated later separately, leading to (4-62).

4. $c_4^0 = 0 < c_1^0, c_3^0 \ll c_2^0$ is another (not frequent) experimental condition. Equation (4-22) becomes for this condition

$$\bar{c}_1 = \frac{c_2^0 + K_{2,1}(2c_1^0 + c_3^0)}{2(K_{2,1} - 1)} \left[1 - \left(1 - \frac{4K_{2,1}(K_{2,1} - 1)(c_1^0 + c_3^0)c_1^0}{[c_2^0 + K_{2,1}(2c_1^0 + c_3^0)]^2} \right)^{1/2} \right]$$

$$(4\text{-}31)$$

Simplification is again possible as long as $c_2^0 \gg K_{2,1}(2c_1^0 + c_3^0)$. One obtains, after expansion of the root and omission of nonlinear terms,

$$\bar{c}_1 = \frac{K_{2,1}c_1^0(c_1^0 + c_3^0)}{c_2^0} \qquad (4\text{-}32)$$

5. $c_1^0 = c_2^0 = 0$ may also be established experimentally; (4-22) becomes

$$\bar{c}_1 = \frac{K_{2,1}(c_3^0 + c_4^0)}{2(K_{2,1} - 1)}\left[1 - \left(1 - \frac{4K_{2,1}(K_{2,1} - 1)c_3^0c_4^0}{[K_{2,1}(c_3^0 + c_4^0)]^2}\right)^{1/2}\right] \qquad (4\text{-}33)$$

Buffering is here equivalent to $c_4^0 \ll c_3^0$, allowing expansion of the root for $c_4^0 \ll K_{2,1}c_3^0$ and omission of nonlinear terms. One obtains

$$\bar{c}_1 = c_4^0 \qquad (4\text{-}34)$$

If in addition to $c_1^0 = c_2^0 = 0$, the concentrations $c_3^0 = c_4^0 > 0$, the derivation may be highly simplified by using only (1-32), (4-11), and the specific conditions. The result is

$$\bar{c}_1 = \frac{c_3^0}{1 + (K_{1,2})^{1/2}} \qquad (4\text{-}35)$$

This equation is quite similar in structure to (4-25), as expected from similarity of conditions.

6. For the full expression of the signal, one has to combine (4-3) with (4-10), (4-11), and (4-21), resulting (for the linearized case) in

$$S_T - S_0 = \eta_2(c_2^0 - c_1^0) + \eta_3(c_1^0 + c_3^0) + \eta_4(c_1^0 + c_4^0) + (\eta_1 + \eta_2 - \eta_3 - \eta_4)\bar{c}_1 \qquad (4\text{-}36)$$

The most general equation to be inserted for $\bar{c}_1$ is given by (4-22). But it is so complex that it is of little value for convenient evaluations. The conditions leading to (4-27) are much more useful. With them (4-36) simplifies to

$$S_T - S_0 = \eta_2 c_2^0 + \eta_3 c_3^0 + \eta_4(c_1^0 + c_4^0)$$
$$+ (\eta_1 + \eta_2 - \eta_3 - \eta_4)\frac{K_{2,1}c_3^0}{K_{2,1}c_3^0 + c_2^0}(c_1^0 + c_4^0) \qquad (4\text{-}37)$$

The use of a buffer generally means that one may set $\eta_2 = \eta_3 = 0$ for the concentrations employed. This further restriction simplifies (4-37) considerably, giving

$$S_T - S_0 = \left[\eta_4 + (\eta_1 - \eta_4)\frac{K_{2,1}c_3^0}{K_{2,1}c_3^0 + c_2^0}\right](c_1^0 + c_4^0) \qquad (4\text{-}38)$$

η_1 and η_4 are easily determined in isolated systems. If $\eta_1 = \eta_4$, the equilibrium constant cannot be evaluated.

There are two special cases with most favorable spectral conditions. $\eta_1 \gg \eta_4$ gives (within limits)

$$\frac{S_T - S_0}{\eta_1(c_1^0 + c_4^0)} = \frac{K_{2,1}c_3^0}{K_{2,1}c_3^0 + c_2^0} \tag{4-39}$$

The maximum of the relative signal is reached at $c_2^0 \ll K_{2,1}c_3^0$. At the half-point of the concentration dependent part, it is $K_{2,1}c_3^0 = c_2^0$, permitting the determination of $K_{2,1}$ directly. $\eta_1 \ll \eta_4$ gives

$$\frac{S_T - S_0}{\eta_4(c_1^0 + c_4^0)} = \frac{c_2^0}{K_{2,1}c_3^0 + c_2^0} \tag{4-40}$$

Here, maximum of the relative signal is reached at $c_2^0 \gg K_{2,1}c_3^0$, while, at half-maximum, $c_2^0 = K_{2,1}c_3^0$. One may easily incorporate one of the other simplified expressions for $\bar{c}_1$, omitted here.

4-2. TWO-STEP MECHANISMS

A. Three Components in Equilibrium

As mentioned in Section 3-2A, only one two-step mechanism can be set up with three components, given by (3-10). There exists only one analytical (or "initial") concentration, defined by

$$c_1^0 = \bar{c}_1 + \bar{c}_2 + \bar{c}_3 \tag{4-41}$$

The differentials in (3-11) and (3-13) are zero at equilibrium, leading directly to the definition of the equilibrium constants. With these equilibrium constants (4-41) may be written

$$c_1^0 = \bar{c}_1(1 + K_{1,2} + K_{1,2}K_{3,4}) \tag{4-42}$$

or in any other desired way. As no equilibrium concentration needs to be inserted in either (3-41) or (3-42), "extended kinetics" with analytical concentrations does not exist for system (3-10).

B. Four Components in Equilibrium

1. An association reaction, *followed* by a monomolecular interconversion, is given by (3-43). The equilibrium constants are derivable from (3-44) and (3-45), where $dc_i/dt = 0$. One may then distinguish two analytical

concentrations (or eventually one, if $\bar{c}_1 = \bar{c}_2$ and c_3^0 or c_4^0 comprise the components),

$$c_1^0 = \bar{c}_1 + \bar{c}_3 + \bar{c}_4 \tag{4-43}$$

$$c_2^0 = \bar{c}_2 + \bar{c}_3 + \bar{c}_4 \tag{4-44}$$

Equations (3-50), (3-51), and (3-53) contain the equilibrium concentrations $\bar{c}_1$ and $\bar{c}_2$. Thus one ought to solve for these concentrations. Equations (4-43) and (4-44) become, after substitution of equilibrium constants,

$$c_1^0 = \bar{c}_1(1 + K_{1,2}\bar{c}_2[1 + K_{3,4}]) \tag{4-45}$$

$$c_2^0 = \bar{c}_2(1 + K_{1,2}\bar{c}_1[1 + K_{3,4}]) \tag{4-46}$$

Substituting the expression for $\bar{c}_2$ from the second equation in the first gives initially

$$c_1^0 = \bar{c}_1\left(1 + \frac{K_{1,2}c_2^0[1 + K_{3,4}]}{1 + K_{1,2}\bar{c}_1[1 + K_{3,4}]}\right) \tag{4-47}$$

The solving of this equation proceeds via a quadratic equation with the root [for the most practical case $c_1^0 < c_2^0 + K_{2,1}(1 + K_{3,4})^{-1}$]

$$\bar{c}_1 = \frac{1}{2}\left(\frac{K_{2,1}}{1 + K_{3,4}} + c_2^0 - c_1^0\right)$$
$$\times \left\{\left[1 + \frac{4K_{2,1}(1 + K_{3,4})^{-1}c_1^0}{[K_{2,1}(1 + K_{3,4})^{-1} + c_2^0 - c_1^0]^2}\right]^{1/2} - 1\right\} \tag{4-48}$$

This equation is rather similar to (4-12) with $c_3^0 \to 0$. Only the dissociation constant $K_{2,1}$ there has to be multiplied with $(1 + K_{3,4})^{-1}$ to give full agreement between (4-12) and (4-48). This modification is then also valid for (4-13) to (4-17). The generalized equation (4-48) was derived previously (1). As was already shown there, $\bar{c}_2$ can simply be obtained from (4-48) by index exchange in the concentrations.

If one now employs (4-3), the monomolecular equilibrium constant, and (4-45), one finally obtains, without any restrictions on the η_i,

$$S_T - S_0 = \eta_2(c_2^0 - c_1^0) + \frac{\eta_3 + \eta_4 K_{3,4}}{1 + K_{3,4}}\,c_1^0 + \left(\eta_1 + \eta_2 = \frac{\eta_3 + \eta_4 K_{3,4}}{1 + K_{3,4}}\right)\bar{c}_1 \tag{4-49}$$

This equation is quite similar in structure to (4-13), although the term with η_3 is here much more involved, owing to the coupled-in monomolecular step. One may then insert for $\bar{c}_1$ any of the various equations. At proper spectral selection, some of the η_i may vanish. But simplifications associated with vanishing η_i will not be treated here. A specific example of this type was recently treated in the literature (2).

2. An association reaction, *preceded* by a monomolecular interconversion, is given by (3-54). $K_{2,1}$ is defined as in the previous section, and $K_{4,3}$ may easily be derived from the (vanishing) differential equation for the left step in (3-54); it is

$$K_{4,3} \equiv \frac{k_4}{k_3} = \frac{\bar{c}_4}{\bar{c}_2} \tag{4-50}$$

The analytical concentrations are now defined as

$$c_1^0 = \bar{c}_1 + \bar{c}_3 \tag{4-51}$$

$$c_2^0 = \bar{c}_2 + \bar{c}_3 + \bar{c}_4 \tag{4-52}$$

These two equations contain four unknown equilibrium concentrations. One may solve for the unknown concentrations, if one incorporates also the definitions of the equilibrium constants. One obtains then (as the most practical roots)

$$\bar{c}_1 = \tfrac{1}{2}[K_{2,1}(1 + K_{4,3}) + c_2^0 - c_1^0]$$

$$\times \left\{ \left[1 + \frac{4K_{2,1}c_1^0(1 + K_{4,3})}{[K_{2,1}(1 + K_{4,3}) + c_2^0 - c_1^0]^2} \right]^{1/2} - 1 \right\} \tag{4-53}$$

$$\bar{c}_2 = \frac{1}{2}\left[K_{2,1} + \frac{c_1^0 - c_2^0}{1 + K_{4,3}} \right] \left\{ \left[1 + \frac{4K_{2,1}c_2^0(1 + K_{4,3})}{[K_{2,1}(1 + K_{4,3}) + c_1^0 - c_2^0]^2} \right]^{1/2} - 1 \right\}$$

$$\tag{4-54}$$

These equations may also be easily obtained from equations derived earlier in a quite similar manner (1). But (4-54) can no longer be obtained from (4-53) by index exchange in the concentrations, which is due to the unsymmetrical nature of the reaction.

If one now employs (4-3) in conjunction with (4-50) to (4-52), one obtains (3)

$$S_T - S_0 = \eta_3 c_1^0 + \frac{\eta_2 + \eta_4 K_{4,3}}{1 + K_{4,3}}(c_2^0 - c_1^0) + \left[\eta_1 - \eta_3 + \frac{\eta_2 + \eta_4 K_{4,3}}{1 + K_{4,3}} \right] \bar{c}_1$$

$$\tag{4-55}$$

Frequently one may find $\eta_2 = \eta_4$. Equation (4-55) will then be considerably simplified. Some vanishing η_i may simplify the relationship further.

C. Five Components in Equilibrium

1. **Association from two sides,** as given by (3-60).

a. **Two analytical concentrations only.** One may rewrite (3-60) in a somewhat different way,

$$Y_1 + Y_2 \underset{k_3}{\overset{k_4}{\rightleftharpoons}} Y_5 \longleftrightarrow Y_3 + Y_4 \tag{4-56}$$

This reaction will now be contrasted with

$$Y_1 + Y_2 \underset{k_2}{\overset{k_1}{\rightleftharpoons}} Y_3 + Y_4 \tag{1-30}$$

The (over-all) equilibrium constant of *both* reactions is defined by

$$K_{2,1} \equiv \frac{k_2}{k_1} = \frac{\bar{c}_1 \bar{c}_2}{\bar{c}_3 \bar{c}_4} \tag{1-32}$$

In addition, there is another equilibrium constant for (4-56), defined by

$$K_{3,4} \equiv \frac{k_3}{k_4} = \frac{\bar{c}_1 \bar{c}_2}{\bar{c}_5} \tag{4-57}$$

This dissociation constant may be considered "immeasurably large" for reaction system (1-30).

In equilibrium experiments on system (1-30) one measures, for instance, the optical density difference between components Y_1 and Y_4 [index 4 refers, for instance, to reduced cytochrome c; index 1 to oxidized cytochrome c; and index 2 to the ferrohexacyanide ion (4)]. Upon fulfillment of Beer-Lambert's law, one may then write

$$\Delta_{\text{ext}} = \eta_4' \bar{c}_4 + \eta_1' \bar{c}_1 - \eta_1' c_1^0 \tag{4-58}$$

η_i' is here distinguished from η_i, as the latter refers to the "specific signal change" and is measured, for instance, in millivolts per micromole. As extinction, on the other hand, is dimensionless, η_i' should be termed "specific extinction" and carries a dimension of reciprocal micromolar (for example). Equation (4-58) implies that under all conditions of reference

$$\eta_2', \eta_3' \ll \eta_1', \eta_4' \tag{4-59}$$

Equation (4-58) also contains the condition that the test cell carries the full reaction system, while the reference cell carries only Y_1, at the same analytical concentration as in the test cell:

$$c_1^0 = \bar{c}_1 + \bar{c}_4 \tag{4-60}$$

To simplify the analysis of the experimental results, Section 4-1C3 is applied: $c_3^0 = c_4^0 = 0 < c_1^0 \ll c_2$. These conditions lead simultaneously to

$$c_2^0 = \bar{c}_2 + \bar{c}_3 \doteq \bar{c}_2 \qquad (4\text{-}61)$$

One may then apply (4-29). The particularly selected experimental case (4) fortunately offers another simplification: $K_{2,1} \gg 1$, by which (4-29) is altered to

$$\bar{c}_1 = \frac{2K_{2,1}c_1^0 + c_2^0}{2K_{2,1}} \left\{ 1 - \left[1 - \frac{4K_{2,1}^2(c_1^0)^2}{(2K_{2,1}c_1^0 + c_2^0)^2} \right]^{1/2} \right\} \qquad (4\text{-}62)$$

This equation may be simplified to (4-30) for $c_2^0 \gg 2K_{2,1}c_1^0$. Equation (4-62) may be normalized to give

$$\frac{\bar{c}_1}{c_1^0} = \left(1 + \frac{c_2^0}{2K_{2,1}c_1^0} \right) \left[1 - \left(1 - \left\langle 1 + \frac{c_2^0}{2K_{2,1}c_1^0} \right\rangle^{-2} \right)^{1/2} \right] \qquad (4\text{-}63)$$

For $\bar{c}_1/c_1^0 = 0.50$, one computes as the analytical concentration for Y_2 the value $c_2^0 = \frac{1}{2}K_{2,1}c_1^0$, which allows a very easy experimental determination of $K_{2,1}$. A normalized plot with $c_2^0(K_{2,1}c_1^0)^{-1}$ as the independent variable and $\bar{c}_1/c_1^0$ as the ordinate is shown as the solid curve in Figure 4.1.

The (experimental) equation (4-58) may be combined with (4-60) and divided by c_1^0, resulting in

$$\frac{\Delta_{\text{ext}}}{c_1^0} = (\eta_4' - \eta_1')(1 - \bar{c}_1/c_1^0) \qquad (4\text{-}64)$$

One immediately realizes that one should plot

$$\frac{\Delta_{\text{ext}} \text{ at specific } c_2^0/c_1^0}{\Delta_{\text{ext}} \text{ for limiting } c_2^0/c_1^0} = 1 - \frac{\bar{c}_1}{c_1^0} \qquad (4\text{-}65)$$

The "limiting c_2^0/c_1^0" means $\bar{c}_4 \rightarrow c_1^0$ associated with $\bar{c}_1 \rightarrow 0$. If this limiting value is not directly accessible, one may obtain it with some other reagent and assume that both reagents act basically in a similar manner.

If some component Y_5, a binary complex, is present, (4-58) would have to be altered to

$$\Delta_{\text{ext}} = \eta_1'\bar{c}_1 + \eta_4'\bar{c}_4 + \eta_5'\bar{c}_5 - \eta_1'c_1^0 \qquad (4\text{-}66)$$

The new "specific extinction" η_5' may have any value in relation to η_1' and η_4'. If no new band appears within the spectral range, one has either $\eta_5' \ll \eta_1', \eta_4'$, or $\eta_5' = \eta_4'$, or $\eta_5' = \eta_1'$. The latter equality is here selected for evaluation. The binary complex Y_5 could then be considered a diffusion complex, which does not alter the specific extinction of Y_1. Equations (4-60) and (4-61) now become

$$c_1^0 = \bar{c}_1 + \bar{c}_4 + \bar{c}_5 \qquad (4\text{-}67)$$

$$c_2^0 = \bar{c}_2 + \bar{c}_3 + \bar{c}_5 \doteq \bar{c}_2 \qquad (4\text{-}68)$$

The latter approximate equality is valid for the experimentally established condition $c_2^0 \gg c_1^0$.

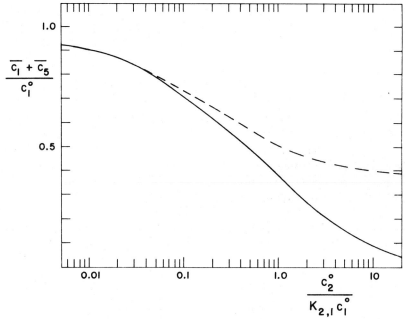

Figure 4-1. A semilog plot of $(\bar{c}_1 + \bar{c}_5)/c_1^0$ versus $c_2^0/K_{2,1}c_1^0$ according to (4-63) (full curve, $\bar{c}_5 \to 0$) and to (4-73) (dashed curve) with $\alpha = 1$ for comparison, (4-76).

Combining (4-66) with (4-67) and (4-68) results for the stated conditions in

$$\Delta_{\text{ext}} = (\eta_4' - \eta_1')c_1^0 - (\eta_4' - \eta_1')(\bar{c}_5 + \bar{c}_1) \qquad (4\text{-}69)$$

One obtains, from (4-57), the stated conditions

$$(\bar{c}_5 + \bar{c}_1) = (1 + c_2^0/K_{3,4})\bar{c}_1 \qquad (4\text{-}70)$$

To obtain a new expression for $\bar{c}_1$ one has to employ (1-32), (4-57),

(4-67), and (4-68), leading with $\bar{c}_3 = \bar{c}_4$ to a quadratic equation. The usable root of this equation is

$$\bar{c}_1 = \frac{2K_{2,1}c_1^0(1 + c_2^0/K_{3,4}) + c_2^0 - c_1^0}{2[K_{2,1}(1 + c_2^0/K_{3,4})^2 - 1]}$$

$$\times \left[1 - \left(1 - \frac{4K_{2,1}(c_1^0)^2[K_{2,1}(1 + c_2^0/K_{3,4})^2 - 1]}{[2K_{2,1}c_1^0(1 + c_2^0/K_{3,4}) + c_2^0 - c_1^0]^2}\right)^{1/2}\right] \qquad (4\text{-}71)$$

This equation assumes only the experimental condition $c_3^0 = c_4^0$, which in turn allowed $\bar{c}_3 = \bar{c}_4$. If one now employs the additional conditions $c_1^0 \ll c_2^0$ and $K_{2,1} \gg 1$ and divides (4-71) by c_1^0, one obtains

$$\frac{\bar{c}_1}{c_1^0} = \left[\frac{1}{1 + c_2^0/K_{3,4}} + \frac{c_2^0}{2K_{2,1}c_1^0(1 + c_2^0/K_{3,4})^2}\right]$$

$$\times \left[1 - \left(1 - \left\langle 1 + \frac{c_2^0}{2K_{2,1}c_1^0(1 + c_2^0/K_{3,4})}\right\rangle^{-2}\right)^{1/2}\right] \qquad (4\text{-}72)$$

Now employing (4-70) results in the simplified equation

$$\frac{\bar{c}_1 + \bar{c}_5}{c_1^0} = \left[1 + \frac{c_2^0}{2K_{2,1}c_1^0(1 + c_2^0/K_{3,4})}\right]$$

$$\times \left[1 - \left(1 - \left\langle 1 + \frac{c_2^0}{2K_{2,1}c_1^0(1 + c_2^0/K_{3,4})}\right\rangle^{-2}\right)^{1/2}\right] \qquad (4\text{-}73)$$

The structure of this equation is quite similar to the structure of (4-63)—except for the denominator of the variable parameter, which contains the factor $(1 + c_2^0/K_{3,4})$ in (4-73) but not in (4-63). The much more extensive equation (4-71) is structurally similar to (4-29) and converts to the latter for "infinitely large" $K_{3,4}$.

The combination of (4-73) with (4-69) gives initially

$$\frac{\Delta_{\text{ext}}}{c_1^0} = (\eta_4' - \eta_1')\left(1 - \frac{\bar{c}_1 + \bar{c}_5}{c_1^0}\right) \qquad (4\text{-}74)$$

Experimentally one should again plot

$$\frac{\Delta_{\text{ext}} \text{ at specific } c_2^0/c_1^0}{\Delta_{\text{ext}} \text{ for limiting } c_2^0/c_1^0} = 1 - \frac{\bar{c}_1 + \bar{c}_5}{c_1^0} \qquad (4\text{-}75)$$

The equation practically agrees with (4-65). They differ only in the equation applicable for the varying term: It is (4-63) for (4-65) and (4-73) for (4-75). It becomes therefore of interest to see how a plot of (4-73) deviates from a plot of (4-63).

To present a normalized plot, $K_{3,4}$ has to be expressed in terms of $K_{2,1}c_1^0$, at least temporarily for purposes of evaluation:

$$K_{3,4} = \alpha K_{2,1} c_1^0 \tag{4-76}$$

For $\alpha \gg 1$, dissociation into the components is large and (4-73) becomes (4-63) over the whole concentration range. An interesting reference value is $\alpha = 1$. This case is plotted in Figure 4.1 as a dashed curve. This curve clearly demonstrates that full conversion of Y_1 to Y_4 never occurs.

Certain limiting values of (4-73) are of interest for the evaluation of the equilibrium constants $K_{2,1}$ and $K_{3,4}$. If

$$\frac{c_1^0}{\bar{c}_1 + \bar{c}_5} = r \tag{4-77}$$

a general relation for this inverse ratio is

$$rc_2^0 = (r - 1)^2 K_{2,1} c_1^0 (1 + c_2^0 / K_{3,4}) \tag{4-78}$$

One then obtains for $r = 2$ [half-conversion denoted by $c_2^0(\tfrac{1}{2})$] and $r = 3$ [with $c_2^0(\tfrac{1}{3})$];

$$K_{2,1} c_1^0 [1 + c_2^0(\tfrac{1}{2}) / K_{3,4}] = 2c_2^0(\tfrac{1}{2}) \tag{4-79}$$

$$4 K_{2,1} c_1^0 [1 + c_2^0(\tfrac{1}{3}) / K_{3,4}] = 3c_2^0(\tfrac{1}{3}) \tag{4-80}$$

Certainly, c_1^0 has to be kept constant for proper evaluations: only c_2^0 varies. After $c_2^0(\tfrac{1}{2})$ and $c_2^0(\tfrac{1}{3})$ have been taken off the experimental plot, one may solve (4-79) and (4-80) for $K_{2,1}$ and $K_{3,4}$. If $K_{3,4}$ becomes much larger than the upper limit of c_2^0, it may contain a rather large error, may even be nonexistent, at least for practical purposes. Otherwise, one should use the computed values of $K_{2,1}$ and $K_{3,4}$ and insert them in (4-73) for a theoretical plot. It is also evident from (4-73) that a relatively large $K_{3,4}$ can only be detected if c_2^0 is made sufficiently large; the size of c_1^0 is of little influence, as long as one maintains $c_2^0 \gg c_1^0$ for any value of c_1^0.

In the treatment of (4-66) three different conditions among η_5' and η_1', η_4' are possible if Y_5 shows no separate absorption band. $\eta_1' = \eta_5'$ was originally selected for further consideration. Now employing $\eta_5' = \eta_4'$, (4-66) and (4-67) leads to

$$\frac{\Delta_{ext} \text{ at finite } c_2^0 / c_1^0}{\Delta_{ext} \text{ for "full conversion"}} = 1 - \frac{\bar{c}_1}{c_1^0} \tag{4-81}$$

This equation then has to be combined with (4-72), as $\bar{c}_5$ is still assumed to be present.

The advantage of (4-65), (4-75), and (4-81) is that the individual η_i' need not be directly known. Only actually measured parameters are inserted (aside from the equilibrium constants $K_{2,1}$ and $K_{3,4}$) and well separated. This simplicity unfortunately is no longer available for the third condition, $\eta_5' \ll \eta_1', \eta_2'$. One obtains

$$\frac{\Delta_{ext} \text{ at } c_2^0/c_1^0}{\Delta_{ext} \text{ at full conversion}} = 1 - \frac{\bar{c}_1}{c_1^0}\left(1 + \frac{c_2^0}{K_{3,4}}\langle 1 - r_E\rangle^{-1}\right) \quad (4\text{-}82)$$

with

$$r_E = \frac{\text{extinction at fully } unconverted\ c_1^0}{\text{extinction at fully converted } c_1^0} \quad (4\text{-}83)$$

Analytical concentrations appear on the right side only. But the ratio of extinction changes appears on the left side of the equation, while a ratio of extinctions appears also on the right side. It is generally not $r_E \ll 1$, so that a combination with (4-72) allows no simplification.

   b.   One component buffered. As (3-60) is symmetric, one may consider any one side rapid and thus buffered. Equation (3-61) demonstrates that k_3 and k_4 were considered to be associated with the slow step. One must then choose Y_2 as the component being buffered. Y_2 may be a part of the solvent (like H^+ and OH^- for water), a metal ion, some anion, or anything else buffered, so it is not responding to changes in the four rate constants of (3-60). But upon change of some external parameter, the concentration $\bar{c}_2$ may impose a change of its own due to the (defined) response of the buffering agents.

   Owing to the nature of Y_2, one may then define as analytical concentrations,

$$c_4^0 = \bar{c}_4 + \bar{c}_3 + \bar{c}_1 \quad (4\text{-}84)$$

$$c_5^0 = \bar{c}_5 + \bar{c}_3 + \bar{c}_1 \quad (4\text{-}85)$$

As $\bar{c}_2$ is separately determined—and fixed—by the buffer ratio, one may set $\bar{c}_2 \to \bar{\bar{c}}_2 \doteq$ fixed concentration of Y_2. The solution of the equations reduces then to one of a quadratic equation, proceeding via equations like (4-45) and (4-46),

$$c_4^0 = \bar{c}_4[1 + K_{4,3}\bar{c}_5(1 + K_{2,1}/\bar{\bar{c}}_2)] \quad (4\text{-}86)$$

$$c_5^0 = \bar{c}_5[1 + K_{4,3}\bar{c}_4(1 + K_{2,1}/\bar{\bar{c}}_2)] \quad (4\text{-}87)$$

Substituting the expression for $\bar{c}_5$ from the second equation in the first one gives initially

$$c_4^0 = \bar{c}_4\left[1 + \frac{K_{4,3}c_5^0(1 + K_{2,1}/\bar{\bar{c}}_2)}{1 + K_{4,3}\bar{c}_4(1 + K_{2,1}/\bar{\bar{c}}_2)}\right] \quad (4\text{-}88)$$

Solving for $\bar{c}_4$ proceeds via a quadratic equation, the suitable root of which is

$$\bar{c}_4 = \frac{1}{2}\left(\frac{K_{3,4}}{1 + K_{2,1}/\bar{c}_2} + c_5^0 - c_4^0\right)$$
$$\times \left(\left\{1 + \frac{4K_{3,4}(1 + K_{2,1}/\bar{c}_2)^{-1}c_4^0}{[K_{3,4}(1 + K_{2,1}/\bar{c}_2)^{-1} + c_5^0 - c_4^0]^2}\right\}^{1/2} - 1\right) \qquad (4\text{-}89)$$

This equation is quite similar in structure to (4-48). The equation for $\bar{c}_5$ is simply obtained by index exchange.

Equation (4-89) may easily be simplified under the two experimental conditions:

1. $c_4^0 = c_5^0$. One obtains from (4-89),

$$\bar{c}_4 = \frac{K_{3,4}/2}{1 + K_{2,1}/\bar{c}_2}\left(\left\{1 + \frac{4c_4^0(1 + K_{2,1}/\bar{c}_2)}{K_{3,4}}\right\}^{1/2} - 1\right) \qquad (4\text{-}90)$$

Such an equation is certainly not difficult to handle at all, in spite of the more complex system.

2. $c_4^0 \ll c_5^0$ results in the simple relationship

$$\bar{c}_4 = c_4^0\left[1 + \frac{c_5^0}{K_{3,4}}(1 + K_{2,1}/\bar{c}_2)\right]^{-1} \qquad (4\text{-}91)$$

In obtaining (4-91), the square root was expanded, making (4-91) only an approximation, which approaches equality with increasing ratio c_5^0/c_4^0.

---

2. TWO CONSECUTIVE ASSOCIATIONS. Another, less symmetric case—compared to the previous one—is given by scheme (3-64). As already shown in Chapter 3, one thus has to differentiate between the two possible cases.

a. The "left step" is very fast, which also means: buffering in Y_2, as in Section 4-1C1. The analytical concentrations are now given by

$$c_4^0 = \bar{c}_4 + \bar{c}_5 \qquad (4\text{-}92)$$
$$c_1^0 = \bar{c}_1 + \bar{c}_3 + \bar{c}_5 \qquad (4\text{-}93)$$

Again $\bar{c}_2$ represents the buffered concentration. The two dissociation constants are defined by

$$K_{2,1} = \frac{\bar{c}_1\bar{c}_2}{\bar{c}_3} \qquad (4\text{-}94)$$

$$K_{4,3} = \frac{\bar{c}_3\bar{c}_4}{\bar{c}_5} \qquad (4\text{-}95)$$

Combining (4-92) to (4-94) gives first

$$c_4^0 = \bar{c}_4(1 + K_{3,4}\bar{c}_3) \tag{4-96}$$

$$c_1^0 = \bar{c}_3(K_{2,1}/\bar{c}_2 + 1 + K_{3,4}\bar{c}_4) \tag{4-97}$$

and upon substitution of $\bar{c}_3$, for instance,

$$c_4^0 = \bar{c}_4\left(1 + \frac{K_{3,4}c_1^0}{K_{2,1}/\bar{c}_2 + 1 + K_{3,4}\bar{c}_4}\right) \tag{4-98}$$

Solving for $\bar{c}_4$ gives (c_4^0 again smaller than the remaining terms in the parentheses)

$$\bar{c}_4 = \tfrac{1}{2}[K_{4,3}(1 + K_{2,1}/\bar{c}_2) + c_1^0 - c_4^0]$$

$$\times \left(\left\{1 + \frac{4c_4^0(1 + K_{2,1}/\bar{c}_2)K_{4,3}}{[K_{4,3}(1 + K_{2,1}/\bar{c}_2) + c_1^0 - c_4^0]^2}\right\}^{1/2} - 1\right) \tag{4-99}$$

This equation is quite similar *in structure* to (4-53).

One may solve (4-96) and (4-97) for $\bar{c}_3$ also, giving in the end (for the practical root),

$$\bar{c}_3 = \tfrac{1}{2}\left(K_{4,3} + \frac{c_4^0 - c_1^0}{1 + K_{2,1}/\bar{c}_2}\right)\left(\left\{1 + \frac{4c_1^0 K_{4,3}(1 + K_{2,1}/\bar{c}_2)}{c_4^0 - c_1^0 + K_{4,3}(1 + K_{2,1}/\bar{c}_2)]^2}\right\}^{1/2} - 1\right)$$

$$\tag{4-100}$$

This equation is quite similar *in structure* to (4-54). These comparisons of (4-89), (4-99), and (4-100) with previous equations show that a rapid bimolecular step may effectively be reduced by buffering to a "pseudo-monomolecular" step. This way, the treatment of mechanisms with one or more monomolecular steps gains in importance.

The last two equations may be simplified under certain experimental conditions.

1. $c_1^0 = c_4^0$. Equation (4-99) reduces to

$$\bar{c}_4 = \tfrac{1}{2}K_{4,3}\left(1 + \frac{K_{2,1}}{\bar{c}_2}\right)\left(\left\{1 + \frac{4c_4^0}{K_{4,3}(1 + K_{2,1}/\bar{c}_2)}\right\}^{1/2} - 1\right) \tag{4-101}$$

Equation (4-100), on the other hand, reduces to

$$\bar{c}_3 = \tfrac{1}{2}K_{4,3}\left(\left\{1 + \frac{4c_1^0}{K_{4,3}(1 + K_{2,1}/\bar{c}_2)}\right\}^{1/2} - 1\right) \tag{4-102}$$

The small difference between (4-101) and (4-102) is interesting, contained only in one single factor.

2. If $c_4^0 \ll c_1^0$, one should consider (4-99), giving

$$\bar{c}_4 = c_4^0\left[1 + \frac{c_1^0}{K_{4,3}(1 + K_{2,1}/\bar{c}_2)}\right]^{-1} \tag{4-103}$$

If, however, $c_4^0 \gg c_1^0$, one would have to consider (4-100), leading to

$$\bar{c}_3 = \frac{c_1^0}{1 + K_{2,1}/\bar{c}_2 + c_4^0/K_{4,3}} \tag{4-104}$$

Certainly, one could also consider the positive root, as discussed following (2-28). It is quite apparent that the three equations (4-91), (4-103), and (4-104) are all somewhat similar, although each one carries its distinct characteristic.

b. The "right step" is very fast. This means that buffering in component Y_4 is of advantage in handling this (generalized) system. The analytical concentrations are then defined somewhat differently,

$$c_1^0 = \bar{c}_1 + \bar{c}_3 + \bar{c}_5 \tag{4-93}$$

$$c_2^0 = \bar{c}_2 + \bar{c}_3 + \bar{c}_5 \tag{4-105}$$

The equilibrium constants are defined by (4-94) and (4-95), *except* for one interchange: the second bar is removed from c_2 and placed on c_4. The symbol $\bar{c}_4$ then indicates "fixed by buffering." Proceeding now as following (4-95) gives (employing the useful "negative" root)

$$\bar{c}_1 = \frac{1}{2}\left\langle \frac{K_{2,1}}{1 + K_{3,4}\bar{c}_4} + c_2^0 - c_1^0 \right\rangle \left(\left\{ 1 + \frac{4c_1^0 K_{2,1}(1 + K_{3,4}\bar{c}_4)^{-1}}{\langle K_{2,1}(1 + K_{3,4}\bar{c}_4)^{-1} + c_2^0 - c_1^0 \rangle^2} \right\}^{1/2} - 1 \right) \tag{4-106}$$

$$\bar{c}_3 = \frac{1}{2}\left\langle \frac{K_{2,1}}{(1 + K_{3,4}\bar{c}_4)^2} + \frac{c_1^0 + c_2^0}{1 + K_{3,4}\bar{c}_4} \right\rangle$$
$$\times \left(1 - \left\{ 1 - \frac{4c_1^0 c_2^0}{\langle K_{2,1}(1 + K_{3,4}\bar{c}_4)^{-1} + c_1^0 + c_2^0 \rangle^2} \right\}^{1/2} \right) \tag{4-107}$$

$$\bar{c}_5 = \frac{1}{2}\left\langle \frac{K_{2,1}K_{4,3}/\bar{c}_4}{(1 + K_{4,3}/\bar{c}_4)^2} + \frac{c_1^0 + c_2^0}{1 + K_{4,3}/\bar{c}_4} \right\rangle$$
$$\times \left(1 - \left\{ 1 - \frac{4c_1^0 c_2^0}{\langle K_{2,1}(1 + \bar{c}_2/K_{4,3})^{-1} + c_1^0 + c_2^0 \rangle^2} \right\}^{1/2} \right) \tag{4-108}$$

The equation for $\bar{c}_2$ has been omitted, as it may easily be obtained from (4-106) by index exchange: old $\bar{c}_1 \rightarrow$ new $\bar{c}_2$, c_2^0 (of old $\bar{c}_1$) $\rightarrow c_1^0$ (of new $\bar{c}_2$) and c_1^0 (of old $\bar{c}_1$) $\rightarrow c_2^0$ (of new $\bar{c}_2$). Equation (4-106) is quite similar to (4-48); the only dissimilarity consists in the replacement of $K_{3,4}$ there by the product $K_{3,4}\bar{c}_4$ here. With these results on hand, one may now directly derive the equations which are valid for the simplifying experimental conditions.

1. $c_1^0 = c_2^0$. One obtains from (4-106) the quite simple relationship

$$\bar{c}_1 = \frac{K_{2,1}/2}{1 + K_{3,4}\bar{c}_4}\left(\left\{ 1 + \frac{4c_1^0(1 + K_{3,4}\bar{c}_4)}{K_{2,1}} \right\}^{1/2} - 1 \right) \tag{4-109}$$

from (4-107):

$$\bar{c}_3 = \left\langle \frac{K_{2,1}/2}{(1 + K_{3,4}\bar{c}_4)^2} + \frac{c_1^0}{1 + K_{3,4}\bar{c}_4} \right\rangle \left(1 - \left\{ 1 - \frac{4(c_1^0)^2}{\langle K_{2,1}(1 + K_{3,4}\bar{c}_4)^{-1} + 2c_1^0 \rangle^2} \right\}^{1/2} \right)$$

(4-110)

and from (4-108):

$$\bar{c}_5 = \left\langle \frac{\frac{1}{2}K_{2,1}K_{4,3}/\bar{c}_4}{(1 + K_{4,3}/\bar{c}_4)^2} + \frac{c_1^0}{1 + K_{4,3}/\bar{c}_4} \right\rangle$$

$$\times \left(1 - \left\{ 1 - \frac{4(c_1^0)^2}{\langle K_{2,1}(1 + \bar{c}_4/K_{4,3})^{-1} + 2c_1^0 \rangle^2} \right\}^{1/2} \right) \quad (4\text{-}111)$$

An equation which is structurally identical with (4.109) was actually derived some time ago in conjunction with investigations on malate dehydrogenase (5) [Eq. (30) of cited paper]. Actually, (4-101) and (4-90) were also derived there, although with different indexing [(4-101) corresponds to Eq. (15) in the paper and (4-90) to (24) there].

2. $c_1^0 \ll c_2^0$. This condition leads for (4-106), (4-107), and (4-108) to

$$\bar{c}_1 = c_1^0 \left(1 + \frac{c_2^0}{K_{2,1}} (1 + K_{3,4}\bar{c}_4) \right)^{-1}$$

(4-112)

$$\bar{c}_3 = \bar{c}_1^0 (1 + K_{3,4}\bar{c}_4 + K_{2,1}/c_2^0)^{-1}$$

(4-113)

$$\bar{c}_5 = c_1^0 \left(1 + \frac{K_{2,1}}{c_2^0} \frac{K_{4,3}/\bar{c}_4}{1 + K_{4,3}/\bar{c}_4} \right)^{-1}$$

(4-114)

The condition, where $\bar{c}_1 = \frac{1}{2}c_1^0$, may very easily be obtained from these three equations. It is also evident from (4-113) that no finite c_2^0 can fulfill the equation $\bar{c}_3 = \frac{1}{2}c_1^0$, if $K_{3,4}\bar{c}_4 \geqslant 1$.

3. MONOMOLECULAR INTERCONVERSION PLUS FOUR-COMPONENT REACTION. The system is chemically described by (3-69). One should handle this system without buffering and as composed of two analytical concentrations, defined by

$$c_1^0 = \bar{c}_1 + \bar{c}_3 + \bar{c}_5$$

(4-115)

$$c_2^0 = \bar{c}_2 + \bar{c}_4$$

(4-116)

These analytical concentrations may or may not be identical with the two initial concentrations of the components, originally combined to establish the equilibrium. One may replace c_1^0 by c_5^0 (or c_3^0) and (simultaneously for initial concentrations) c_2^0 by c_4^0, for instance. The equilibrium constant $K_{2,1}$ is defined by (1-32), while from (3-70),

$$K_{4,3} = \frac{\bar{c}_3}{\bar{c}_5}$$

(4-117)

Equation (4-115) simplifies with (4-117) to

$$c_1^0 = \bar{c}_1 + \bar{c}_3(1 + K_{3,4}) \tag{4-118}$$

In (4-116) and (4-118) there are a total of four concentration variables; as only three independent equations are available [namely (1-32), (4-116), and (4-118)], a fourth one has to be derived from the condition of preparing the solutions.

a. Y_1 and Y_2 mixed. If it is assumed that c_1^0 and c_2^0 are also the *initial* analytical concentrations, one obtains from stoichiometry and the law of conservation of mass,

$$\bar{c}_4 = \bar{c}_3(1 + K_{3,4}) \tag{4-119}$$

One may now solve for $\bar{c}_1$ and obtain

$$\bar{c}_1 = \frac{(c_2^0 - c_1^0)(1 + K_{3,4}) + 2K_{2,1}c_1^0}{2(K_{2,1} - 1 - K_{3,4})}$$

$$\times \left\{ 1 - \left\langle 1 - \frac{4(c_1^0)^2 K_{2,1}(K_{2,1} - 1 - K_{3,4})}{[(c_2^0 - c_1^0)(1 + K_{3,4}) + 2c_1^0 K_{2,1}]^2} \right\rangle^{1/2} \right\} \tag{4-120}$$

This rather complex equation (4-120) converts easily into the (simplified, which is $c_3^0 = c_4^0 = 0$) equation (4-22) by realizing that for $\bar{c}_5 \to 0$, also $K_{3,4} \to 0$. The equilibrium concentration $\bar{c}_2$ is simply obtained by index exchange in the concentration parameters.

One more expression for an equilibrium concentration would have to be derived directly, which may be any one of the three remaining; $\bar{c}_3$ is chosen here. One obtains the somewhat simpler equation

$$\bar{c}_3 = \frac{c_1^0 + c_2^0}{2(K_{2,1} - 1 - K_{3,4})} \left\{ \left\langle 1 + \frac{4c_1^0 c_2^0(K_{2,1} - 1 - K_{3,4})}{(1 + K_{3,4})(c_1^0 + c_2^0)^2} \right\rangle^{1/2} - 1 \right\} \tag{4-121}$$

One may again set $K_{3,4} \to 0$ and obtain the properly simplified equation (4-22) after some rearrangements (and with $\bar{c}_3 \to \bar{c}_1$, $c_3^0 \to c_1^0$, $c_4^0 \to c_2^0$, $c_1^0 \to c_3^0$, $c_2^0 \to c_4^0$, $K_{2,1} \to K_{1,2}$, and *then* $c_3^0 = c_4^0 = 0!$). On the other hand, (4-121) may easily be converted to one-half of (5-19) for $K_{3,4} \to 0$. The equations for $\bar{c}_4$ and $\bar{c}_5$ can be derived from (4-117) and (4-119), employing (4-121). One may now easily employ further experimental restrictions.

1. $c_1^0 = c_2^0$. Equation (4-120) simplifies to

$$\bar{c}_1 = \frac{K_{2,1}c_1^0}{K_{2,1} - (1 + K_{3,4})} \left\{ 1 - \left\langle \frac{1 + K_{3,4}}{K_{2,1}} \right\rangle^{1/2} \right\} \tag{4-122}$$

Under certain conditions this equation may have to be changed to

$$\bar{c}_1 = \frac{K_{2,1}c_1^0}{1 + K_{3,4} - K_{2,1}} \left\{ \left\langle \frac{1 + K_{3,4}}{K_{2,1}} \right\rangle^{1/2} - 1 \right\} \tag{4-123}$$

It is apparent from the simple structures that (4-122) is identical with (4-123), but these two equations cannot be used for $K_{2,1} - (1 + K_{3,4}) \to 0$. In such a case, one has to expand the square root in (4-120) and obtains finally,

$$\bar{c}_1 \to c_1^0/2 \qquad \text{for } K_{2,1} - (1 + K_{3,4}) \to 0 \qquad (4\text{-}124)$$

If $\bar{c}_3$ is desired for the condition $c_1^0 = c_2^0$, one obtains from (4-121),

$$\bar{c}_3 = \frac{c_1^0}{K_{2,1} - 1 - K_{3,4}} \left(\left\langle \frac{K_{2,1}}{1 + K_{3,4}} \right\rangle^{1/2} - 1 \right) \qquad (4\text{-}125)$$

This equation is valid, as long as $K_{2,1} \neq 1 + K_{3,4}$. For equality (or its close approach) one obtains a very simple expression by expanding the square root of (4-121).

2. $c_1^0 \ll c_2^0$. Equation (4-120) simplifies considerably if, for instance, $2K_{2,1}c_1^0 \ll (1 + K_{3,4})c_2^0$ also, to

$$\bar{c}_1 = \frac{(c_1^0)^2}{c_2^0} \frac{K_{2,1}}{1 + K_{3,4}} \qquad (4\text{-}126)$$

This result is a limiting one [similar to (4-30)] for the more general expression

$$\bar{c}_1 = \frac{(1 + K_{3,4})c_2^0 + 2K_{2,1}c_1^0}{2(K_{2,1} - 1 - K_{3,4})} \left\{ 1 - \left\langle 1 - \frac{4(c_1^0)^2 K_{2,1}(K_{2,1} - 1 - K_{3,4})}{[(1 + K_{3,4})c_2^0 + 2K_{2,1}c_1^0]^2} \right\rangle^{1/2} \right\} \qquad (4\text{-}127)$$

Equation (4-121) becomes for any size $K_{2,1}c_1^0$,

$$\bar{c}_3 = \frac{c_2^0}{2(K_{2,1} - 1 - K_{3,4})} \left[\left\langle 1 + \frac{4c_1^0(K_{2,1} - 1 - K_{3,4})}{c_2^0(1 + K_{3,4})} \right\rangle^{1/2} - 1 \right] \qquad (4\text{-}128)$$

The expression for the concentration $\bar{c}_3$ becomes very simple for $K_{2,1}c_1^0 \ll c_2^0$ (with $K_{3,4} \lesssim 1$).

b. Y_3 (or Y_5) and Y_4 mixed. To better distinguish this new possibility from the previous one, (4-116) and (4-118) are rewritten

$$c_3^0 = \bar{c}_1 + \bar{c}_3(1 + K_{3,4}) \qquad (4\text{-}129)$$

$$c_4^0 = \bar{c}_2 + \bar{c}_4 \qquad (4\text{-}130)$$

Equation (4-119) is no longer valid and has to be replaced by

$$\bar{c}_1 = \bar{c}_2 \qquad (4\text{-}131)$$

One may now solve for $\bar{c}_1$ and obtains (as a more practical root)

$$\bar{c}_1 = \frac{1}{2} \frac{c_3^0 + c_4^0}{K_{1,2}(1 + K_{3,4}) - 1} \left\{ \left\langle 1 + \frac{4c_3^0 c_4^0 [K_{1,2}(1 + K_{3,4}) - 1]}{(c_3^0 + c_4^0)^2} \right\rangle^{1/2} - 1 \right\} \qquad (4\text{-}132)$$

This equation is valid for any $K_{2,1}(1 + K_{3,4})^{-1} \neq 1$. Equation (4-132) converts to (4-22) with $c_1^0 = c_2^0 = 0$, if $\bar{c}_5 \to 0$, which produces $K_{3,4} \to 0$. One may solve the same initial equations for $\bar{c}_3$ and obtains

$$\bar{c}_3 = \frac{c_4^0 - c_3^0 + 2K_{1,2}(1 + K_{3,4})c_3^0}{2(1 + K_{3,4})[1 - K_{1,2}(1 + K_{3,4})]}$$

$$\times \left\{ \left\langle 1 + \frac{4K_{1,2}(1 + K_{3,4})[1 - K_{1,2}(1 + K_{3,4})](c_3^0)^2}{[c_4^0 - c_3^0 + 2K_{1,2}(1 + K_{3,4})c_3^0]^2} \right\rangle^{1/2} - 1 \right\} \quad \text{(4-133)}$$

This equation is valid for any $K_{1,2}(1 + K_{3,4}) \neq 1$, as long as $c_4^0 > c_3^0[1 - 2K_{1,2}$ $(1 + K_{3,4})]$. If, however, $c_4^0 < c_3^0[1 - 2K_{1,2}(1 + K_{3,4})]$, one has to employ the alternative equation

$$\bar{c}_3 = \frac{1}{2} \frac{c_3^0[2K_{1,2}(1 + K_{3,4}) - 1] + c_4^0}{(1 + K_{3,4})[K_{1,2}(1 + K_{3,4}) - 1]}$$

$$\times \left\{ 1 - \left\langle 1 - \frac{4(c_3^0)^2(1 + K_{3,4})K_{1,2}[K_{1,2}(1 + K_{3,4}) - 1]}{[c_4^0 + c_3^0\{2K_{1,2}(1 + K_{3,4}) - 1\}]^2} \right\rangle^{1/2} \right\} \quad \text{(4-134)}$$

Upon proper index exchange and simplifications, (4-133) can also be reduced to (4-22) for $K_{3,4} \to 0$. One may now introduce further experimental restrictions.

1. $c_3^0 = c_4^0$. Equation (4-132) directly simplifies to

$$\bar{c}_1 = \frac{c_3^0}{K_{1,2}(1 + K_{3,4}) - 1} \left(\left\langle \frac{1 + K_{3,4}}{K_{2,1}} \right\rangle^{1/2} - 1 \right) \quad \text{(4-135)}$$

The similarity in structure to (4-125) is quite striking. Equations (4-133) and (4-134) simplify for the stated experimental condition to

$$\bar{c}_3 = \frac{K_{1,2}c_3^0}{1 - K_{1,2}(1 + K_{3,4})} \left(\left\langle \frac{K_{2,1}}{1 + K_{3,4}} \right\rangle^{1/2} - 1 \right) \quad \text{(4-136)}$$

This last equation is identical to (4-125) [for $c_1^0 \to c_3^0$].

2. $c_3^0 \ll c_4^0$. For the general case, the simplifications are small. One thus obtains from (4-132),

$$\bar{c}_1 = \frac{c_4^0/2}{K_{1,2}(1 + K_{3,4}) - 1} \left\{ \left\langle 1 - \frac{4c_3^0}{c_4^0} [K_{1,2}(1 + K_{3,4}) - 1] \right\rangle^{1/2} - 1 \right\} \quad \text{(4-137)}$$

and, from (4-133),

$$\bar{c}_3 = \frac{c_4^0 + 2K_{1,2}(1 + K_{3,4})c_3^0}{2(1 + K_{3,4})[1 - K_{1,2}(1 + K_{3,4})]}$$

$$\times \left\{ \left\langle 1 + \frac{4K_{1,2}(1 + K_{3,4})[1 - K_{1,2}(1 + K_{3,4})](c_3^0)^2}{[c_4^0 + 2K_{1,2}(1 + K_{3,4})c_3^0]^2} \right\rangle^{1/2} - 1 \right\} \quad \text{(4-138)}$$

Considerable simplification is possible, if c_4^0 is large enough, such that

$c_4^0 \gg 2K_{1,2}(1 + K_{3,4})c_3^0$. Equations (4-137) and (4-138) become in the limit $\bar{c}_1 \to c_3^0$ and $\bar{c}_3 \to K_{1,2}(c_3^0)^2/c_4^0$, respectively; $\bar{c}_3$ thus becomes similar in structure to (4-126). Unfortunately these extreme conditions are not very favorable, if Y_1, for instance, is the indicating parameter and $\bar{c}_1 = c_3^0$. One may thus deduce again that extreme ratios in analytical concentrations with reference to equilibrium constants are not necessarily desirable on experimental grounds.

3. $c_3^0 \gg c_4^0$. Of particular interest for this case is the application of (4-134). One obtains initially with this relation,

$$\bar{c}_3 = \frac{c_3^0}{2(1 + K_{3,4})} \frac{2K_{1,2}(1 + K_{3,4}) - 1}{K_{1,2}(1 + K_{3,4}) - 1}$$

$$\times \left\{ 1 - \left\langle 1 - \frac{4(1 + K_{3,4})K_{1,2}[K_{1,2}(1 + K_{3,4}) - 1]}{[2K_{1,2}(1 + K_{3,4}) - 1]^2} \right\rangle^{1/2} \right\} \qquad (4\text{-}139)$$

Considerable further simplification is possible for two conditions:

(a) $K_{1,2}(1 + K_{3,4}) \gg 1$ leads to

$$\bar{c}_3 = c_3^0(1 + K_{3,4})^{-1} \qquad (4\text{-}140)$$

(b) $K_{1,2}(1 + K_{3,4}) \ll 1$ gives $\bar{c}_3 < 0$, also with the use of (4-133). One thus has to use the positive square root under these conditions, leading also to (4-140). This example shows that (4-132) to (4-134) also have their limitation in use, as previously elaborated following (2-28).

4-3. THREE-STEP MECHANISMS

A. Four Components

Only one three-step mechanism with four components can be set up. Equation (3-171) already represented this system. The third (the longest) relaxation time is either given by (3-174) or by (3-183), depending upon whether the middle reaction or one of the terminal reactions is slowest. Equilibrium concentrations do not appear in either equation. But the measured signal changes of individual relaxation steps would still be dependent upon the equilibrium concentrations of individual components. Their relationship to analytical concentrations would therefore have to be established.

At equilibrium, differential equations (3-11), (3-12), and (3-177) vanish, leading to

$$K_{2,1} = \bar{c}_1/\bar{c}_2 \qquad (1\text{-}4)$$

$$K_{4,3} = \bar{c}_2/\bar{c}_3 \qquad (4\text{-}141)$$

$$K_{6,5} = \bar{c}_3/\bar{c}_4 \qquad (4\text{-}142)$$

The analytical concentration is given by

$$c_1^0 = \sum_{i=1}^{4} \bar{c}_i \qquad (4\text{-}143)$$

Only one c_i^0 may be introduced, but one may choose any one as index. Combining the last four equations gives, for instance,

$$c_1^0 = \bar{c}_1[1 + K_{1,2}(1 + K_{3,4}\langle 1 + K_{5,6}\rangle)] \tag{4-144}$$

Certainly, one could select any one $\bar{c}_i$, leading to somewhat different structures for each expression. But there is no difficulty at all in solving (1-4) and (4-141) to (4-143) at any time for any $\bar{c}_i$.

B. Five Components

A three-step mechanism with five components has to be composed of one bimolecular association step and two monomolecular interconversion steps. These three steps may be combined in three possible modes, which are given by (3-186), (3-191), and (3-195). Only the first possibility will be discussed thoroughly with reference to analytical concentrations, as it is by far the most useful one. Fortunately, in "statics" there is no distinction between fast and slow steps; all steps have to be in equilibrium.

There are three different equilibrium constants, referring to system (3-186), namely (1-4), (4-141), and

$$K_{6,5} = \frac{\bar{c}_3}{\bar{c}_4 \bar{c}_5} \tag{4-145}$$

One has to introduce two equations for analytical concentrations, to establish the five relations necessary for the solution of this system. Most suitable are

$$c_4^0 = \bar{c}_1 + \bar{c}_2 + \bar{c}_3 + \bar{c}_4 \tag{4-146}$$

$$c_5^0 = \bar{c}_1 + \bar{c}_2 + \bar{c}_3 + \bar{c}_5 \tag{4-147}$$

One may now combine the five equations and solve for either one of four equilibrium concentrations—because of symmetry, the solution for $\bar{c}_4$ gives also the solution for $\bar{c}_5$ (by index exchange). One obtains the following expressions for the equilibrium concentrations:

$$\bar{c}_1 = \frac{\frac{1}{2}}{1 + K_{1,2}(1 + K_{3,4})} \left\{ c_4^0 + c_5^0 + K_0 \right\} \left[1 - \left\langle 1 - \frac{4c_4^0 c_5^0}{(c_4^0 + c_5^0 + K_0)^2} \right\rangle^{1/2} \right] \tag{4-148}$$

$$\bar{c}_4 = \frac{1}{2}(c_5^0 - c_4^0 + K_0) \left[\left\langle 1 + \frac{4c_4^0 K_0}{(c_5^0 - c_4^0 + K_0)^2} \right\rangle^{1/2} - 1 \right] \tag{4-149}$$

K_0 is the "over-all dissociation constant" and is defined by

$$K_0 \equiv \frac{\bar{c}_4 \bar{c}_5}{\bar{c}_1 + \bar{c}_2 + \bar{c}_3} \tag{4-150}$$

This equation may also be written in terms of defined equilibrium constants, for instance,

$$K_0 = \frac{K_{5,6}}{1 + K_{4,3}(1 + K_{2,1})} \tag{4-151}$$

Equation (4-149) is in structure quite similar to (4-12), with $c_3^0 \equiv 0$ (becoming identical upon proper reindexing). The equation for $\bar{c}_2$ is obtained from (4-148) and (1-4), while $\bar{c}_3 = K_{1,2}K_{3,4}\bar{c}_1$ according to (1-4) and (4-141), with $\bar{c}_1$ from (4-148).

One may now again employ (4-3). If there is one η_i, which is much larger than any other, the concentration associated with this η_i determines the equilibrium signal. As an example, which is related to an investigated system (6), one may choose $i = 2$. Experimentally, one may then select two simplifying analytical conditions: $c_4^0 = c_5^0$ and $c_4^0 \ll c_5^0$. For equality of the concentrations, one obtains from (4-148) with (1-4),

$$\bar{c}_2 = \frac{c_5^0 + \frac{1}{2}K_0}{1 + K_{2,1} + K_{3,4}}\left[1 - \left\langle 1 - \left(\frac{c_5^0}{c_5^0 + \frac{1}{2}K_0}\right)^2\right\rangle^{1/2}\right] \tag{4-152}$$

For small differences $S_0 - S_T$, this equilibrium concentration $\bar{c}_2$ may be multiplied with η_2 to give this difference directly. For strong unequality of the concentrations, the square root in (4-148) may be expanded and higher terms neglected, leading then with (1-4) to

$$\bar{c}_2 = \frac{c_4^0}{1 + K_{2,1} + K_{3,4}}\frac{c_5^0}{K_0 + c_5^0} \tag{4-153}$$

Both (4-152) and (4-153) indicate as the most suitable experimental range for c_5^0,

$$\tfrac{1}{10}K_0 \leqslant c_5^0 \leqslant 10K_0$$

This relation is equivalent to similar ones early in this chapter, where the "overall dissociation constant" corresponds to just one single step.

PROBLEMS

1. Derive a usable expression from (4-20), if $\eta_1 \ll \eta_3$.
2. Derive (4-22) in detail; discuss both roots.
3. Simplify (4-22), if (4-23) is sufficiently well approximated.
4. Solve (1-32), (4-10), (4-11), and (4-21) for $\bar{c}_2$ *directly* (via the quadratic equation).
5. Derive (4-25) from the simplified initial equations and from (4-24).
6. Obtain $\bar{c}_1$ for $c_3^0 = c_4^0 > 0 < c_1^0$, c_2^0 from (4-22).
7. Show that the second term under the root of (4-26) is small for *any* value of $K_{2,1}$ under the otherwise specified conditions.

8. Show that the square root in (4-29) cannot be eliminated for $c_2^0 = 2K_{2,1}c_1^0$.
9. Derive (4-35) directly from the initial conditions and from (4-33).
10. Find the typographical error mentioned in conjunction with Ref. *3* and derive that equation as indicated in the reference [related to (4-55)].
11. Use $\alpha = 2$ in (4-76) and plot the resulting curve of (4-73) with $c_2^0/K_{2,1}c_1^0$ as the independent variable.
12. Derive the general form of (4-78).
13. Derive the full equation for $\bar{c}_2$ directly from (1-32), (4-116), (4-118), and (4-119), to reach an equation similar to (4-120).
14. Derive (4-121) from (1-32), (4-116), (4-118), and (4-119).
15. Derive an equation for $\bar{c}_1$ which is similar to (4-120) but carries a sum, *not* a difference, under the root and leads directly to (4-123) for $c_1^0 = c_2^0$.
16. Starting with (4-121), show that $\bar{c}_3 \rightarrow c_1^0 c_2^0 (1 + K_{3,4})^{-1}(c_1^0 + c_2^0)^{-1}$ for the case $K_{2,1} - (1 + K_{3,4}) \rightarrow 0$.
17. Derive both (4-133) and (4-134) directly from (4-129), (4-130), (4-131), (4-117), and (1-32).
18. Derive the expression for $\bar{c}_3$ directly from (1-4), (4-141), and (4-145) to (4-147); investigate the concentration behavior of $\bar{c}_3/K_0$ versus c_5^0/K_0 with $c_4^0 \ll c_5^0$ and $K_{1,2} = K_{3,4} = 1$.
19. Demonstrate that after proper index exchange, (4-152) is actually identical with Eq. (17) of Ref. *6* [compare (4-151)!].

REFERENCES

1. G. Czerlinski, *J. Theoret. Biol.*, **7**, 463 (1964).
2. G. Czerlinski and G. Schreck, *J. Biol., Chem.*, **239**, 913 (1964), App. I.
3. Equation (7.9) of *J. Theoret. Biol.* **7**, 463 (1964) by expressing $S_T - S_0$ in terms of $\bar{c}_3$, using (4-51)—except for a typographical error.
4. G. Czerlinski and G. Hess, *J. Biol. Chem.* (1966), in preparation.
5. G. Czerlinski and G. Schreck, *Biochemistry*, **3**, 89 (1964).
6. G. Czerlinski and J. Malkewitz, *Biochemistry*, **4**, 1127 (1965).

CHAPTER 5

EXTENDED KINETICS

In Chapter 3 the kinetics of chemical relaxation was treated. The final equations contained equilibrium concentrations whenever a bimolecular step entered into the kinetics. But equilibrium concentrations are not directly accessible experimentally. The experimentally accessible parameters are the initial (analytical) concentrations c_i^0. One should therefore express the chemical-relaxation-time constants in terms of these analytical concentrations. A plot of the theoretical curves of τ versus c_i^0 could then easily be compared with experimental data. The desired expressions are obtained by combining the relevant equations of Chapter 3 with the associated ones in Chapter 4. Although this combination is quite straightforward, a separate chapter is reserved to develop the simplifications peculiar to individual systems. It is important for an investigator to recognize in the shape of a curve the mechanism actually present. This chapter is therefore essential for the interpretation of the experimental data.

5–1. ONE-STEP MECHANISMS

A. The Monomolecular Interconversion

Equation (3-3) shows no concentration dependence. Individual velocity constants can therefore not be derived from a plot of τ as a function of any analytical concentration. One could only give an upper limit for the velocity constants, but not decide to which one of the two constants it should be attributed.

B. Dissociation–Association

Equation (3-7) gives the time constant derived from

$$Y_1 + Y_2 \underset{k_2}{\overset{k_1}{\rightleftharpoons}} Y_3 \qquad (1\text{-}12)$$

One realizes from (4-10) and (4-11) that (in general)

$$\bar{c}_1 + \bar{c}_2 = c_1^0 + c_2^0 + 2(c_3^0 - \bar{c}_3) \tag{5-1}$$

Introduction of (5-1) together with the general equation (4-13) in (3-7) results after rearrangements and squaring in [with at least one of the $c_i^0 \equiv 0$; see the discussion of (5-6)]

$$\tau^{-2} = k_1^2[(c_1^0 - c_2^0)^2 + 2K_{2,1}(c_1^0 + c_2^0 + 2c_3^0)] + k_2^2 \tag{5-2}$$

This general equation is still somewhat difficult to solve, since it requires prior knowledge of $K_{2,1}$. But experimentally one may be able to establish various conditions which simplify (5-2) considerably and which do not require prior knowledge of $K_{2,1}$.

1. $c_1^0 = c_2^0 > 0 = c_3^0$ is the condition which seems particularly attractive for the simplification of (5-2). One obtains

$$\tau^{-2} = 4k_1k_2c_1^0 + k_2^2 \tag{5-3}$$

The intercept with the ordinate gives k_2^2, that with the abscissa $-\frac{1}{4}K_{2,1}$. Another special case may be derived by $c_1^0 = c_2^0 = 0 < c_3^0$, leading also to (5-3) with c_1^0 replaced by c_3^0.

2. Large c_2^0 represents a buffering condition for detection at Y_1

a. $c_1^0 = 0$; it is, for *any* c_3^0,

$$\tau^{-2} = k_1^2(c_2^0)^2 + 2k_1k_2(c_2^0 + 2c_3^0) + k_2^2 \tag{5-4}$$

and for the more frequent case $c_3^0 \ll c_2^0$,

$$\tau^{-1} = k_1c_2^0 + k_2 \tag{5-5}$$

This latter equation is also obtained directly from (3-7) by employing $\bar{c}_1 \ll \bar{c}_2 \doteq c_2^0$. The intercepts with the coordinates are easily obtained.

b. $c_3^0 = 0$; condition $c_1^0 \ll c_2^0$ leads immediately to (5-5) but the special condition is a restricting one, necessary for detection via Y_1. If detection is accomplished via component Y_3, c_1^0 does not need to be small compared to c_2^0. The (simplified) equation (5-2) would have to be used. The special case $c_1^0 = c_2^0$ was already treated after (5-3).

C. The Four-Component System

Equation (3-9) gives the time constant of

$$Y_1 + Y_2 \xrightarrow{\ k_1\ }_{k_2} Y_3 + Y_4 \tag{1-30}$$

The indicating component is Y_1 and should be present in relatively small concentration; its initial concentration may be represented by

$$c_1^0 = \bar{c}_1 + \bar{c}_4 \tag{5-6}$$

which eliminates c_4^0 (by $c_4^0 \equiv 0$). One should omit either c_1^0 or c_4^0 due to the dependence of one of the two upon the equilibrium constant [this is also valid for (5-3) and (5-4), leading to their simplified expressions]. Equation (4-22) may then be slightly simplified. Equation (4-22) was not simplified at its original place, since one is largely free in selecting the vanishing c_i^0, if buffering is not employed. One actually can quite generally state that if N is the number of components in a reaction system and n the number of individual reaction steps (equilibria), $N - n$ is the number of analytical concentrations one is free to select. But each equality $c_i^0 = c_j^0$ ($i \neq j$) must also be counted, as well as every (additional) $c_k^0 = 0$; see (5-19). [Later on it is shown that buffering of a component reduces the number of "free" analytical concentrations further; see the discussion of (5-29).] If more than $N - n$ (nonzero) analytical concentrations *are* selected, one should merge suitable ones to facilitate evaluations.

Equation (4-22) may be rewritten for $\bar{c}_2$, and one obtains for $\bar{c}_1 + \bar{c}_2$ an expression with two square roots, which cannot be combined in the most general case. Similarly, one obtains for $\bar{c}_3 + \bar{c}_4$ an expression with two noncombinable square roots. To facilitate the treatment, one should add at least one other condition. The various possible ones will now be discussed.

1. $c_1^0 = c_2^0 > 0$. The two roots in $\bar{c}_1 + \bar{c}_2$ can be immediately added and one obtains [from (4-24) and an equivalent equation for $\bar{c}_2$]

$$\bar{c}_1 + \bar{c}_2 = \frac{K_{2,1}(2c_1^0 + c_3^0)}{K_{2,1} - 1} \left\{ 1 - \left[1 - \frac{4(K_{2,1} - 1)c_1^0(c_1^0 + c_3^0)}{K_{2,1}(2c_1^0 + c_3^0)^2} \right]^{1/2} \right\} \tag{5-7}$$

the two roots in $\bar{c}_3 + \bar{c}_4$ cannot be directly eliminated except if one employs (4-10), (4-11), and (5-6), which give

$$\bar{c}_3 + \bar{c}_4 = c_1^0 + c_2^0 + c_3^0 - (\bar{c}_1 + \bar{c}_2) \tag{5-8}$$

Employing $c_1^0 = c_2^0$, (5-7) and (5-8) give

$$\bar{c}_3 + \bar{c}_4 = \frac{K_{2,1}(2c_1^0 + c_3^0)}{K_{2,1} - 1} \left[1 - \frac{4(K_{2,1} - 1)c_1^0(c_1^0 + c_3^0)}{K_{2,1}(2c_1^0 + c_3^0)^2} \right]^{1/2} - \frac{2c_1^0 + c_3^0}{K_{2,1} - 1} \tag{5-9}$$

The equation for the reciprocal relaxation time, (3-9), then becomes

$$\tau^{-1} = k_2(2c_1^0 + c_3^0)[1 - 4(K_{2,1} - 1)c_1^0(c_1^0 + c_3^0)K_{2,1}^{-1}(2c_1^0 + c_3^0)^{-2}]^{1/2} \tag{5-10}$$

Squaring of (5-10) leads, with simplification, to

$$\tau^{-2} = k_2^2(c_3^0)^2 + 4k_1k_2c_1^0(c_1^0 + c_3^0) \tag{5-11}$$

A plot of $(\tau c_3^0)^{-2}$ as a function of $c_1^0(c_1^0 + c_3^0)(c_3^0)^{-2}$ gives a straight line of slope $4k_1k_2$, intercept with the ordinate of k_2^2, and intercept with the abscissa of $-\frac{1}{4}K_{2,1}$. This result is thus quite similar to that of (5-3) for a three-component-system.

To be able to measure the velocity constants in (5-11) individually with adequate security, one should vary the two terms in (5-11) from

$$k_2^2(c_3^0)^2 \ll 4k_1k_2c_1^0(c_1^0 + c_3^0) \qquad \text{to} \qquad k_2^2(c_3^0) \gg 4k_1k_2c_1^0(c_1^0 + c_3^0)$$

The "center of variation" is given by

$$k_2^2(c_3^0)^2 = 4k_1k_2c_1^0(c_1^0 + c_3^0) \tag{5-12}$$

One may solve for c_3^0 and obtain

$$c_3^0 = \frac{2c_1^0}{K_{2,1}}[1 + (1 + K_{2,1})^{1/2}] \tag{5-13}$$

One may show the correctness of this equation immediately for $K_{2,1} \ll 1$, leading to $c_3^0 = 4c_1^0K_{2,1} - 1$, which is equivalent to $c_3^0 \gg c_1^0$. If $K_{2,1} \gg 1$, (5-13) becomes $c_3^0 = 2c_1^0(K_{1,2})^{1/2}$, which corresponds to $c_3^0 \ll c_1^0$ but is not permissible for reasons of detection! If thus $K_{2,1} \gg 1$, the initial condition $c_1^0 = c_2^0$ is not suitable.

2. $c_1^0 \ll c_2^0$. The derivation is quite straightforward, as condition (5-6) allows:

$$\bar{c}_1 + \bar{c}_2 \doteq c_2^0 \tag{5-14}$$

One then obtains immediately from (5-14), with (5-8) and $c_3^0 \gg c_1^0$,

$$\bar{c}_3 + \bar{c}_4 \doteq c_3^0 \tag{5-15}$$

[Experimentally, one may also establish $c_3^0 = 0$, which leads to a relationship discussed in conjunction with (5-19).]

The "full buffering condition" is given by $c_1^0 \ll c_2^0$, c_3^0 and leads for (3-9) to the very simple relationship [see (1-45)!]

$$\tau^{-1} = k_1c_2^0 + k_2c_3^0 \tag{5-16}$$

The "center of variation" is given by

$$k_1c_2^0 = k_2c_3^0 \tag{5-17}$$

One may immediately solve for c_3^0:

$$c_3^0 = c_2^0/K_{2,1} \tag{5-18}$$

If $K_{2,1}$ becomes rather large, it is difficult to maintain the requirements for (5-15), and one better establishes the next condition.

3. $c_3^0 = 0$. As $c_4^0 = 0$ also, the equation for $\bar{c}_3 + \bar{c}_4$ may be simplified, as the roots can now be added:

$$\bar{c}_3 + \bar{c}_4 = \frac{K_{1,2}(c_1^0 + c_2^0)}{K_{1,2} - 1}\left\{1 - \left[1 - \frac{4(K_{1,2} - 1)c_1^0 c_2^0}{K_{1,2}(c_1^0 + c_2^0)^2}\right]^{1/2}\right\} \quad (5-19)$$

If $c_3^0 = c_4^0 \equiv 0$, stoichiometry gives $\bar{c}_3 = \bar{c}_4$, which immediately results in an equation for the individual equilibrium concentrations. This equation (5-19) is rather similar in structure to (5-7), as similar conditions prevail; here $c_3^0 = c_4^0 = 0$, there $c_1^0 = c_2^0 > 0$. One obtains $\bar{c}_1 + \bar{c}_2$ from (5-19) with (5-8):

$$\bar{c}_1 + \bar{c}_2 = \frac{K_{1,2}(c_1^0 + c_2^0)}{K_{1,2} - 1}\left[1 - \frac{4(K_{1,2} - 1)c_1^0 c_2^0}{K_{1,2}(c_1^0 + c_2^0)^2}\right]^{1/2} - \frac{c_1^0 + c_2^0}{K_{2,1} - 1} \quad (5-20)$$

One may now incorporate (5-19) and (5-20) in the equation for the chemical relaxation time constant of this system, (3-9). One then obtains

$$\tau^{-1} = k_1(c_1^0 + c_2^0)\left[1 + \frac{4(K_{2,1} - 1)c_1^0 c_2^0}{(c_1^0 + c_2^0)^2}\right]^{1/2} \quad (5-21)$$

If this equilibrium constant $K_{2,1}$, defined by (1-32), approaches unity, (5-21) cannot be used. One would have to expand the square root at a much earlier stage of the derivation, as mentioned in the discussion of (4-22).

a. $K_{2,1} \gg 1$. Equation (5-21) may be slightly simplified, and squaring leads still to a somewhat complex equation:

$$[\tau(c_1^0 + c_2^0)]^{-2} = k_1^2 + \frac{4k_1 k_2 c_1^0 c_2^0}{(c_1^0 + c_2^0)^2} \quad (5-22)$$

Assuming Y_1 as the indicating component, one should select for suitable detection $c_1^0 \leqslant c_2^0$. The equilibrium constant, defined by (1-32), demonstrates that $\bar{c}_1$ would be quite small (relative to $\bar{c}_3$ and $\bar{c}_4$) for $K_{2,1} \gg 1$ *and* $c_1^0 = c_2^0$. It was shown upon discussion of (4.82) that $\bar{c}_1/c_1^0 = \frac{1}{2}$ at $c_2^0 = \frac{1}{2}K_{2,1}c_1^0$. One should therefore vary c_2^0/c_1^0 in the neighborhood of $\frac{1}{2}K_{2,1}$ (one order of magnitude both ways). $K_{2,1} \gg 1$ then leads to $c_2^0 \gg c_1^0$ (for the whole concentration span, the practical condition is $K_{2,1} > 100$). This relationship among the concentrations facilitates further simplification of (5-22), now employing c_2^0/c_1^0 as the independent variable:

$$\frac{1}{(\tau c_2^0)^2} = k_1^2 + 4k_1 k_2 \frac{c_1^0}{c_2^0} \quad (5-23)$$

A plot of the experimental $(\tau c_2^0)^{-2}$ versus c_1^0/c_2^0 gives $4k_1k_2$ as slope and k_1^2 as intercept with the ordinate. Both terms contribute equally to $(\tau c_2^0)^{-2}$, if $c_2^0 = 4K_{2,1}c_1^0$. k_1 can therefore only be determined if one progresses experimentally all the way to $c_2^0 \gg 4K_{2,1}c_1^0$.

b. $K_{2,1} \ll 1$. It becomes evident that k_2 is inaccessible for the condition $c_3^0 = c_4^0 = 0$. The condition $c_4^0 = c_3^0 = 0$ with its equation (5-21) is therefore unsuitable for $K_{2,1} \ll 1$. Inspection of the equilibrium equation (1-32) shows also that then $\bar{c}_1 \ll \bar{c}_3$, $\bar{c}_4$ always for $c_1^0 \leqslant c_2^0$ (condition for detectability). (An index exchange and mixing in opposite direction would take care of the problem, as case a with $K \gg 1$ would result.)

c. $c_1^0 = c_2^0$ for a $K_{2,1}$ of any magnitude. Equation (5-21) simplifies to

$$\tau^{-1} = 2(k_1k_2)^{1/2}c_1^0 \tag{5-24}$$

This result may also be obtained from (5-11) for $c_3^0 \equiv 0$. The reciprocal relaxation time changes linearly with c_1^0, with intercept at the origin!

4. SEVERAL OTHER EXPERIMENTAL CONDITIONS ARE NOT SUITABLE TO BE EMPLOYED FOR SIMPLIFICATION

a. $c_1^0 = c_2^0 = 0$ is against the condition that $c_4^0 = 0$. One may exchange indices and use case 3.

b. $c_2^0 = 0$ does not give any reaction, as required by (5-6).

c. $c_1^0 \gg c_2^0$ represents "inverse buffering"; no effects are detectable via Y_1.

d. $c_3^0 \gg c_1^0$, c_2^0 makes smallest concentration for Y_4. If this should become necessary, one should reindex and employ case 2.

D. Dimerization

This very simple reaction was only briefly treated thus far (in Section 3-1F1). The extended kinetics may be treated here quite briefly (1). The dissociation constant of the dimers is given by (D represents dimer)

$$K_{2,1} = \frac{(\bar{c}_1)^2}{\bar{c}_D} \tag{5-25}$$

The analytical concentration used in the system is given by

$$c_1^0 = \bar{c}_1 + 2\bar{c}_D \tag{5-26}$$

One may now solve for $\bar{c}_1$ and obtain

$$\bar{c}_1 = \frac{K_{2,1}}{4}\left[\left(1 + \frac{8c_1^0}{K_{2,1}}\right)^{1/2} - 1\right] \tag{5-27}$$

Using this equation in conjunction with (3-90) gives

$$\tau^{-1} = k_2 \left(1 + \frac{8c_1^0}{K_{2,1}} \right)^{1/2} \tag{5-28}$$

This equation may be squared to obtain a linear relationship between τ^{-2} and c_1^0.

E. The Buffer Derivation

So far the buffering condition was always inserted *after* the relaxation time constant had been derived. Equation (1-30) was repeated in the beginning of Section 5-1C. This reaction scheme may have given the true representation of the system, but at a detailed look one might have recognized the exchange of a part of the molecule, such as, for instance,

$$AH + B \underset{k'_2}{\overset{k'_1}{\rightleftharpoons}} BH + A \tag{5-29}$$

H does not need to represent a proton [charges are omitted in (5-29)]. H may be a metal ion, or a cation or anion, or may even be an atom, electron, or group. Hypothetically, one may then "split" (5-28) into two equations:

$$A + H \underset{k_2}{\overset{k_1}{\rightleftharpoons}} AH \tag{5-30}$$

$$B + H \underset{k_4}{\overset{k_3}{\rightleftharpoons}} BH \tag{5-31}$$

If one of the component pairs in (5-29) is now in great excess, one may have established the buffering condition for the two reactions (5-30) and (5-31). Buffering *is* established, if, for instance,

$$\bar{c}_B, \bar{c}_{BH} \gg \bar{c}_A, \bar{c}_{AH} \tag{5-32}$$

The concentrations of B and BH remain then virtually unchanged in chemical relaxation processes. They are therefore directly accessible analytically. One obtains

$$c_B^0 \doteq \bar{c}_B \qquad c_{BH}^0 \doteq \bar{c}_{BH} \tag{5-33}$$

Only one other analytical concentration is then "free":

$$c_A^0 = \bar{c}_A + \bar{c}_{AH} \tag{5-34}$$

The following two equations determine this system fully, together with (5-33) and (5-34):

$$K_{A,H} = \frac{\bar{c}_A \bar{c}_H}{\bar{c}_{AH}} = \frac{k_2}{k_1} \tag{5-35}$$

$$K_{B,H} = \frac{\bar{c}_B \bar{c}_H}{\bar{c}_{BH}} = \frac{k_4}{k_3} \tag{5-36}$$

An additional consideration is necessary with reference to the magnitude of $\bar{c}_H$. Equations (5-33) remain valid only as long as

$$\bar{c}_B, \bar{c}_{BH} \gg \bar{c}_H \tag{5-37}$$

If (5-37) is no longer true, the equations become somewhat more complicated. However, if the invalidity of (5-37) leads to

$$\bar{c}_H \gg \bar{c}_A, \bar{c}_{AH} \tag{5-38}$$

one may omit components B and BH and use the buffering by H directly. Here only the validity of (5-37) will be considered.

If Equation (5-37) is valid, one may simplify the kinetic derivation for the system (5-29). One may employ a derivation starting with (5-30) only. But it should be pointed out that this equation does not necessarily represent the actual kinetic process. This equation is only used to arrive at a simplified derivation, labeled above as the "buffer derivation." Equation (5-30) will therefore now be considered only.

Buffering in H leads to one fundamental relation which is different from all previous ones:

$$\Delta c_H \ll \Delta c_A, \Delta c_{AH} \tag{5-39}$$

This relation includes that for all practical purposes $d\,\Delta c_H/dt \equiv 0$. (This actually is a kinetic relationship, establishing pre-equilibration.) The remaining two differential equations become

$$\frac{d\,\Delta c_A}{dt} = -\frac{d\,\Delta c_{AH}}{dt} = -k_1(\bar{c}_A\,\Delta c_H + \bar{c}_H\,\Delta c_A) + k_2\,\Delta c_{AH} \tag{5-40}$$

As $\Delta c_A = -\Delta c_{AH}$ [compare former equation (3-5), which corresponds to this treatment], one obtains, with (5-39),

$$\frac{d\,\Delta c_A}{dt} = -(k_1\bar{c}_H + k_2)\,\Delta c_A \tag{5-41}$$

The relaxation time is immediately evident and coincides with (5-5) for $\bar{c}_H = c_2^0$. One realizes that (5-5) is not only obtained by a relatively large c_2^0 but also by a buffered one.

It is quite important to realize that (5-41) does *not* necessarily give the true kinetic representation of the system. On the contrary, most of the conversion may proceed via mechanism (5-29), where the proton transfer occurs directly between buffering base B and indicating acid A. Equation (5-16) is then valid and written in the terminology of mechanism (5-29),

$$\tau^{-1} = k_1' c_B^0 + k_2' c_{BH}^0 \tag{5-42}$$

In the pH range 6 to 8, this equation represents almost exclusively the actual mechanism of proton transfer.

System (5-29) may also be split in the following two subsystems:

$$AH + OH \xrightarrow[k_2]{k_1} A(+H_2O) \tag{5-43}$$

$$BH + OH \xrightarrow[k_4]{k_3} B(+H_2O) \tag{5-44}$$

H_2O is omitted, as it is (quite generally) considered to be a solvent molecule. Again, (5-32) is valid, and the derivation proceeds similarly to the one given following (5-32). One finally obtains

$$\tau^{-1} = k_1 \bar{c}_{OH} + k_2 \tag{5-45}$$

If the reaction proceeds thus via OH, the reciprocal relaxation time is given by (5-45). Distinction between these three available mechanisms becomes possible on the grounds of the detailed concentration dependence of τ^{-1}.

Differentiation among these three possible mechanisms is lost when a relaxation process is considered which is much slower than this proton exchange. If the slower process is followed, the faster (protonic) process appears as an equilibrium term. And in an equilibrium term the various expressions may be freely exchanged. But one should still keep in mind that the faster step may proceed via a different mechanism than shown in the equations for the slower relaxation process. On the other hand, the smaller the number of components, the simpler the equations (a recommendation to employ buffering, whenever possible; see later sections of this chapter and following ones.) Buffering will frequently be indicated by two bars over the specific concentration symbol for example, $\bar{\bar{c}}_H$.

5–2. TWO-STEP MECHANISMS

A. Three Components

The relaxation times of a two-step mechanism with three components are given by (3-41) and (3-42), demonstrating no concentration dependence.

B. Four Components

A bimolecular and a monomolecular reaction may be combined in two different ways, as was already pointed out at appropriate places in previous chapters.

1. An association reaction, *followed* by a monomolecular interconversion, as defined by (3-43). All relevant relaxation times contain the

concentrations $\bar{c}_1$ and $\bar{c}_2$ as a sum. The unabbreviated expression for $\bar{c}_1$ is given by (4-48). The appropriate expression for $\bar{c}_2$ is then obtained by index exchange in the concentration terms. Adding the two concentrations results in

$$\bar{c}_1 + \bar{c}_2$$

$$= \frac{1}{2}\left(\frac{K_{2,1}}{1+K_{3,4}} + c_2^0 - c_1^0\right)\left[1 + \frac{4K_{2,1}c_1^0}{1+K_{3,4}}\left(\frac{K_{2,1}}{1+K_{3,4}} + c_2^0 - c_1^0\right)^{-2}\right]^{1/2}$$

$$+ \frac{1}{2}\left(\frac{K_{2,1}}{1+K_{3,4}} + c_1^0 - c_2^0\right)\left[1 + \frac{4K_{2,1}c_2^0}{1+K_{3,4}}\left(\frac{K_{2,1}}{1+K_{3,4}} + c_1^0 - c_2^0\right)^{-2}\right]^{1/2}$$

$$- \frac{K_{2,1}}{1+K_{3,4}} \tag{5-46}$$

It is immediately evident by what *experimental* conditions this equation may be simplified.

a. $c_1^0 = c_2^0$ leads immediately to

$$\bar{c}_1 + \bar{c}_2 = \frac{K_{2,1}}{1+K_{3,4}}\left\{\left[1 + \frac{4c_1^0(1+K_{3,4})}{K_{2,1}}\right]^{1/2} - 1\right\} \tag{5-47}$$

This result may directly be combined with (3-50), giving, upon simplification,

$$\tau_1^{-1} = \frac{k_2}{1+K_{3,4}}\left\{\left[1 + \frac{4c_1^0(1+K_{3,4})}{K_{2,1}}\right]^{1/2} + K_{3,4}\right\} \tag{5-48}$$

The intercept with the ordinate ($c_1^0 \to 0$) results directly in k_2. At *high* c_1^0 the slope of a plot of τ_1^{-1} versus $(c_1^0)^{1/2}$ becomes equal to $[4k_1k_2/(1+K_{3,4})]^{1/2}$.

Similarly, one obtains, from (3-51),

$$\tau_2^{-1} = k_3\left\{1 + \frac{1+K_{3,4}}{[1 + 4(1+K_{3,4})c_1^0/K_{2,1}]^{1/2} - 1}\right\}^{-1} + k_4 \tag{5-49}$$

This equation is substantially identical to (6-3) of a slightly different derivation already published (2). The intercept with the ordinate ($c_1^0 \to 0$) gives k_4. At very large c_1^0 ($\to \infty$) the ordinate reaches a limiting value of $k_3 + k_4$. At the "half-point of change" the ordinate is at $k_4 + \frac{1}{2}k_3$, while

$$(c_1^0)_{1/2} = \frac{K_{2,1}}{1+K_{3,4}}(\tfrac{1}{4}K_{3,4}^2 + K_{3,4} + \tfrac{3}{4}) \tag{5-50}$$

These derivations are only valid for the case of a fast bimolecular step followed by a slow monomolecular interconversion.

The other possible case is that of a fast monomolecular interconversion followed by a slow bimolecular step. The fast reciprocal relaxation time for this case is given by (3-52), τ_2^{-1} is given by (3-53). Only the latter equation requires incorporation of (5-47), resulting after simplification in

$$\tau_2^{-1} = \frac{k_2}{1 + K_{3,4}} \left[1 + \frac{4c_1^0(1 + K_{3,4})}{K_{2,1}} \right]^{1/2} \tag{5-51}$$

for $c_1^0 \to 0$ one obtains $\tau_2^{-1} \to k_2(1 + K_{3,4})^{-1}$, and for $c_1^0 \to \infty$ one obtains a slope of $[4k_1k_2/(1 + K_{3,4})]^{1/2}$ from a plot of τ_2^{-1} versus $(c_1^0)^{1/2}$. A linear relationship is obtained from (5-51) by squaring:

$$\tau_2^{-2} = \left(\frac{k_2}{1 + K_{3,4}} \right)^2 + \frac{4k_1k_2}{1 + K_{3,4}} c_1^0 \tag{5-52}$$

If $K_{3,4}$ is not known, only a lower limit for k_2 could be given. If τ_1, on the other hand, was experimentally detectable, k_2 cannot be expected to be 10 times larger than the given lower limit. In comparing (5-52) with (5-3), one realizes that both equations are experimentally indistinguishable; distinction requires prior knowledge of $K_{3,4}$ by some experimental means.

b. One of the c_i^0 is much larger than the other one. If detection proceeds via Y_1: $c_2^0 \gg c_1^0$. If detection proceeds via Y_3 or Y_4, any condition is possible, but the larger c_i^0 should be of the magnitude of the dissociation constant. If $c_2^0 \gg c_1^0$, one also has $\bar{c}_2 \gg \bar{c}_1$ and one obtains, from (3-50),

$$\tau_1^{-1} = k_1c_2^0 + k_2 \tag{5-53}$$

from (3-51),

$$\tau_2^{-1} = k_3 \frac{c_2^0}{K_{2,1} + c_2^0} + k_4 \tag{5-54}$$

and from (3-53),

$$\tau_2^{-1} = k_1c_2^0 + k_2(1 + K_{3,4})^{-1} \tag{5-55}$$

These equations are *much* simpler than the previous ones and should therefore preferably be used. But if $K_{2,1}$ is quite small (in the micromolar range) and if there is no species in the system with outstanding detection properties ($\eta_i \gg \eta_j$ for any $j \neq i$) or both, the more complex equations of Section 5-2B1a have to be used.

c. One of the $\bar{c}_i$ is buffered, say $\bar{c}_2$. Equations (5-53), (5-54), and (5-55) may again be used with $c_2^0 \to \bar{c}_2$, the buffered concentration. But it should be stated again that it is very unlikely that (5-53) and (5-55) represent the actual mechanism. Only (5-54) could be considered a true representation. The concentration $\bar{c}_2$ there may be replaced as well by a term containing the dissociation constant of the buffer and the two concentrations of the buffering species [compare the left section of (5-35) for $\bar{c}_2 = \bar{c}_H$].

2. An association reaction, preceded by a monomolecular interconversion, as defined by (3-54). It is now no longer of interest to form the sum $\bar{c}_1 + \bar{c}_2$, since this sum appears in only part of the relaxation times. The expressions for $\bar{c}_1$ and $\bar{c}_2$ are now also more complex than in Section 5-2B1, as signified by (4-53) and (4-54). Specific cases will now be treated directly.

a. $c_1^0 = c_2^0$ gives for $\bar{c}_1$ from (4-53),

$$\bar{c}_1 = \tfrac{1}{2}[K_{2,1}(1 + K_{4,3})]\left\{\left[1 + \frac{4c_1^0}{K_{2,1}(1 + K_{4,3})}\right]^{1/2} - 1\right\} \quad (5\text{-}56)$$

$$\bar{c}_2 = \tfrac{1}{2}K_{2,1}\left\{\left[1 + \frac{4c_1^0}{K_{2,1}(1 + K_{4,3})}\right]^{1/2} - 1\right\} \quad (5\text{-}57)$$

Equation (3-50) is also valid here and leads upon proper substitution to

$$\tau_1^{-1} = k_2\left[\left\{\left[1 + \frac{4c_1^0}{K_{2,1}(1 + K_{4,3})}\right]^{1/2} - 1\right\}\left(1 + \frac{K_{4,3}}{2}\right) + 1\right] \quad (5\text{-}58)$$

One obtains for $c_1^0 \to 0$ as limit $\tau_1^{-1} \to k_2$ and for $c_1^0 \to \infty$ in a plot of τ_1^{-1} versus $(c_1^0)^{1/2}$ as slope $2k_2(1 + \tfrac{1}{2}K_{4,3})[K_{2,1}(1 + K_{4,3})]^{-1/2}$, which allows computation of k_1 after τ_2^{-1} has been evaluated. Equation (3-57) gives, with (5-56) and (5-57), the inverse slow relaxation time for the process of a fast bimolecular step and a slow monomolecular one:

$$\tau_2^{-1} = k_3 + k_4\left[1 + \frac{1 + K_{4,3}}{1 + 2\{[1 + 4c_1^0/[(1 + K_{4,3})K_{2,1}]]^{1/2} - 1\}^{-1}}\right]^{-1} \quad (5\text{-}59)$$

This equation is identical to (6.5) published earlier (2). A plot of τ_2^{-1} versus c_1^0 gives a sigmoid-like curve with $\tau_2^{-1} \to k_3 + k_4$ for $c_1^0 \to 0$ and $\tau_2^{-1} \to k_3 + k_4(2 + K_{4,3})^{-1}$ for $c_1^0 \to \infty$. This was one of two possible kinetic cases.

In the other possible case, the monomolecular interconversion is fast, while the bimolecular association is slow. The fast relaxation process is determined by (3-52) with no concentration dependence of τ_1^{-1}. The second (much longer) relaxation time is given by (3-53), which contains equilibrium concentrations and would have to be combined with (5-56) and (5-57). One obtains

$$\tau_2^{-1} = k_2\left[1 + \frac{4c_1^0}{K_{2,1}(1 + K_{4,3})}\right]^{1/2} \quad (5\text{-}60)$$

A plot of τ_2^{-1} versus $(c_1^0)^{1/2}$ gives a monotonic curve with $\tau_2^{-1} \to k_2$ for $c_1^0 \to 0$ and a slope of $[4k_1k_2(1 + K_{4,3})^{-1}]^{-1/2}$ for $c_1^0 \to \infty$. A simple linear relationship is obtained by squaring:

$$\tau_2^{-2} = k_2^2 + 4k_1k_2(1 + K_{4,3})^{-1}c_1^0 \tag{5-61}$$

The structure of this equation should be compared with that of (5-52) and (5-3). Again $K_{4,3}$ should be known; otherwise, only a lower limit could be given for k_1.

b. One of the c_i^0 is much larger than the other one. If detection proceeds via Y_1, $c_2^0 \gg c_1^0$. If detection proceeds via Y_2 or Y_4, $c_1^0 \gg c_2^0$. Any condition is possible for detection via Y_3. But the larger c_i^0 should always be of the order of magnitude of the dissociation constant. While in Section 5-2B1b there was no fundamental difference between $c_1^0 \gg c_2^0$ and $c_2^0 \gg c_1^0$, this is no longer true for reaction system (3-54).

One obtains from (4-53) for $c_1^0 \gg c_2^0$: $\bar{c}_1 \doteq c_1^0$. Under the same conditions, one also has $\bar{c}_2 \ll K_{2,1}$. Thus one obtains for a fast bimolecular step and a slow monomolecular one, from (3-50),

$$\tau_1^{-1} = k_1c_1^0 + k_2 \tag{5-62}$$

and, from (3-57),

$$\tau_2^{-1} = k_3 + k_4\frac{K_{2,1}}{K_{2,1} + c_1^0} \tag{5-63}$$

On the other hand, one obtains for a fast monomolecular step and a slow bimolecular one (3-52) for τ_1^{-1} and, from (3-58),

$$\tau_2^{-1} = \frac{k_1}{1 + K_{4,3}} c_1^0 + k_2 \tag{5-64}$$

The limits in these equations for plotting any τ^{-1} versus c_1^0 are easily seen.

Now if $c_2^0 \gg c_1^0$, one obtains, from (4-54),

$$\bar{c}_2 = \frac{c_2^0}{1 + K_{4,3}} \tag{5-65}$$

If $K_{4,3} < 10$, one may still consider $\bar{c}_2 \gg \bar{c}_1$. Under these conditions one obtains, from (3-50),

$$\tau_1^{-1} = \frac{k_1}{1 + K_{4,3}} c_2^0 + k_2 \tag{5-66}$$

and, from (3-57),

$$\tau_2^{-1} = k_3 + k_4 \tag{5-67}$$

This latter equation demonstrates no concentration dependence. The individual constants can therefore not be evaluated under these conditions. To evaluate these constants, one therefore has to establish conditions which lead to (5-59).

For a fast monomolecular step, (3-52) remains valid. The slow step is then given by (3-58), which becomes

$$\tau_2^{-1} = \frac{k_1}{1 + K_{4,3}} c_2^0 + k_2 \qquad (5\text{-}68)$$

under the condition $c_2^0 \gg c_1^0$ and for any size $K_{4,3}$. The right side of this equation is identical to (5-66). It can only be distinguished from (5-66) by the fact that a slower relaxation time follows after (5-66), whereas (5-68) requires a (prior) fast step.

c. The case of buffering seems applicable only to (5-63), (5-64), and (5-68) with $c_1^0 \rightarrow \bar{c}_i$ [(5-67) is not useful]. Equation (5-64) is quite similar to (5-68), while (5-63) is rather different in structure. If buffering is used, one should be very careful in the interpretation of the mechanisms related to (5-64) and (5-68). Buffering may be applied without reservation to (5-63) [but not to (5-62)].

C. Five Components

1. Four-component-step coupled to Monomolecular One. This is represented by (3-69). As was already mentioned in Chapter 3, the indicated reaction is quite unsymmetric and would therefore have to be treated in two ways.

a. The multicomponent step is much faster than the monomolecular interconversion. Although the fast step is determined by (3-9), the replacement of equilibrium concentrations by analytical concentrations leads to an expression which is certainly more complex than (5-23) or (5-24). As there are two ways in which two components may be mixed, additional subdivisions become necessary.

1. Y_1 and Y_2 Are Initially Brought Together. Equations (4-116) and (4-118) determine the equilibrium concentrations as a function of analytical concentrations in a multivariable form. Although some simplification is possible by the introduction of (4-120) and (4-121), considerably more simplification is obtained by introducing the simplifying experimental conditions:

a. $c_1^0 = c_2^0$. One may employ (4-122) [with $\bar{c}_1 = \bar{c}_2$] and the simplified equation (4-121), leading to

$$\tau_1^{-1} = \frac{2k_2 c_1^0}{K_{2,1} - (1 + K_{3,4})}\left[1 + \left\langle 1 + \frac{K_{3,4}}{2}\right\rangle\left\langle \frac{K_{2,1}}{1 + K_{3,4}}\right\rangle^{1/2}\right]$$
$$\times \left(1 - \left\langle \frac{1 + K_{3,4}}{K_{2,1}}\right\rangle^{1/2}\right) \quad (5\text{-}69)$$

If $K_{3,4} \to 0$, this equation may be converted to the former very simple relation (5-24). Equation (5-69) has the unfortunate feature that a plot of τ_1^{-1} versus c_1^0 gives only a slope which is given by a complex expression.

Equation (5-69) is equally valid for $K_{2,1} > 1 + K_{3,4}$ and for $K_{2,1} < 1 + K_{3,4}$. If these interrelations are extreme, further simplifications are possible,

$$\tau_1^{-1} \to 2c_1^0\langle k_1 k_2(1 + K_{3,4})^{-1}\rangle^{1/2} \qquad \text{for } K_{2,1} \to 0 \quad (5\text{-}70)$$

$$\tau_1^{-1} \to (2 + K_{3,4})c_1^0\langle k_1 k_2(1 + K_{3,4})^{-1}\rangle^{1/2} \qquad \text{for } K_{2,1} \to \infty \quad (5\text{-}71)$$

But these extreme conditions are not favorable for the detection of small concentration changes; in other words, the condition $c_1^0 = c_2^0$ is unsuitable as an experimental condition, if $K_{2,1}$ is very much different from $1 + K_{3,4}$.

The second relaxation process may be written in a very simple manner,

$$\tau_2^{-1} = k_4 + k_3(1 - k_2 \tau_1 \bar{c}_4) \quad (5\text{-}72)$$

with $\bar{c}_4$ from (4-119) and (4-121). If the expressions for τ_1 and $\bar{c}_4$ are inserted, one obtains after rearrangement,

$$\tau_2^{-1} = k_4 + k_3\left[1 + (1 + K_{3,4})\left(2\left\langle \frac{1 + K_{3,4}}{K_{2,1}}\right\rangle^{1/2} + 1\right)^{-1}\right]^{-1} \quad (5\text{-}73)$$

The condition $c_1^0 = c_2^0$ results thus here in an expression for τ_2 which is concentration-independent. One should therefore definitely avoid the condition $c_1^0 = c_2^0$.

b. $c_1^0 \ll c_2^0$, *Giving Also* $\bar{c}_1 \ll \bar{c}_2 \doteq c_2^0$. It is then sufficient to employ (4-128) only, giving

$$\tau_1^{-1} = k_1 c_2^0 + k_2(2 + K_{3,4})\frac{c_2^0}{2[K_{2,1} - (1 + K_{3,4})]}$$
$$\times \left(\left\langle 1 + \frac{4c_1^0(K_{2,1} - 1 - K_{3,4})}{c_2^0(1 + K_{3,4})}\right\rangle^{1/2} - 1\right) \quad (5\text{-}74)$$

Further simplification is possible, if not only $c_1^0 \ll c_2^0$, but also $K_{2,1}c_1^0 \ll c_2^0$, leading (for $K_{2,1} > 1 + K_{3,4}$) to

$$\tau_1^{-1} = k_1 c_2^0 + k_2 c_1^0 [1 + (1 + K_{3,4})^{-1}] \tag{5-75}$$

If $K_{3,4} \to 0$, (5-75) reduces to (5-21) *with* $c_1^0 \ll c_2^0$. Unfortunately, the conditions for (5-75) are rather unfavorable for detecting a signal change; these conditions are more related to the limiting case. The most favorable condition for detection is approximately [from (6-25)] given by $c_2^0 = 2c_1^0 K_{2,1}(1 + K_{3,4})^{-1}$, which leads for $c_2^0 \gg c_1^0$ to $K_{2,1}(1 + K_{3,4})^{-1} \gg 1$.

The second relaxation time is again given by (5-72), but with $\bar{c}_4$ from (4-119) and (4-128). Upon substitution of the proper expressions in (5-72), one obtains

$$\tau_2^{-1} = k_4 + k_3 \left(1 + \left\{ \frac{2[K_{2,1} - (1 + K_{3,4})]}{K_{2,1}(1 + K_{3,4})} \right. \right.$$

$$\left. \left. \times \left[\left\langle 1 + \frac{4c_1^0(K_{2,1} - 1 - K_{3,4})}{c_2^0(1 + K_{3,4})} \right\rangle^{1/2} - 1 \right]^{-1} + \frac{1}{1 + K_{3,4}} \right\}^{-1} \right)^{-1} \tag{5-76}$$

If α denotes the second term under the root, one obtains for $\alpha \to 0$, the limit $\tau^{-1} \to k_3 + k_4$ and for $\alpha \to \infty$ the limit $\tau_2^{-1} \to k_4 + k_3(2 + K_{3,4})^{-1}$. It is quite apparent from these estimations on the concentration-dependent term α that τ_2^{-1} passes a concentration-dependent range.

2. Y_3 (or Y_5) and Y_4 Are Mixed. This leads to a redefinition of the analytical concentrations according to (4-129) and (4-130). One may easily insert the complex equations (4-132) and (4-133) in (3-9). At this place, only the two limiting experimental conditions will be considered.

a. $c_3^0 = c_4^0$. Equation (3-9) becomes upon substitution by (4-131), (4-135), (4-136), and (4-130),

$$\tau_1^{-1} = \frac{k_1 c_3^0}{K_{1,2}(1 + K_{3,4}) - 1} \left[(2 - K_{2,1}) \left\langle \frac{1 + K_{3,4}}{K_{2,1}} \right\rangle^{1/2} \right.$$

$$\left. + K_{3,4} - \left\langle \frac{K_{2,1}}{1 + K_{3,4}} \right\rangle^{1/2} \right] \tag{5-77}$$

This equation has the origin again as intercept, permitting no direct determination of k_2.

The second relaxation process is again given by (5-72), but $\bar{c}_4$ is now given by (4-130), leading, together with (4-135), to

$$\tau_2^{-1} = k_4 + k_3 \left[1 - k_2 \tau_1 c_3^0 \frac{K_{1,2}(1 + K_{3,4}) - \langle K_{1,2}(1 + K_{3,4}) \rangle^{1/2}}{K_{1,2}(1 + K_{3,4}) - 1} \right] \quad (5\text{-}78)$$

The quotient in the brackets is positive for any $K_{2,1} \neq (1 + K_{3,4})$. One may also incorporate τ_1 from (5-77), leading to

$$\tau_2^{-1} = k_4 + k_3 \left[1 + \frac{\langle K_{1,2}(1 + K_{3,4}) \rangle^{1/2} - 1}{K_{1,2}(1 + K_{3,4}) - 1} (1 + K_{3,4}) \right]^{-1} \quad (5\text{-}79)$$

The quotient in the brackets is again positive for any $K_{2,1} \neq 1 + K_{3,4}$. In addition, no analytical concentration appears in (5-79); τ_2 is therefore independent of concentration [in contrast to the appearance of (3-73)].

b. $c_3^0 \ll c_4^0$. Equation (3-9) becomes upon substitution by (4-131) and (4-136), and with $\bar{c}_3 \ll \bar{c}_4 \doteq c_4^0$,

$$\tau_1^{-1} = \frac{k_1 c_4^0}{K_{1,2}(1 + K_{3,4}) - 1}$$

$$\times \left\{ \left\langle 1 + 4 \frac{c_3^0}{c_4^0} [K_{1,2}(1 + K_{3,4}) - 1] \right\rangle^{1/2} - 1 \right\} + k_2 c_4^0 \quad (5\text{-}80)$$

The limits of this equation are

$$\tau_1^{-1} \to k_1 2c_3^0 + k_2 c_4^0 \qquad \text{for } c_4^0 \to \infty$$

$$\tau_1^{-1} \to k_1 \langle 4c_3^0 c_4^0 [K_{1,2}(1 + K_{3,4})]^{-1} \rangle^{1/2} + k_2 c_4^0 \qquad \text{for } c_4^0 \to 0$$

One then obtains for the second relaxation time,

$$\tau_2^{-1} = k_3 (1 + \tau_1 k_1 c_4^0)^{-1} + k_4 \quad (5\text{-}81)$$

The limits for this equation may easily be derived from the limits of the square root in (5-80).

b. The multicomponent step is much slower than the monomolecular interconversion. The relaxation time for the fast step is always given by (3-52). It is therefore only necessary to discuss the slow step. Again, there are two ways in which two components may be mixed.

1. Y_1 and Y_2 Are Initially Brought Together. Equations (4-116) and (4-118) then define the analytical concentrations in terms of the individual equilibrium concentrations. One may then incorporate (4-120) and (4-121).

These equations do not simplify the over-all expression substantially, and therefore the special experimental conditions are introduced.

a. $c_1^0 = c_2^0$, which results in $\bar{c}_1 = \bar{c}_2$. Equation (3-74) is then combined with (4-122), the simplified (4-121), and (4-119), leading to

$$\frac{1}{\tau_2} = 2c_1^0 \left\langle \frac{k_1 k_2}{1 + K_{3,4}} \right\rangle^{1/2} \tag{5-82}$$

One derives from (3-70) that $K_{3,4} = \bar{c}_5/\bar{c}_3$; thus if $\bar{c}_5 \to 0$, which is equivalent to the nonexistence of the equilibrium with $K_{3,4}$, one obtains $K_{3,4} \to 0$ and (5-82) simplifies to (5-24). Equation (5-82) is very simple, but gives only the slope and thus the product of the two rate constants. To evaluate the individual rate constants, one would have to employ some additional analytical condition. The employment of (5-82) is difficult, if the equilibrium constant $K_{2,1}$ is considerably different from unity; the difficulty lies in the indication of equilibrium changes, as extreme equilibrium concentration ratios are associated with $K_{2,1} \gg 1$ or $K_{2,1} \ll 1$ and $c_1^0 = c_2^0$. The indicating species must then have a relatively quite high extinction coefficient (or fluorescence yield).

b. $c_1^0 \ll c_2^0$. One has to combine (3-74) with (4-128), (4-119), and the simplification $\bar{c}_1 \ll \bar{c}_2 \doteq c_2^0$, leading to

$$\frac{1}{\tau_2 c_2^0} = k_1 + \frac{k_2}{K_{2,1} - (1 + K_{3,4})} \left[\left\langle 1 + \left(\frac{4c_1^0}{c_2^0} \right) \left(\frac{K_{2,1}}{1 + K_{3,4}} - 1 \right) \right\rangle^{1/2} - 1 \right] \tag{5-83}$$

Considerable further simplifications are only possible if $K_{2,1} \gg 1 + K_{3,4}$. But this relationship is particularly useful for $c_1^0 \ll c_2^0$. One obtains, with $K_{2,1} \gg 1 + K_{3,4}$,

$$\frac{1}{(\tau_2 c_2^0)^2} = k_1^2 + \frac{4k_1 k_2}{1 + K_{3,4}} \frac{c_1^0}{c_2^0} \tag{5-84}$$

This equation is quite similar to (5-23), but vastly different from (5-74) or (5-75), which is simply due to the different sequencing of the individual reaction steps.

2. *Y₃ (or Y₅) and Y₄ Are Initially Brought Together.* Equations (4-129) and (4-130) then define the analytical concentration in terms of equilibrium concentrations. One may then generally employ (4-132) and (4-133) or use the simplifying analytical conditions.

a. $c_3^0 = c_4^0$. Equations (4-119) and (4-131) are valid; (3-74) is combined with (4-135) and (4-136), resulting in

$$\frac{1}{\tau_2} = 2c_3^0 \left\langle \frac{k_1 k_2}{1 + K_{3,4}} \right\rangle^{1/2} \tag{5-85}$$

The similarity to (5-82) is quite striking. But the same problems are associated with the use of this equation as with (5-82).

b. $c_3^0 \ll c_4^0$, associated with $\bar{c}_3 \ll \bar{c}_4 \doteq c_4^0$. Equation (3-74) becomes, with (4-131) and (4-137),

$$\frac{1}{\tau_2 c_4^0} = \frac{k_1}{K_{1,2}(1 + K_{3,4}) - 1} \left\{ \left\langle 1 + \frac{4c_3^0}{c_4^0} [K_{1,2}(1 + K_{3,4}) - 1] \right\rangle^{1/2} - 1 \right\}$$
$$+ \frac{k_2}{1 + K_{3,4}} \tag{5-86}$$

Considerable further simplification becomes possible for $K_{1,2}(1 + K_{3,4}) \gg 1$, leading to

$$(\tau_2 c_4^0)^{-2} = \left(\frac{k_2}{1 + K_{3,4}}\right)^2 + 4k_1 k_2 (1 + K_{3,4}) \frac{c_3^0}{c_4^0} \tag{5-87}$$

This equation has considerable similarity in structure compared to (5-84). Employment of (5-87) is most useful for $K_{2,1} \ll 1 + K_{3,4}$ and (5-84) is most useful for $K_{2,1} \gg 1 + K_{3,4}$. If, however, $K_{2,1} \approx 1 + K_{3,4}$, the case of "full buffering" is most suitable (and is discussed below).

3. "Full buffering" means either $\bar{c}_1, \bar{c}_3 \gg \bar{c}_2, \bar{c}_4$ or $\bar{c}_2, \bar{c}_4 \gg \bar{c}_1, \bar{c}_3$. Analytically most suitable is $c_2^0, c_4^0 \gg c_3^0$, with c_3^0 given by (4-129). With these conditions, (3-74) immediately becomes

$$\frac{1}{\tau_2} = k_1 c_2^0 + \frac{k_2}{1 + K_{3,4}} c_4^0 \tag{5-88}$$

If $K_{2,1} \approx 1$, the ratio c_2^0/c_4^0 should vary between $0.1K_{2,1}$ and $10K_{2,1}$, to obtain both rate constants easily. Because of its simplicity, this equation is not discussed any further.

---

2. **TWO CONSECUTIVE ASSOCIATIONS.** This rather unsymmetric case is given by reaction scheme (3-64). One has to distinguish according to the relative speeds of the reaction steps.

a. **The "left step" is very rapid.** It was assumed previously [preceding (4-92)] that Y_2 is buffered. As will be seen later, this buffering is a very important property for solving the equations easily. The equation for τ_1 is then almost trivial and was already given earlier in this chapter: Eq. (5-5). This reaction step may quite easily be investigated by just omitting the addition of component Y_4. Actually, one may solve the kinetics of this step in any way, if Y_4 is omitted.

Equation (3-66) is valid for the second step with the factor at $\bar{c}_4$ reduced to $\bar{c}_2(K_{2,1} + \bar{c}_2)^{-1}$. The two bars above the concentration term c_2 indicate "fixation by buffering." One may now directly incorporate (4-99) and (4-100) in (3-66), leading by contraction of the equations to

$$\frac{1}{\tau_2} = k_3 \left(K_{4,3} + \frac{c_4^0 - c_1^0}{1 + K_{2,1}/\bar{c}_2} \right) \left[\left\langle 1 + \frac{4c_4^0 K_{4,3}(1 + K_{2,1}/\bar{c}_2)}{[K_{4,3}(1 + K_{2,1}/\bar{c}_2) + c_1^0 - c_4^0]^2} \right\rangle^{1/2} - 1 \right] 2k_4 \tag{5-89}$$

This result is still rather complex, but further simplifications are easily possible by the choice of analytical conditions.

1. $c_1^0 = c_4^0$ with their definition by (4-92) and (4-93) or by (4-96) and (4-97). Equation (5-89) reduces for this equality to

$$\tau_2^{-2} = k_4^2 + \frac{4k_3 k_4 c_4^0}{1 + K_{2,1}/\bar{c}_2} \tag{5-90}$$

An evaluation is easily possible and may be conducted as described earlier for (5-3). It is also apparent that only rate constant k_3 is dependent upon the concentration of Y_2, and in a very simple manner.

2. $c_1^0 \gg c_4^0$. One obtains from (4-96) and (4-103) as the relation for $\bar{c}_3$,

$$\bar{c}_3 = \frac{c_1^0}{1 + K_{2,1}/\bar{c}_2} \tag{5-91}$$

Combining now (4-103) and (5-91) with the (simplified) equation (3-66) results quite generally in

$$\frac{1}{\tau_2} = \frac{k_3 c_1^0}{1 + K_{2,1}/\bar{c}_2} \left[1 + \frac{1 + K_{2,1}/\bar{c}_2}{1 + K_{3,4} c_1^0 (1 + K_{2,1}/\bar{c}_2)^{-1}} \frac{c_4^0}{c_1^0} \right] + k_4 \tag{5-92}$$

The term in the brackets is most frequently much smaller than unity. This term becomes only comparable with unity when the factor in front of c_4^0/c_1^0 becomes very large, which is the case for $K_{2,1} \gg \bar{c}_2$ plus $K_{3,4} c_1^0 \lesssim 1$. But the condition $K_{2,1} \gg \bar{c}_2$ affects the first term drastically and, whenever the factor in front of c_4^0/c_1^0 becomes much larger than c_1^0/c_4^0, one obtains the limiting case $\tau_2^{-1} \to k_3 c_4^0 + k_4$.

3. $c_4^0 \gg c_1^0$. For the general derivation, one has to proceed as before. Equation (4-104) gives the value for $\bar{c}_3$, while that for $\bar{c}_4$ is obtained from (4-96) and (4-104):

$$\bar{c}_4 = \frac{c_4^0}{1 + K_{3,4} c_1^0 (1 + K_{2,1}/\bar{c}_2 + c_4^0/K_{4,3})^{-1}} \tag{5-93}$$

Insertion of the equilibrium concentrations into the simplified equation (3-66) leads to

$$\frac{1}{\tau_2} = \frac{k_3}{1 + K_{2,1}/\bar{c}_2} c_4^0 + k_4 \tag{5-94}$$

This equation does not show the limiting value, which (5-92) may reach at very small $\bar{c}_2$.

b. The "right step" is very rapid. Now, the investigation of the slow left step is most easily accomplished by simply *not* adding component Y_4. One then has an abbreviated scheme, with (3-7) giving the relaxation time of the *slow* step. Equations (5-3) and (5-4) give the relaxation time under suitable analytical conditions. This three-component system will not be considered further, only a system with all five components present. The slow relaxation time will now be rewritten in terms of the special analytical conditions. It is also specified that Y_2 is no longer buffered but Y_4 instead, denoted by $\bar{c}_4$.

1. $c_1^0 = c_2^0$. Adequately good buffering of $\bar{c}_4$ changes (3-68) to

$$\frac{1}{\tau_2} = 2k_1\bar{c}_1 + \frac{k_2}{1 + \bar{c}_4/K_{4,3}} \tag{5-95}$$

The equilibrium concentration $\bar{c}_1$ may now be substituted by the expression from (4-109), giving, upon rearrangement,

$$\tau_2^{-2} = \left(\frac{k_2}{1 + \bar{c}_4/K_{4,3}}\right)^2 + \frac{4k_1k_2}{1 + \bar{c}_4/K_{4,3}} c_1^0 \tag{5-96}$$

This equation has considerable similarity with (5-90) and may be converted for $\bar{c}_4 \ll K_{4,3}$ and directly to the former equation (5-3).

2. $c_1^0 \ll \bar{c}_2 \doteq c_2^0$, changing (3-68) for well-buffered Y_4 to

$$\tau_2^{-1} = k_1c_2^0 + k_2(1 + \bar{c}_4/K_{4,3})^{-1} \tag{5-97}$$

This quite simple equation shows best "response" (equivalent to optimal signal change) for $c_2^0 \doteq K_{2,1}(1 + \bar{c}_4/K_{4,3})^{-1}$.

3. The short relaxation time can only be investigated in the full system. Equation (3-67) has to be applied, although buffering of Y_4 is not suitable (the high concentrations of the buffer components would determine the speed of the reaction). A reasonably elementary treatment of the system can still be given under the following conditions.

a. $c_1^0 \gg c_2^0$ (*or alternatively* $c_2^0 \gg c_1^0$), defining then as analytical concentration of Y_2:

$$c_2^0 = \bar{c}_3 + \bar{c}_5 \tag{5-98}$$

Any further consideration of c_1^0 is then unnecessary, and the fast reaction step simply becomes one of a three-component system, already treated earlier in this chapter.

b. Y_1 *(or* Y_2 *alternatively) is strongly buffered.* The ratio $\bar{c}_1/K_{2,1}$ then defines $\bar{c}_3$ on the right side of (5-97) by

$$\frac{\bar{c}_1}{K_{2,1}} = \frac{\bar{c}_3}{\bar{c}_2} \tag{5-99}$$

The concentration $\bar{c}_2$ may be neglected (relative to $\bar{c}_3$) whenever $\bar{c}_1 \gg K_{2,1}$, leading again to validity of (5-98).

c. $c_1^0 = c_2^0 \gg K_{2,1}$, which is equivalent to "negligible dissociation of Y_3 into Y_1 and Y_2." Equation (5-98) is again valid and the treatment again becomes one of a three-component system.

3. ASSOCIATION *FROM* AND *TOWARD* TWO SIDES. Systems (3-60) and (3-62) are considered simultaneously and in a simplified manner. Because of their symmetry, one may consider either side as the much more rapid one. In both cases the rapid reaction step is considered on the left side. For the investigation of the slow step, strong buffering is considered to occur via component Y_1, denoted later by $\bar{c}_1$.

a. System (3-60). Equation (3-61) becomes, for the mentioned buffering,

$$\tau_2^{-1} = k_3(1 + K_{2,1}/\bar{c}_1)^{-1} + k_4(\bar{c}_4 + \bar{c}_5) \tag{5-100}$$

Further treatment becomes most simplified for $c_4^0 \gg c_5^0$ (with the equivalence $c_5^0 = c_2^0$ which may be used interchangeably under these *specific* conditions), as then $\bar{c}_5 \ll \bar{c}_4 \doteq c_4^0$, giving

$$\tau_2^{-1} = k_3(1 + K_{2,1}/\bar{c}_1)^{-1} + k_4 c_4^0 \tag{5-101}$$

The ("vertical") response upon perturbation is largest for $c_4^0 \doteq K_{3,4}(1 + K_{2,1}/\bar{c}_1)^{-1}$, as long as $\bar{c}_1$ is not too much smaller than $K_{2,1}$ (at some limit the mentioned simplifications are no longer allowable).

b. System (3-62). Equation (3-63) becomes, for buffering via component Y_1,

$$\tau_2^{-1} = k_3[\bar{c}_2 + \bar{c}_4(1 + \bar{c}_1/K_{2,1})^{-1}] + k_4 \tag{5-102}$$

As Y_2 reacts both with Y_1 and Y_4, the treatment becomes quite simple (and without additional restrictions) by $c_4^0 \gg c_2^0$. The concentration $\bar{c}_4$ may then directly be replaced by c_4^0, and $\bar{c}_2$ may be neglected, giving

$$\tau_2^{-1} = k_3(1 + \bar{c}_1/K_{2,1})^{-1} c_4^0 + k_4 \tag{5-103}$$

The relaxation time is optimally measurable, as long as c_4^0 is in the neighborhood of $K_{4,3}(1 + \bar{c}_1/K_{2,1})$.

D. Six Components

1. The reaction sequence is given by

$$\tag{3-75}$$

Because of the unsymmetry of the reaction, a large number of possibilities actually could be considered. Here only that case will be treated where (3-9) represents the fast relaxation time with Y_6 being strongly buffered, Y_3 and Y_4 being initially brought together, *and $c_3^0 \ll c_4^0$*. For all these conditions one obtains

$$\tau_1^{-1} = \frac{k_1 c_4^0}{K_{1,2}(1 + K_{3,4}/\bar{c}_6) - 1} \left\{ \left\langle 1 + \frac{4 c_3^0}{c_4^0}\left[K_{1,2}\left(1 + \frac{K_{3,4}}{\bar{c}_6}\right) - 1 \right] \right\rangle^{1/2} - 1 \right\} + k_2 c_4^0$$

(5-104)

This equation is quite similar to (5-80). $K_{3,4}$ is a dissociation constant, which has to be divided by the concentration of the buffered component, such as, for instance, in (5-101) for $K_{2,1}$. Equation (5-104) may be simplified for $K_{1,2}(1 + K_{3,4}/\bar{c}_6) \gg 1$ *and $\bar{c}_6 \gg K_{3,4}$*. One then obtains

$$(\tau_1 c_4^0)^{-1} = k_2^2 + 4 k_1 k_2 \frac{c_3^0}{c_4^0}$$

(5-105)

This equation is identical in structure to (5-23).

2. The reaction sequence is given by

$$Y_1 \underset{k_2}{\overset{k_1}{\rightleftharpoons}} Y_3 \underset{k_4}{\overset{k_3}{\rightleftharpoons}} Y_5$$

(3-80)

$$Y_2 \qquad Y_4 \qquad Y_6$$

Again, a larger number of possibilities actually could be treated. But again, only that case will be treated where equation (3-9) represents the fast relaxation time with Y_6 being strongly buffered, Y_3 and Y_4 being initially brought together, *and $c_3^0 \ll c_4^0$*. For all these conditions, one obtains

$$\tau_1^{-1} = \frac{k_1 c_4^0}{K_{1,2}(1 + \bar{c}_6/K_{4,3}) - 1} \left\{ \left\langle 1 + \frac{4 c_3^0}{c_4^0}\left[K_{1,2}\left(1 + \frac{\bar{c}_6}{K_{4,3}}\right) - 1 \right] \right\rangle^{1/2} - 1 \right\} + k_2 c_4^0$$

(5-106)

This equation is similar to (5-80). $K_{4,3}$ is now the dissociation constant, which has to be divided by the concentration of the buffered component, such as, for instance, in (5-103) for $K_{2,1}$. If $K_{1,2}(1 + \bar{c}_6/K_{4,3}) \gg 1$ and $\bar{c}_6 \ll K_{4,3}$, one obtains from (5-106) (5-105) again, as under quite equivalent conditions from (5-104).

3. The above treatment on two systems with six components has been selected because of its relation to the electron transfer between oxidized cytochrome c (with c_3^0) and ferrohexacyanide (with c_4^0) (3). In the case of system (3-75) the component Y_6 corresponds to H^+, and in the case of system (3-80) the buffered component Y_6 corresponds to OH^-. A kinetic differentiation between the two possibilities of H^+ or OH^- uptake cannot be obtained from equations (5-104) and (5-106). Under such circumstances the proton-uptake mechanism of system (3-75) may be chosen; the pH scale then becomes the variable parameter.

5-3. THREE-STEP MECHANISMS

A. Four Components

The system is represented by (3-171). The two possible relaxation times are given by (3-174) and (3-183), neither of them showing concentration dependence. Equilibrium concentrations, therefore, need not be substituted by analytical concentrations.

B. Five Components

The most useful combination is given by (3-186). One may then derive three different forms for the slowest relaxation time, depending upon which one of the three reaction steps is slowest. Kinetics of this reaction sequence will now be developed extensively.

1. $a_{22} \ll a_{11}, a_{33}$. The faster relaxation times may be derived directly, as they are separated by the slowest step. But because of this separation, the two fast relaxations have to be detected by using different components of the system as indicating species. One relaxation time is given by (3-3) and can only be detected via components Y_1 or Y_2 of (3-186). The other relaxation time is given by

$$\tau^{-1} = k_5 + k_6(\bar{c}_4 + \bar{c}_5) \tag{5-107}$$

To obtain the expression in terms of analytical concentrations, one may employ (4-149) and its alternative form for $\bar{c}_5$. If on the other hand, $c_4^0 = c_3^0$, one obtains

$$\tau^{-1} = \frac{k_5}{1 + K_{3,4}(1 + K_{2,1})^{-1}} + \left[\frac{k_5 k_6}{1 + K_{4,3}(1 + K_{2,1})}\right]^{1/2} \langle K_0 + 4c_4^0\rangle^{1/2} \tag{5-108}$$

If one plots τ^{-1} versus $\langle K_0 + 4c_4^0\rangle^{1/2}$, one obtains the first term as intercept with the ordinate and $\{k_5 k_6/[1 + K_{4,3}(1 + K_{2,1})]\}^{1/2}$ as slope. The necessity of the knowledge of K_0 is inconvenient. This over-all equilibrium constant must have been obtained prior to relaxation experiments. The precision in obtaining the intercept with the ordinate is not high, as the values along the abscissa are limited by $(K_0)^{1/2}$. There is no difference in evaluating whether the monomolecular (left) reaction step or the bimolecular (right) reaction step is faster.

Equation (5-107) may be considerably simplified, if $c_5^0 \gg c_4^0$, giving

$$\tau^{-1} = k_5 + k_6 c_5^0 \tag{5-109}$$

Although this equation permits direct evaluation of k_5 and k_6, the equilibrium constants of the two monomolecular reactions cannot yet be evaluated.

The third relaxation time is given by (3-188). The simplest case again prevails, if $c_5^0 \gg c_4^0$, simplifying (3-188) to

$$\tau_3^{-1} = k_3(1 + K_{2,1})^{-1} + k_4 \frac{c_5^0}{K_{5,6} + c_5^0} \tag{5-110}$$

A plot of τ_3^{-1} versus c_5^0 gives a sigmoid curve with $k_3(1 + K_{2,1})^{-1}$ as intercept with the ordinate and $k_3(1 + K_{2,1})^{-1} + k_4$ as limiting value for very high c_5^0; when τ_3^{-1} is halfway in between the two limits, it is $c_5^0 = K_{5,6}$. One thus obtains another check on $K_{5,6}$. The equilibrium constant $K_{4,3}$ is not directly obtainable, only the combined constant $K_{4,3}(1 + K_{2,1})$. Now $c_4^0 = c_5^0$, (3-188) becomes, together with (4-149),

$$\tau_3^{-1} = \frac{k_3}{1 + K_{2,1}}$$
$$+ k_4 \left\{ 1 + \left[\left\langle \frac{K_0 + 4c_4^0}{K_{5,6}[1 + K_{4,3}(1 + K_{2,1})]} \right\rangle^{1/2} - \langle 1 + K_{4,3}(1 + K_{2,1}) \rangle^{-1} \right]^{-1} \right\}^{-1}$$

$$(5\text{-}111)$$

This rather complex equation may certainly be written in various ways. The shown expression contains only one square root, and c_4^0 appears only once.

2. $a_{11} \ll a_{22}, a_{33}$. The slowest time constant is now treated first and then the two possible sequences of the faster relaxation processes.

a. The third relaxation time constant is given by (3-189). One may distinguish two different relationships among the analytical concentrations.

1. $c_5^0 \gg c_4^0$. Equation (3-189) immediately simplifies to

$$\tau_3^{-1} = k_1 + k_2[1 + K_{3,4}(1 + K_{5,6}/c_5^0)]^{-1} \tag{5-112}$$

In a plot of τ_3^{-1} versus c_5^0 one obtains: as lower limit, τ_3^{-1} (for $c_5^0 \to 0) = k_1$, and, as upper limit, τ_3^{-1} (for $c_5^0 \to \infty) = k_1 + k_2(1 + K_{3,4})^{-1}$; at $c_5^0 = K_{5,6}$ one obtains $\tau_3^{-1} = k_1 + k_2(1 + 2K_{3,4})^{-1}$. Although k_1 can be obtained from the lower limit, k_2 cannot from the upper limit.

2. $c_5^0 = c_6^0$. Equation (3-189) has to be combined with the simplified equation (4-149), leading to

$$\tau_3^{-1} = k_1 + k_2 \left\{ 1 + K_{3,4} \left[1 + \frac{1 + K_{4,3}(1 + K_{2,1})}{\langle 1 + 4c_4^0/K_0 \rangle^{1/2} - 1} \right] \right\}^{-1} \tag{5-113}$$

This equation is quite complex. But in a plot of τ_3^{-1} versus c_4^0 one obtains for $c_4^0 \to 0$ the limit $\tau_3^{-1} \to k_1$. If, on the other hand, $c_4^0 \to \infty$, one obtains as upper limit $\tau_3^{-1} \to k_1 + k_2(1 + K_{3,4})^{-1}$. The limits are the same as the ones for (5-112).

b. One possibility among the faster relaxation times is given by $a_{22} \ll a_{33}$, corresponding to the natural sequence.

1. The fastest relaxation time for this possibility is given by (5-107). One may then distinguish two different relationships among the analytical concentrations.

a. $c_5^0 \gg c_4^0$. Equation (5-109) results directly. One obtains thus the two rate constants k_5 and k_6, and thus also the dissociation constant $K_{5,6}$.

b. $c_5^0 = c_4^0$. Equation (5-108) results, and it is here referred to its discussion above.

2. The slower time constant may be derived from (3-51). One obtains, by proper index exchange,

$$\tau_2^{-1} = k_3 + k_4 \frac{\bar{c}_4 + \bar{c}_5}{K_{5,6} + \bar{c}_4 + \bar{c}_5} \tag{5-114}$$

In the further evaluation of this equation one may then distinguish two different relationships among the analytical concentrations.

a. $c_5^0 \gg c_4^0$. Equation (5-114) simplifies to

$$\tau_2^{-1} = k_3 + k_4 \frac{c_5^0}{K_{5,6} + c_5^0} \tag{5-115}$$

In a plot of τ_2^{-1} versus c_5^0, one obtains $\tau_2^{-1} = k_3$ for low c_5^0 and $\tau_2^{-1} = k_3 + k_4$ for high c_5^0. The change between these given limits is half completed at $c_5^0 = K_{5,6}$. And this $K_{5,6}$ should agree with $K_{5,6}$ obtained from (5-109).

b. $c_5^0 = c_4^0$. Equation (5-114) has to be combined with the simplified equation (4-149), giving

$$\tau_2^{-1} = k_3 + k_4 \left[1 + \frac{1 + K_{4,3}(1 + K_{2,1})}{\langle 1 + 4c_4^0/K_0 \rangle^{1/2} - 1} \right]^{-1} \tag{5-116}$$

One obtains the same limits here for c_4^0 as with reference to (5-115) for c_5^0 as independent variable: k_3 and $k_3 + k_4$.

c. The other possibility among the faster relaxation times is given by $a_{33} \ll a_{22}$.

1. The fastest relaxation time for this second possibility is given by

$$\tau_1^{-1} = k_3 + k_4 \tag{5-117}$$

This time constant shows no concentration dependence and the individual rate constants cannot be evaluated.

2. The equation for the second relaxation time is given by

$$\tau_2^{-1} = \frac{k_5}{1 + K_{4,3}} + k_6(\bar{c}_4 + \bar{c}_5) \tag{5-118}$$

This equation is quite similar to (5-107), differing only in the first term. One may now introduce the two simplifying conditions among the analytical concentrations.

a. $c_5^0 \gg c_4^0$. Equation (5-118) simplifies directly to

$$\tau_2^{-1} = k_5(1 + K_{4,3})^{-1} + k_6 c_5^0 \tag{5-119}$$

A plot of τ_2^{-1} versus c_5^0 gives $k_5(1 + K_{4,3})^{-1}$ as the intercept with the ordinate and k_6 as the slope.

b. $c_5^0 = c_4^0$. Equation (5-118) has to be combined with the simplified equation (4-149), to give

$$\tau_2^{-1} = \frac{k_5}{(1 + K_{4,3})[1 + K_{3,4}(1 + K_{2,1})^{-1}]}$$
$$+ \left[\frac{k_5 k_6}{1 + K_{4,3}(1 + K_{2,1})} \right]^{1/2} (K_0 + 4c_4^0)^{1/2} \qquad (5\text{-}120)$$

This equation is even more complex than (5-108), although one may again plot τ_2^{-1} versus $\langle K_0 + 4c_4^0 \rangle^{1/2}$ according to (5-120); the slope of (5-120) agrees with that of (5-108), but the intercepts have a somewhat different structure.

3. $a_{33} \ll a_{11}, a_{22}$. Again, the slowest time constant will be treated first and then the two possible sequences of the faster time constants.

a. The third relaxation time is given by (3-190). The two relations between the analytical concentrations may now be employed.

1. $c_5^0 \gg c_4^0$. Equation (3-190) is easily converted to

$$\tau_3^{-1} = k_5[1 + K_{4,3}(1 + K_{2,1})]^{-1} + k_6 c_5^0 \qquad (5\text{-}121)$$

Slope and intercept in a plot of τ_3^{-1} versus c_5^0 are immediately realized.

2. $c_5^0 = c_4^0$. Equation (3-190) has to be combined with the simplified equation (4-149), resulting in

$$\tau_3^{-2} = \left[\frac{k_5}{1 + K_{4,3}(1 + K_{2,1})} \right]^2 + \frac{4 k_5 k_6 c_4^0}{1 + K_{4,3}(1 + K_{2,1})} \qquad (5\text{-}122)$$

This final equation is quite similar in structure to the much earlier equation (5-3).

b. $a_{22} \ll a_{11}$ represents one sequence in the speed of the reaction steps.

1. The faster step is given by (3-3), demonstrating no concentration dependence.

2. The slower one of the two steps is given by (3-42), which is again concentration-independent, therefore making the evaluation of individual rate constants quite difficult.

c. $a_{11} \ll a_{22}$ represents the other sequence in the speed of the reaction steps.

1. The faster step is given by (3-52), again containing no equilibrium concentration.

2. The slower step is given by

$$\tau_2^{-1} = k_1 + k_2(1 + K_{3,4})^{-1} \qquad (5\text{-}123)$$

This latter equation corresponds in structure to (3-42). The concentration independence of all four relaxation times makes it practically impossible to differentiate between them. Choice of the indicating component may eventually assist in locating the position of the fastest step: If a_{11} is largest, τ_1 can only be detected via Y_1 and Y_2; if a_{22} is largest, τ_1 can only be detected via Y_2 and Y_3; and if a_{33} is largest, the change may only be detected via components Y_3, Y_4, and Y_5.

4. THE BUFFER CONDITION. True buffering of this system is only of interest for a few equations—namely (5-110), (5-112), and (5-115); c_5^0 in these equations should then be replaced by $\bar{c}_5$ to indicate buffering. This buffering condition is not very desirable for these simple equations. But it certainly becomes of very high interest for reactions with several bimolecular steps.

PROBLEMS

1. Derive (5-2) according to the text.
2. Write out the full expressions for $\bar{c}_1 + \bar{c}_2$ and $\bar{c}_3 + \bar{c}_4^*$, belonging to (1-30) and employing (5-6).
3. Derive (5-11) under its specific conditions.
4. Derive (5-22) under its specific conditions.
5. Buffering with $c_i^0 \to \bar{c}_i$ can only be applied to (5-63) without reservations on the interpretation [compare (5-62) to (5-68)]. Why?
6. Derive (5-69) from (3-9), (4-121), (4-122), and with the proper simplifications; show that (5-69) converts to (5-24) for $K_{3,4} \to 0$.
7. Derive (5-77).
8. Derive (5-82) and (5-85).
9. Derive (5-90) from the simplified equation (3-66) with (4-101) and (4-102).

REFERENCES

1. G. Czerlinski and F. Hommes, *Biochem. Biophys. Acta*, **79**, 46 (1964).
2. G. Czerlinski, *J. Theoret. Biol.*, **7**, 463 (1964).
3. G. Czerlinski and G. Hess, *J. Biol. Chem.* (1966), in preparation.

CHAPTER 6

EQUILIBRIUM CONCENTRATION CHANGES (THERMODYNAMICS)

6-1. ONE-STEP MECHANISMS

A. The Monomolecular Interconversion

The monomolecular interconversion was represented by (1-1) and treated in Section 2-4. The fundamental conditions were also given there. Several of the equations may be considered as the "final result." It is not here referred to any one in particular.

B. Dissociation–Association

Equation (2-57) applied to (1-14) gives

$$\frac{\Delta K_{2,1}}{K_{2,1}} = \frac{\Delta \bar{c}_1}{\bar{c}_1} + \frac{\Delta \bar{c}_2}{\bar{c}_2} - \frac{\Delta \bar{c}_3}{\bar{c}_3} \tag{6-1}$$

Equations (2-12) and (2-14) are also valid for *equilibrium* concentration changes. If Y_1 is the indicating component, one should solve (6-1) with (2-12) and (2-14) for $\Delta \bar{c}_1/\bar{c}_1$, giving

$$\frac{\Delta \bar{c}_1}{\bar{c}_1} = \frac{\Delta K_{2,1}}{K_{2,1}} \left(1 + \frac{\bar{c}_1}{\bar{c}_2} + \frac{K_{2,1}}{\bar{c}_2} \right)^{-1} \tag{6-2}$$

If no further relation for the equilibrium concentrations is given, one has to substitute the general expressions for $\bar{c}_1$ and $\bar{c}_2$ which were derived in Chapter 4 [Eq. (4-12) for $\bar{c}_1$, and after reindexing for $\bar{c}_2$]. But there, and in Chapter 5, some simplifying conditions were already mentioned. Here we shall maintain the subdivision of Chapter 5. But first we have to remember that $\Delta \bar{c}_3/\bar{c}_3$ has a somewhat different solution. It is

$$\frac{\Delta \bar{c}_3}{\bar{c}_3} = -\frac{\Delta K_{2,1}}{K_{2,1}} \left(1 + \frac{\bar{c}_1}{K_{2,1}} + \frac{\bar{c}_2}{K_{2,1}} \right)^{-1} \tag{6-3}$$

1. $c_1^0 = c_2^0$. This condition leads automatically to $\bar{c}_1 = \bar{c}_2$ and to the applicability of (4-15) (or its alternative for $\bar{c}_2$). Employing (4-15) and its condition, (6-2) appears in a rather complicated form. One immediately recognizes simplifying possibilities, when the expression behind the relative change in the equilibrium constant is carefully written out. After some simple conversions, one obtains (with either $c_1^0 = 0$ or $c_3^0 = 0$)

$$\left\{ 1 + \frac{1}{[1 + 4(c_1^0 + c_3^0)K_{2,1}^{-1}]^{\frac{1}{2}} - 1} \right\}^{-1} = 1 - \left[1 + \frac{4(c_1^0 + c_3^0)}{K_{2,1}} \right]^{-1/2} \quad (6\text{-}4)$$

The relative concentration change is thus given by

$$\frac{\Delta \bar{c}_1}{\bar{c}_1} = \frac{\Delta K_{2,1}}{2K_{2,1}} \left\{ 1 - \left[1 + \frac{4(c_1^0 + c_3^0)}{K_{2,1}} \right]^{-1/2} \right\} \quad (6\text{-}5)$$

This equation was originally given as Eq. (10.3) of Ref. *1* (generally $c_3^0 \equiv 0$).

Applying the condition $\bar{c}_1 = \bar{c}_2$ to (6-3) and employing (4-15) leads easily to

$$\frac{\Delta \bar{c}_3}{\bar{c}_3} = \frac{\Delta K_{2,1}}{K_{2,1}} \left[1 + \frac{4(c_1^0 + c_3^0)}{K_{2,1}} \right]^{-1/2} \quad (6\text{-}6)$$

As $\Delta \bar{c}_2/\bar{c}_2 = \Delta \bar{c}_1/\bar{c}_1$, one realizes that the sum of (6-1) gives, with (6-5) and (6-6), $\Delta K_{2,1} K_{2,1}^{-1}$ again, as is to be expected. One also realizes from (6-5) and (6-6) that detection of relative equilibrium concentration changes is most effective *via* component Y_1, if $4(c_1^0 + c_3^0) \gg K_{2,1}$, and most effective *via* component Y_3, if $4(c_1^0 + c_3^0) \ll K_{2,1}$. The largest *relative* equilibrium concentration change is only obtainable by observation *via* Y_3 and is $|\Delta \bar{c}_3/\bar{c}_3| = |\Delta K_{2,1}/K_{2,1}|$; this limit is reached for $4(c_1^0 + c_3^0)/K_{2,1} \ll 1$, which is unfavorable on grounds of the absolute signal height.

In following the dependence of $\Delta \bar{c}_i/\bar{c}_i$ upon $(c_1^0 + c_3^0)$, the point halfway between zero and maximum ordinate is of interest. One immediately realizes that for this point,

$$\left[1 + \frac{4(c_1^0 + c_3^0)}{K_{2,1}} \right]^{1/2} = 2 \quad (6\text{-}7)$$

This equation is easily solved, leading for "half-maximal transfer" to

$$(c_1^0 + c_3^0)_{1/2} = \tfrac{3}{4} K_{2,1} \quad (6\text{-}8)$$

The "half-maximal point" is therefore quite useful in the determination of an unknown $K_{2,1}$. It corresponds to the "center of variation," introduced with (5-12) for a four-component system. It may also be derived from (5-3), giving

$$(c_1^0 + c_3^0)_{1/2} = \tfrac{1}{4} K_{2,1} \tag{6-9}$$

One realizes that the two points do not need to coincide, when derived from kinetics or from equilibrium concentration changes. One covers both points by establishing as experimental range

$$\tfrac{1}{10} K_{2,1} \leqslant (c_1^0 + c_3^0) \leqslant 10 K_{2,1} \tag{2-47}$$

Equations (6-5) and (6-6) [as well as (6-8)] do not consider that either one of the c_i^0 should vanish [compare the discussion following (5-6)]. There are thus the two alternatives

$$c_1^0 = c_2^0 > 0 = c_3^0$$

$$c_1^0 = c_2^0 = 0 < c_3^0$$

Either one of the two concentrations vanishes in the above equations, but their structure remains unaltered. How these relative equilibrium *concentration* changes affect the relative equilibrium *signal* changes will be demonstrated in Chapter 7.

2. $c_1^0 \ll c_2^0$. This condition is associated with the simplification $c_2^0 \doteq \bar{c}_2 \gg \bar{c}_1$. Equation (6-1) contains then a vanishingly small $\Delta \bar{c}_2 / \bar{c}_2$ and one obtains, from (6-2), after rearrangement,

$$\frac{\Delta \bar{c}_1}{\bar{c}_1} = \frac{\Delta K_{2,1}}{K_{2,1}} \frac{c_2^0}{K_{2,1} + c_2^0} \tag{6-10}$$

One recognizes the upper and lower values immediately. Plotting $\Delta \bar{c}_1 / \bar{c}_1$ as function of c_2^0 gives with logarithmic abscissa a sinusoidal curve. Half the maximum value is reached at $c_2^0 = K_{2,1}$. The experimental range is given by

$$\tfrac{1}{10} K_{2,1} \leqslant c_2^0 \leqslant 10 K_{2,1} \tag{2-44}$$

This equation is valid for both "subconditions":

$$c_2^0 \gg c_1^0 > c_3^0 = 0$$

$$c_2^0 \gg c_3^0 > c_1^0 = 0$$

The second condition is rare. But one realizes from the derivation of (6-10) that the (rare) second condition does not need to be fulfilled that strictly: c_3^0 may become comparable with c_2^0. But if $\bar{c}_1 \ll \bar{c}_2$, $\bar{c}_3$, the second and the third term in (6-1) vanish and one obtains

$$\frac{\Delta \bar{c}_1}{\bar{c}_1} = \frac{\Delta K_{2,1}}{K_{2,1}} \tag{6-11}$$

with

$$\bar{c}_1 = K_{2,1} \frac{c_3^0}{c_2^0} \tag{6-12}$$

This "full buffering" gives the simplest relation. One has always "maximum transfer" from $\Delta K_{2,1}/K_{2,1}$. But kinetics remains governed by relation (2-44), as one realizes from (5-5).

C. The Four-Component System

Equation (2-57) applied to (1-32) gives

$$\frac{\Delta K_{2,1}}{K_{2,1}} = \frac{\Delta \bar{c}_1}{\bar{c}_1} + \frac{\Delta \bar{c}_2}{\bar{c}_2} - \frac{\Delta \bar{c}_3}{\bar{c}_3} - \frac{\Delta \bar{c}_4}{\bar{c}_4} \tag{6-13}$$

Equations (2-12) and (2-14) are also valid for equilibrium concentration changes. Combining these equations with (6-13) leads to an equation which cannot be substantially simplified without special conditions:

$$\frac{\Delta \bar{c}_1}{\bar{c}_1} = \frac{\Delta K_{2,1}}{K_{2,1}} \left(\frac{\bar{c}_1 + \bar{c}_2}{\bar{c}_2} + K_{2,1} \frac{\bar{c}_3 + \bar{c}_4}{\bar{c}_2} \right)^{-1} \tag{6-14}$$

Equation (6-14) was written in a form which can later be used for the conditions between the analytical concentrations.

1. $c_1^0 = c_2^0 > 0$. The two sums $\bar{c}_1 + \bar{c}_2$ and $\bar{c}_3 + \bar{c}_4$ were already given previously as (5-7) and (5-9). As $\bar{c}_2$ has to be used as denominator, its expression will be given now for the condition $c_4^0 = 0$:

$$\bar{c}_2 = \frac{K_{2,1}}{2(K_{2,1} - 1)} (2c_2^0 + c_3^0) \left\{ 1 - \left[1 - \frac{4(K_{2,1} - 1)(c_2^0 + c_3^0)c_2^0}{K_{2,1}(2c_2^0 + c_3^0)^2} \right]^{1/2} \right\} \tag{6-15}$$

As $c_1^0 = c_2^0$, one may easily divide (5-7) by (6-15), resulting in

$$\frac{\bar{c}_1 + \bar{c}_2}{\bar{c}_2} = 2 \tag{6-16}$$

This simple result could have been derived directly from (4-10), demonstrating the internal consistency of the derivations.

To obtain a concentration dependence of $\Delta \bar{c}_1/\bar{c}_1$, in a facilitated manner, one may establish $c_3^0 \gg c_2^0$ and the concentration relation

$$0.2 \leqslant \frac{K_{2,1}c_3^0}{\bar{c}_2} \leqslant 20 \tag{6-17}$$

with $K_{2,1}c_3^0(\bar{c}_2)^{-1} = 2$ as "center of variation," which may be seen by comparing (6-14) with (6-16). Equation (6-17) immediately establishes $K_{2,1} \ll 1$, and one may convert (6-15) to

$$\bar{c}_2 = \frac{K_{2,1}c_3^0}{2}\left[\left(1 + \frac{4c_2^0}{K_{2,1}c_3^0}\right)^{1/2} - 1\right] \tag{6-18}$$

As $\bar{c}_2$ is of the order of magnitude of c_2^0, (6-18) cannot be further simplified.

Combining (6-14) with (6-16) and (6-18) gives, with the case of extreme concentration difference after simplification,

$$\frac{\Delta \bar{c}_1}{\bar{c}_1} = \frac{1}{2}\frac{\Delta K_{2,1}}{K_{2,1}}\left[1 - \left(1 + \frac{4c_2^0}{K_{2,1}c_3^0}\right)^{-1/2}\right] \tag{6-19}$$

One realizes that the expression in brackets has a value between 0 and 1. It is $\frac{1}{2}$ at $c_2^0 = \frac{3}{4}K_{2,1}c_3^0$. One may again term this value of c_2^0 "the center of variation." But one may use as the independent variable either c_2^0 or c_3^0 or even their *ratio*. Equation (6-17) may then be replaced by

$$\frac{1}{20} \leqslant \frac{K_{2,1}c_3^0}{c_2^0} \leqslant 20 \tag{6-20}$$

These results are similar to those leading to (5-13) for the same conditions.

2. $c_1^0 \ll c_2^0, c_4^0$ represents the most favorable buffering condition for $K_{2,1} \approx 1$. Equation (6-14) may immediately be converted to

$$\frac{\Delta \bar{c}_1}{\bar{c}_1} = \frac{\Delta K_{2,1}}{K_{2,1}}\left(1 + K_{2,1}\frac{c_3^0}{c_2^0}\right)^{-1} \tag{6-21}$$

One realizes as the range of variation,

$$0.1 \leqslant K_{2,1}\frac{c_3^0}{c_2^0} \leqslant 10 \tag{6-22}$$

with its "center" $c_2^0 = K_{2,1}c_3^0$, which is in agreement with (5-18). It is evident that $K_{2,1}$ may deviate somewhat from unity, as long as (6-22) can be fulfilled.

3. $c_3^0 = 0$ is the most useful condition for $K_{2,1} \gg 1$. To compensate for the magnitude of $K_{2,1}$, one has also to fulfill the condition $c_2^0 \gg c_1^0$.

Equation (6-14) becomes under these circumstances,

$$\frac{\Delta \bar{c}_1}{\bar{c}_1} = \frac{\Delta K_{2,1}}{K_{2,1}} \left[(\bar{c}_3 + \bar{c}_4) \frac{K_{2,1}}{c_2^0} + 1 \right]^{-1} \tag{6-23}$$

Equation (5-19) may be simplified further and inserted in (6-23), resulting in

$$\frac{\Delta \bar{c}_1}{\bar{c}_1} = \frac{\Delta K_{2,1}}{K_{2,1}} \left(1 + \frac{2K_{2,1}c_1^0}{c_2^0} \right)^{-1} \tag{6-24}$$

The range of experimental variation is given by

$$0.1 \leqslant 2K_{2,1}c_1^0/c_2^0 \leqslant 10 \tag{6-25}$$

with its "center" at $c_2^0 = 2K_{2,1}c_1^0$. Equation (5-24) becomes twice this value for large $K_{2,1}$. Relation (6-25) is thus valid for both the kinetic and the thermodynamic treatments. If condition $c_3^0 = 0$ is combined with $c_1^0 = c_2^0$, treated previously, one obtains a very simple relationship from the original equation (6-14), together with the appropriately simplified equations (5-7), (5-9), and (6-15):

$$\frac{\Delta \bar{c}_1}{\bar{c}_1} = \frac{\Delta K_{2,1}}{2K_{2,1}} [1 + (K_{2,1})^{1/2}]^{-1} \tag{6-26}$$

There is no concentration dependence of the relative signal change, which becomes negligibly small for $K_{2,1} \gg 1$.

D. Dimerization

Equilibrium constant and analytical concentration are defined by (5-24) and (5-25). Equation (2-57) may be written, with the definition of the mentioned equilibrium constant,

$$\frac{\Delta K_{2,1}}{K_{2,1}} = 2 \frac{\Delta \bar{c}_1}{\bar{c}_1} - \frac{\Delta \bar{c}_D}{\bar{c}_D} \tag{6-27}$$

One derives the relation among the equilibrium concentration changes from (5-25) by applying the law of conservation of mass to small changes:

$$0 = \Delta \bar{c}_1 + 2\Delta \bar{c}_D \tag{6-28}$$

This equation corresponds to (3-89) except for the bar over the concentration symbol and one index.

Combination of the above two equations results in

$$\frac{\Delta K_{2,1}}{K_{2,1}} = 2 \frac{\Delta \bar{c}_1}{\bar{c}_1} \left(1 + \frac{1}{4} \frac{K_{2,1}}{\bar{c}_1} \right) \tag{6-29}$$

One may now solve for the relative change $\Delta \bar{c}_1/\bar{c}_1$ and substitute the remaining $\bar{c}_1$ from (5-27). One obtains, after rearrangement,

$$\frac{\Delta \bar{c}_1}{\bar{c}_1} = \frac{\Delta K_{2,1}}{2K_{2,1}} \left[1 - \left(1 + \frac{8c_1^0}{K_{2,1}} \right)^{-1/2} \right] \tag{6-30}$$

If c_1^0 is very large, the factor in front of the brackets is effective in its full magnitude. If c_1^0 is very small, no relative concentration change will be visible. The factor in front of the brackets will be just half transferred to $\Delta \bar{c}_1/\bar{c}_1$ at

$$(c_1^0)_{1/2} = 3K_{2,1}/8 \tag{6-31}$$

The *change* of $\Delta \bar{c}_1/\bar{c}_1$ with c_1^0 then centers around $(c_1^0)_{1/2}$. The usefulness of (6-30) implies that $\eta_1 \gg \eta_D$. If the inverse relationship holds, (6-30) may be easily converted into the proper equation for $\Delta \bar{c}_D/\bar{c}_D$ by (6-27).

6-2. TWO-STEP MECHANISMS

A. Three Equilibrium Components Participate

1. Two (consecutive) monomolecular interconversions, as originally given by (3-10). As was pointed out following (4-41) (the equation defining the analytical concentration in terms of equilibrium concentrations), the equilibrium constants may be directly derived from (3-11) and (3-13). For small changes in the equilibrium constant, one may then write

$$\frac{\Delta K_{2,1}}{K_{2,1}} = \frac{\Delta \bar{c}_1}{\bar{c}_1} - \frac{\Delta \bar{c}_2}{\bar{c}_2} \tag{6-32}$$

$$\frac{\Delta K_{4,3}}{K_{4,3}} = \frac{\Delta \bar{c}_2}{\bar{c}_2} - \frac{\Delta \bar{c}_3}{\bar{c}_3} \tag{6-33}$$

Because of symmetry, there is no difference which of the two reaction steps is the faster one (except in detection: to follow the fast step, a component participating in this fast step must be the indicating one). The left reaction step (involving $K_{2,1}$) is here considered much faster than the right one. For the fast step, (6-33) is nonexistent. Equation (6-32), on the other hand, is identical with (2-59). Again, (2-60) is valid for the fast step, leading then for this step to (2-61). As (2-61) does not contain any concentration term on the right side, (2-61) directly represents the relative concentration change of the fast step.

In considering the slow step, one may proceed in various ways, depending upon the "point of reference." To make this aspect clear, some new terminology has to be introduced, by adding a second index to all (equilibrium) concentration parameters. In general terms, $\bar{c}_{i,j} \equiv$ concentration of the ith component after equilibration of the jth relaxation process. Certainly, $j = 0$ corresponds now to the equilibrium concentration present before any relaxation process has started, and thus, as before, even imposing a change in the external parameter (to initiate the relaxation process). For two-step mechanisms, the final equilibrium value is then represented by $j = 2$. Not only the concentrations, but also the concentration changes, have a second index j. The meaning of $\Delta \bar{c}_{i,j}$ will now be determined.

Quite early in discussing the basis of chemical relaxation, $\bar{c}_i'$ was defined as the final equilibrium concentration, but was set equal to $\bar{c}_i$ for practical purposes. But in discussing this practical approximation (2-22), it was indicated that concentration differences might limit the use of this approximation. Such differences unfortunately become quite important in the treatment of equilibrium concentration changes of consecutive reaction steps. One may now define

$$\bar{c}_{i,1} \equiv \bar{c}_{i,0} + \Delta \bar{c}_{i,1} \tag{6-34}$$

$$\bar{c}_{i,2} \equiv \bar{c}_{i,0} + \Delta \bar{c}_{i,2} + \Delta \bar{c}_{i,2} \tag{6-35}$$

$$\Delta \bar{c}_{i,0} \equiv \Delta \bar{c}_{i,1} + \Delta \bar{c}_{i,2} \tag{6-36}$$

The fast relaxation process is then (6-32) changed to

$$\frac{\Delta K_{2,1}}{K'_{2,1}} = \frac{\Delta \bar{c}_{1,1}}{\bar{c}_{1,1}} - \frac{\Delta \bar{c}_{2,1}}{\bar{c}_{2,1}} \tag{6-37}$$

The equilibrium constant carries a prime, to signify that it is the equilibrium constant finally to be reached. It is directly fixed by choosing $j = 1$ in $\bar{c}_{i,j}$. If one chose $j = 0$ in $\bar{c}_{i,j}$, (6-32) would become

$$\frac{\Delta K_{2,1}}{K_{2,1}} = \frac{\Delta \bar{c}_{1,1}}{\bar{c}_{1,0}} - \frac{\Delta \bar{c}_{2,1}}{\bar{c}_{2,0}} \tag{6-38}$$

The equilibrium constant is now without a prime, to signify its value before the perturbation process. $\Delta \bar{c}_{3,1}$ does not need to be considered, as it remains unchanged during the time range of the first relaxation process: $\Delta \bar{c}_{3,1} \equiv 0$.

For the appearance of the second relaxation process, one has to consider the following possible pairs of equations:

$$\frac{\Delta K_{2,1}}{K'_{2,1}} = \frac{\Delta \bar{c}_{1,1} + \Delta \bar{c}_{1,2}}{\bar{c}_{1,2}} - \frac{\Delta \bar{c}_{2,1} + \Delta \bar{c}_{2,2}}{\bar{c}_{2,2}} \tag{6-39}$$

$$\frac{\Delta K_{4,3}}{K'_{4,3}} = \frac{\Delta \bar{c}_{2,1} + \Delta \bar{c}_{2,2}}{\bar{c}_{2,2}} - \frac{\Delta \bar{c}_{3,2}}{\bar{c}_{3,2}} \tag{6-40}$$

$$\frac{\Delta K_{2,1}}{K_{2,1}} = \frac{\Delta \bar{c}_{1,1} + \Delta \bar{c}_{1,2}}{\bar{c}_{1,0}} - \frac{\Delta \bar{c}_{2,1} + \Delta \bar{c}_{2,2}}{\bar{c}_{2,0}} \tag{6-41}$$

$$\frac{\Delta K_{4,3}}{K_{4,3}} = \frac{\Delta \bar{c}_{2,1} + \Delta \bar{c}_{2,2}}{\bar{c}_{2,0}} - \frac{\Delta \bar{c}_{3,2}}{\bar{c}_{3,0}} \tag{6-42}$$

$$\frac{\Delta K_{2,1}}{K'_{2,1}} = \frac{\Delta \bar{c}_{1,1} + \Delta \bar{c}_{1,2}}{\bar{c}_{1,1}} - \frac{\Delta \bar{c}_{2,1} + \Delta \bar{c}_{2,2}}{\bar{c}_{2,1}} \tag{6-43}$$

$$\frac{\Delta K_{4,3}}{(K'_{4,3})} = \frac{\Delta \bar{c}_{2,1} + \Delta \bar{c}_{2,2}}{\bar{c}_{2,1}} - \frac{\Delta \bar{c}_{3,2}}{\bar{c}_{3,1}} \tag{6-44}$$

The change $\Delta \bar{c}_{2,1}$ has to appear in the second equation of each pair; this becomes clear immediately for the case that $\Delta K_{2,1} \neq 0$ and $\Delta K_{4,3} \equiv 0$: the change $\Delta \bar{c}_{2,1}$ causes a "concentration jump" with reference to the slow step.

The third pair is nonrealistic, as $\bar{c}_{3,1} = \bar{c}_{3,0}$ and $\bar{c}_{2,1}$ do not contain any concentration change due to the second relaxation process; $K_{4,3}$ in the denominator on the left side of (6-44) is therefore not right (and was thus put in parentheses). But $K_{4,3}$ itself could also not be used.

The over-all law of conservation of mass is

$$\Delta \bar{c}_{1,0} + \Delta \bar{c}_{2,0} + \Delta \bar{c}_{3,0} = 0 \tag{6-45}$$

The corresponding equation for the fast step—previously (2-60)—is now

$$\Delta \bar{c}_{1,1} + \Delta \bar{c}_{2,1} = 0 \tag{6-46}$$

One obtains as the difference between (6-45) and (6-46)—employing the general definition (6-36)—the (derived) law of conservation of mass for the slow process *alone*:

$$\Delta \bar{c}_{1,2} + \Delta \bar{c}_{2,2} + \Delta \bar{c}_{3,2} = 0 \tag{6-47}$$

Two of the three equations (6-45), (6-46), and (6-47) may be considered as independent and may therefore be employed in later derivations. In the first pair of equations, one encounters the difficulty that no $\bar{c}_{i,2}$ is contained in (6-37), making any relation between the fast and the slow process quite complex. It seems therefore most advisable to employ the second pair, consisting of (6-41) and (6-42). The appropriate equation to consider in conjunction with (6-41) and (6-42) is (6-38). This latter equation gives in conjunction with (6-46) and the definition

$$K_{2,1} = \frac{\bar{c}_{1,0}}{\bar{c}_{2,0}} \qquad (6\text{-}48)$$

for the relative concentration change of the rapid step,

$$\frac{\Delta \bar{c}_{1,1}}{\bar{c}_{1,0}} = \frac{\Delta K_{2,1}}{K_{2,1}} (1 + K_{2,1})^{-1} \qquad (6\text{-}49)$$

This result is essentially identical with (2-61). The (initial) equilibrium concentration may be expressed in terms of (4-42) with $\bar{c}_1 \to \bar{c}_{1,0}$. One obtains from (6-49), upon substitution,

$$\Delta \bar{c}_{1,1} = \frac{c_1^0}{(1 + K_{1,2})(1 + K_{1,2} + K_{1,2}K_{3,4})} \frac{\Delta K_{2,1}}{K_{2,1}} \qquad (6\text{-}50)$$

This final result is certainly quite different from the former (2-63), which was derived from a one-step mechanism. The *relative* change $\Delta \bar{c}_{1,1}/c_1^0$ is again independent of c_1^0. But the magnitude of the individual equilibrium constants determines vitally to what extent the reaction enthalpy actually appears in $\Delta \bar{c}_{1,1}/c_1^0$.

The much slower second relaxation process may now be derived in various ways. Formerly, the pair of equations (6-41) and (6-42) was solved first for $\Delta \bar{c}_{i,0}$, and $\Delta \bar{c}_{i,1}$ was subtracted later on (2). The more elaborate writing of the equations now demonstrates a more direct approach. One may subtract (6-38) directly from (6-41), giving

$$0 = \frac{\Delta \bar{c}_{1,2}}{\bar{c}_{1,0}} - \frac{\Delta \bar{c}_{2,2}}{\bar{c}_{2,0}} \qquad (6\text{-}51)$$

As generally $\bar{c}_{1,0} \neq \bar{c}_{2,0}$, it is also $\Delta \bar{c}_{1,2} \neq \Delta \bar{c}_{2,2}$, which is in the expected agreement with (6-47). Now employing

$$K_{4,3} = \frac{\bar{c}_{2,0}}{\bar{c}_{3,0}} \qquad (6\text{-}52)$$

together with equations (6-42), (6-47), (6-49), and (6-51), one obtains for the slow relative equilibrium concentration change of component Y_1 the relation

$$\frac{\Delta \bar{c}_{1,2}}{\bar{c}_{1,0}} = \frac{(\Delta K_{4,3}/K_{4,3}) + (\Delta K_{2,1}/K_{2,1})(1 + K_{1,2})^{-1}}{1 + K_{4,3}(1 + K_{2,1})} \tag{6-53}$$

Employing (4-42) again gives

$$\Delta \bar{c}_{1,2} = \frac{[(\Delta K_{4,3}/K_{4,3}) + (\Delta K_{2,1}/K_{2,1})(1 + K_{1,2})^{-1}]c_1^0}{[1 + K_{4,3}(1 + K_{2,1})][1 + K_{1,2}(1 + K_{3,4})]} \tag{6-54}$$

The corresponding value for component Y_2 is obtained from (6-53) with (6-51). The equilibrium concentration $\bar{c}_{2,0}$ is obtained from (4-41), (6-48), and (6-52), resulting in

$$\bar{c}_{2,0} = c_1^0(K_{2,1} + 1 + K_{3,4})^{-1} \tag{6-55}$$

Introducing this value for the equilibrium concentration gives

$$\Delta \bar{c}_{2,2} = \frac{[(\Delta K_{4,3}/K_{4,3}) + (\Delta K_{2,1}/K_{2,1})(1 + K_{1,2})^{-1}]c_1^0}{[1 + K_{4,3}(1 + K_{2,1})](1 + K_{2,1} + K_{3,4})} \tag{6-56}$$

Equation (6-47) may then be combined with (6-54) and (6-56) to result in

$$\Delta \bar{c}_{3,2} = - \frac{[(\Delta K_{4,3}/K_{4,3}) + (\Delta K_{2,1}/K_{2,1})(1 + K_{1,2})^{-1}]c_1^0}{1 + K_{4,3}(1 + K_{2,1})} A \tag{6-57}$$

with

$$A = [1 + K_{2,1}(1 + K_{3,4})]^{-1} + (1 + K_{2,1} + K_{3,4})^{-1} \tag{6-58}$$

The complexity of the expressions already for the simplest mechanism is not very encouraging concerning the "simplicity" of thermodynamic expressions for more complex multistep mechanisms.

2. A dimerization, coupled to a monomolecular interconversion. One has to distinguish four possibilities:

The dimer interconverts: Dimerization proceeds much faster than interconversion.

The dimer interconverts: Dimerization proceeds much slower than interconversion.

The monomer interconverts: Dimerization proceeds much faster than interconversion.

The monomer interconverts: Dimerization proceeds much slower than interconversion.

These four possibilities certainly give rise to four different derivations. Although such systems were treated in Chapter 3, they are not considered important enough to be treated here.

B. Four Equilibrium Components Participate

1. An association reaction, *followed* by a monomolecular interconversion, as formerly presented by (3-43). One now has to distinguish between two cases, a and b.

a. The association process is much faster than the monomolecular interconversion. Employing dual indexing for the equilibrium concentration (change)-s, one obtains

$$K_{2,1} = \frac{\bar{c}_{1,0}\bar{c}_{2,0}}{\bar{c}_{3,0}} \tag{6-59}$$

$$K_{4,3} = \frac{\bar{c}_{3,0}}{\bar{c}_{4,0}} \tag{6-60}$$

from (3-44) and (3-45) at equilibrium. The second index refers to the relaxation process under observation, as explained in detail in the text preceding (6-34). If the second index (j) is zero, it is referred to the condition before perturbation. Equilibrium changes are now described similar to the treatment in Section 6-2A1.

1. For the initial rapid process, one has

$$\frac{\Delta K_{2,1}}{K_{2,1}} = \frac{\Delta \bar{c}_{1,1}}{\bar{c}_{1,0}} + \frac{\Delta \bar{c}_{2,1}}{\bar{c}_{2,0}} - \frac{\Delta \bar{c}_{3,1}}{\bar{c}_{3,0}} \tag{6-61}$$

For this fast process the law of conservation of mass gives

$$\Delta \bar{c}_{2,1} + \Delta \bar{c}_{3,1} = 0 \tag{6-62}$$

One obtains, in addition,

$$\Delta \bar{c}_{1,1} = \Delta \bar{c}_{2,1} \tag{6-63}$$

from stoichiometry. Of main interest is $\Delta \bar{c}_{1,1}/\bar{c}_{1,0}$, an expression which may be obtained from (6-61) by incorporating (6-59), (6-62), and (6-63):

$$\frac{\Delta K_{2,1}}{K_{2,1}} = \frac{\Delta \bar{c}_{1,1}}{\bar{c}_{1,0}}\left(1 + \frac{\bar{c}_{1,0}}{\bar{c}_{2,0}} + \frac{K_{2,1}}{\bar{c}_{2,0}}\right) \tag{6-64}$$

Although complete expressions with analytical concentrations could be written, they would become quite complex, and it is therefore advisable to introduce the two limiting experimental conditions at this point.

a. $c_1^0 = c_2^0$. c_1^0 and c_2^0 were defined according to (4-43) and (4-44) with each equilibrium concentration carrying the second index zero. This experimental condition also gives $\bar{c}_{1,0} = \bar{c}_{2,0}$. An expression for $\bar{c}_{2,0}$ is obtained from (4-48) by index exchange (1 for 2 and 2 for 1 in all c_i^0). Observing the analytical condition leads to one-half the value of (5-47) for $\bar{c}_{2,0}$. Inserting this value into the (simplified) equation (6-64) gives

$$\frac{\Delta K_{2,1}}{K_{2,1}} = 2\,\frac{\Delta\bar{c}_{1,1}}{\bar{c}_{1,0}}\left\{1 + (1 + K_{3,4})\left[\left\langle 1 + \frac{4c_1^0(1 + K_{3,4})}{K_{2,1}}\right\rangle^{1/2} - 1\right]^{-1}\right\} \quad (6\text{-}65)$$

One immediately recognizes the limits

$$\frac{\Delta\bar{c}_{1,0}}{\bar{c}_{1,0}} \to \frac{\Delta K_{2,1}}{K_{2,1}} \times \begin{cases} 0 & \text{for } c_1^0 \to 0 \\ \tfrac{1}{2} & \text{for } c_1^0 \to \infty \end{cases}$$

This relative concentration change $\Delta\bar{c}_{1,0}/\bar{c}_{1,0}$ reaches $\tfrac{1}{4}(\Delta K_{2,1}/K_{2,1})$ at

$$c_1^0 = \frac{K_{2,1}}{4(1 + K_{3,4})}\,[3 + K_{3,4}(4 + K_{3,4})]$$

To obtain the absolute concentration change as a function of c_1^0, one has to insert the same half-value of (5-47), resulting in

$$\Delta\bar{c}_{1,1} = \frac{\Delta K_{2,1}}{K_{2,1}}\,\frac{K_{2,1}}{1 + K_{3,4}}$$

$$\times\,\frac{1 - \langle 1 + [4c_1^0(1 + K_{3,4})/K_{2,1}]\rangle^{1/2} + [4c_1^0(1 + K_{3,4})/K_{2,1}]}{K_{3,4} + \langle 1 + [4c_1^0(1 + K_{3,4})/K_{2,1}]\rangle^{1/2}}$$

$$(6\text{-}66)$$

One obtains as limits [for the absolute change; those for the relative (to c_1^0) change are quite different!]:

$$\Delta\bar{c}_{1,1} \to \frac{\Delta K_{2,1}}{K_{2,1}}\,\frac{K_{2,1}}{1 + K_{3,4}} \times \begin{cases} 0 & \text{for } c_1^0 \to 0 \\ \infty & \text{for } c_1^0 \to \infty \end{cases}$$

Computation of any intermediate value of c_1^0 is possible but of little interest here (for the given limits). Therefore, no explicit expression for $\Delta\bar{c}_1$ was given in Section 6-1B1 (the plain association reaction without monomolecular interconversion coupled in). The concentration changes $\Delta\bar{c}_{2,1}$ and $\Delta\bar{c}_{3,1}$ may easily be obtained from (6-66) with (6-62) and (6-63). Equation (6-65) may be converted to

$$\frac{\Delta\bar{c}_{1,1}}{\bar{c}_{1,0}} = \frac{\Delta K_{2,1}}{2K_{2,1}}\,\frac{\langle 1 + [4c_1^0(1 + K_{3,4})/K_{2,1}]\rangle^{1/2} - 1}{\langle 1 + [4c_1^0(1 + K_{3,4})/K_{2,1}]\rangle^{1/2} + K_{3,4}} \quad (6\text{-}67)$$

b. $c_1^0 \ll c_2^0$ under the assumption that detection proceeds via component Y_1. Under this condition one obtains, directly from (6-64),

$$\frac{\Delta \bar{c}_{1,1}}{\bar{c}_{1,0}} = \frac{\Delta K_{2,1}}{K_{2,1}} \left(1 + \frac{K_{2,1}}{c_2^0} \right)^{-1} \tag{6-68}$$

This equation is practically identical to (6-10). This type of "buffering" therefore does not reveal any distinction between a plain association process and one with a (slow) interconversion of the associate. Certainly, if $K_{3,4} \ll 1$, (6-67) also cannot be distinguished from (6-5). On the other hand, the expression for $\Delta \bar{c}_{1,1}$ would certainly be different from a comparable expression relating only to a plain association process.

2. For the second, much slower process, one first has

$$\frac{\Delta K_{2,1}}{K_{2,1}} = \frac{\Delta \bar{c}_{1,1} + \Delta \bar{c}_{1,2}}{\bar{c}_{1,0}} + \frac{\Delta \bar{c}_{2,1} + \Delta \bar{c}_{2,2}}{\bar{c}_{2,0}} - \frac{\Delta \bar{c}_{3,1} + \Delta \bar{c}_{3,2}}{\bar{c}_{3,0}} \tag{6-69}$$

$$\frac{\Delta K_{4,3}}{K_{4,3}} = \frac{\Delta \bar{c}_{3,1} + \Delta \bar{c}_{3,2}}{\bar{c}_{3,0}} - \frac{\Delta \bar{c}_{4,2}}{\bar{c}_{4,0}} \tag{6-70}$$

The relations among the $\Delta \bar{c}_{i,2}$ are given by

$$\Delta \bar{c}_{1,2} = \Delta \bar{c}_{2,2} \tag{6-71}$$

$$\Delta \bar{c}_{1,2} + \Delta \bar{c}_{3,2} + \Delta \bar{c}_{4,2} = 0 \tag{6-72}$$

One may now subtract (6-61) from (6-69), giving

$$\frac{\Delta \bar{c}_{1,2}}{\bar{c}_{1,0}} + \frac{\Delta \bar{c}_{2,2}}{\bar{c}_{2,0}} - \frac{\Delta \bar{c}_{3,2}}{\bar{c}_{3,0}} = 0 \tag{6-73}$$

This relation represents full equilibration of the first (fast) step for the time range of the second step.

Initially, it is again assumed that detection of the changes proceeds via component Y_1. Combining equations (6-70), (6-73), (6-71), (6-72), (6-59), and (6-60) then leads to an expression with $\Delta \bar{c}_{1,2}$ as the only concentration change for the slow process:

$$\frac{\Delta \bar{c}_{1,2}}{\bar{c}_{1,0}} \left[1 + \frac{\bar{c}_{1,0}}{\bar{c}_{2,0}} + \frac{K_{2,1}}{\bar{c}_{2,0}} (1 + K_{3,4})^{-1} \right]$$

$$= \left(\frac{\Delta K_{4,3}}{K_{4,3}} - \frac{\Delta \bar{c}_{3,1}}{\bar{c}_{3,0}} \right) \left(1 + K_{4,3} \right)^{-1} \tag{6-74}$$

In this equation a term with $\Delta \bar{c}_{3,1}$ appears. The explicit expression is best derived directly from (6-61) with (6-62) and (6-63), giving, for instance,

$$\frac{\Delta \bar{c}_{3,1}}{\bar{c}_{3,0}} = - \frac{\Delta K_{2,1}}{K_{2,1}} \left(1 + \frac{\bar{c}_{1,0} + \bar{c}_{2,0}}{K_{2,1}} \right)^{-1} \tag{6-75}$$

From (6-70) to (6-73) one may also derive the relations

$$\frac{\Delta \bar{c}_{3,2}}{\bar{c}_{3,0}} \left[1 + K_{4,3} \left(1 + \frac{K_{2,1}}{\bar{c}_{1,0} + \bar{c}_{2,0}} \right) \right] = \frac{\Delta K_{4,3}}{K_{4,3}} - \frac{\Delta \bar{c}_{3,1}}{\bar{c}_{3,0}} \tag{6-76}$$

$$\frac{\Delta \bar{c}_{4,2}}{\bar{c}_{4,0}} \left[1 + K_{3,4} \left(1 + \frac{K_{2,1}}{\bar{c}_{1,0} + \bar{c}_{2,0}} \right)^{-1} \right] = \frac{\Delta K_{4,3}}{K_{4,3}} - \frac{\Delta \bar{c}_{3,1}}{\bar{c}_{3,0}} \tag{6-77}$$

Equation (6-75) would also have to be used for these last two equations. In the general case, one would have to substitute $\bar{c}_{1,0}$ and $\bar{c}_{2,0}$ by their complete expressions, such as (4-48) and (5-46). But considerable simplifications are possible for the two limiting cases.

 a. $c_1^0 = c_2^0$. Upon combining (6-74) with (6-75), one obtains with $\bar{c}_{1,0} = \bar{c}_{2,0}$,

$$\frac{\Delta \bar{c}_{1,2}}{\bar{c}_{1,0}} = \frac{(\Delta K_{4,3}/K_{4,3}) + (\Delta K_{2,1}/K_{2,1})[1 + (2\bar{c}_{1,0}/K_{2,1})]^{-1}}{2(1 + K_{4,3}) + (K_{2,1}/\bar{c}_{1,0})K_{4,3}} \tag{6-78}$$

For $\bar{c}_{1,0}$ one may insert one-half the value of (5-47). As very little simplification in the expression for $\Delta \bar{c}_{1,2}$ is obtained that way, the complete equation is not written down here. But one may easily deduce

If $c_1^0 \to 0$: $\bar{c}_{1,0} \to 0$ and $\Delta \bar{c}_{1,2}/\bar{c}_{1,0} \to 0$

If $c_1^0 \to \infty$: $\bar{c}_{1,0} \to \infty$ and $\Delta \bar{c}_{1,2}/\bar{c}_{1,0} \to (\Delta K_{4,3}/K_{4,3})(2 + 2K_{4,3})^{-1}$

If $c_1^0 = \dfrac{3K_{2,1}}{4(1 + K_{3,4})}$: $\dfrac{K_{2,1}/2}{1 + K_{4,3}} = \bar{c}_{1,0}$

and

$$\frac{\Delta \bar{c}_{1,2}}{\bar{c}_{1,0}} = \frac{1}{4} \left[\frac{\Delta K_{4,3}}{K_{4,3}} (1 + K_{4,3})^{-1} + \frac{\Delta K_{2,1}}{K_{2,1}} (1 + 2K_{4,3})^{-1} \right] \tag{6-79}$$

If, on the other hand, $c_1^0 = 2K_{2,1}/(1 + K_{3,4})$, one obtains $\bar{c}_{1,0} = K_{2,1}/(1 + K_{3,4})$ and

$$\frac{\Delta \bar{c}_{1,2}}{\bar{c}_{1,0}} = \frac{1}{3} \left[\frac{\Delta K_{4,3}}{K_{4,3}} (1 + K_{3,4})^{-1} + \frac{\Delta K_{2,1}}{K_{2,1}} (1 + 3K_{4,3})^{-1} \right] \tag{6-80}$$

At this point it might be mentioned that a result similar to (6-78) was obtained previously by Czerlinski (3), although the derivation there was less rigorous: Eq. (8.8) minus (8.11) there give (6-78) for the limiting case.

Equations (6-76) and (6-77) become for this limiting case, and with (6-75),

$$\frac{\Delta \bar{c}_{3,2}}{\bar{c}_{3,0}} = \left[\frac{\Delta K_{4,3}}{K_{4,3}} + \frac{\Delta K_{2,1}}{K_{2,1}} \left(1 + \frac{2\bar{c}_{1,0}}{K_{2,1}} \right)^{-1} \right] \left[1 + K_{4,3} \left(1 + \frac{K_{2,1}}{2\bar{c}_{2,0}} \right) \right]^{-1}$$

(6-81)

$$\frac{\Delta \bar{c}_{4,2}}{\bar{c}_{4,0}} = \left[\frac{\Delta K_{4,3}}{K_{4,3}} + \frac{\Delta K_{2,1}}{K_{2,1}} \left(1 + \frac{2\bar{c}_{1,0}}{K_{2,1}} \right)^{-1} \right] \left[1 + K_{3,4} \left(1 + \frac{K_{2,1}}{2\bar{c}_{1,0}} \right)^{-1} \right]^{-1}$$

(6-82)

In comparing (6-81) with (6-82), one limit is of special interest—$c_1^0 \to 0$. This limit gives $\bar{c}_{1,0} \to 0$ also, and thus $\Delta \bar{c}_{3,2}/\bar{c}_{3,0} \to 0$, but

$$\Delta \bar{c}_{4,2}/\bar{c}_{4,0} \to \frac{\Delta K_{4,3}}{K_{4,3}} + \frac{\Delta K_{2,1}}{K_{2,1}}$$

Certainly this result is only of theoretical interest.

b. $c_1^0 \ll c_2^0$. One obtains practically $\bar{c}_1 + \bar{c}_2 \doteq c_2^0$, leading to the following simplifications from (6-74), (6-76), and (6-77), incorporating (6-75) also:

$$\frac{\Delta \bar{c}_{1,2}}{\bar{c}_{1,0}} = \left(\frac{\Delta K_{4,3}}{K_{4,3}} + \frac{\Delta K_{2,1}}{K_{2,1}} \frac{K_{2,1}}{K_{2,1} + c_2^0} \right) \left(1 + K_{4,3} \frac{K_{2,1} + c_2^0}{c_2^0} \right)^{-1} = \frac{\Delta \bar{c}_{3,2}}{\bar{c}_{3,0}}$$

(6-83)

$$\frac{\Delta \bar{c}_{4,2}}{\bar{c}_{4,0}} = \left(\frac{\Delta K_{4,3}}{K_{4,3}} + \frac{\Delta K_{2,1}}{K_{2,1}} \frac{K_{2,1}}{K_{2,1} + c_2^0} \right) \left(1 + K_{3,4} \frac{c_2^0}{K_{2,1} + c_2^0} \right)^{-1}$$

(6-84)

Certainly, the changes in $\Delta \bar{c}_{2,2}/c_2^0$ would be negligibly small compared to those of (6-83), owing to the buffering by Y_2.

c. The association process is much slower than the monomolecular interconversion. Equations (6-59) and (6-60) are also valid for this combination.

1. For the initial rapid process it is

$$\frac{\Delta K_{4,3}}{K_{4,3}} = \frac{\Delta \bar{c}_{3,1}}{\bar{c}_{3,0}} - \frac{\Delta \bar{c}_{4,1}}{\bar{c}_{4,0}}$$

(6-85)

One obtains from stoichiometry the relation

$$\Delta \bar{c}_{3,1} = - \Delta \bar{c}_{4,1}$$

(6-86)

Combining equations (6-60), (6-85), and (6-86) gives

$$\frac{\Delta \bar{c}_{3,1}}{\bar{c}_{3,0}} = \frac{\Delta K_{4,3}}{K_{4,3}} (1 + K_{4,3})^{-1} = - K_{3,4} \frac{\Delta \bar{c}_{4,1}}{\bar{c}_{4,0}} \qquad (6\text{-}87)$$

These relative concentration changes are independent of equilibrium concentrations, as also shown for the much simpler system by (2-61).

2. For the second, much slower process, one first has

$$\frac{\Delta K_{2,1}}{K_{2,1}} = \frac{\Delta \bar{c}_{1,2}}{\bar{c}_{1,0}} + \frac{\Delta \bar{c}_{2,2}}{\bar{c}_{2,0}} - \frac{\Delta \bar{c}_{3,1} + \Delta \bar{c}_{3,2}}{\bar{c}_{3,0}} \qquad (6\text{-}88)$$

$$\frac{\Delta K_{4,3}}{K_{4,3}} = \frac{\Delta \bar{c}_{3,1} + \Delta \bar{c}_{3,2}}{\bar{c}_{3,0}} - \frac{\Delta \bar{c}_{4,1} + \Delta \bar{c}_{4,2}}{\bar{c}_{4,0}} \qquad (6\text{-}89)$$

Subtracting (6-85) from (6-89) gives

$$\frac{\Delta \bar{c}_{3,2}}{\bar{c}_{3,0}} - \frac{\Delta \bar{c}_{4,2}}{\bar{c}_{4,0}} = 0 \qquad (6\text{-}90)$$

Furthermore, (6-71) and (6-72) are again valid for this slower process. Combining equations (6-88), (6-90), (6-71), (6-72), (6-59), and (6-60) gives the two relationships

$$\frac{\Delta K_{2,1}}{K_{2,1}} + \frac{\Delta_{3,1}}{\bar{c}_{3,0}} = \frac{\Delta \bar{c}_{1,2}}{\bar{c}_{1,0}} \left[1 + \frac{\bar{c}_{1,0}}{\bar{c}_{2,0}} + \frac{K_{2,1}}{\bar{c}_{2,0}} (1 + K_{3,4})^{-1} \right] \qquad (6\text{-}91)$$

$$\frac{\Delta K_{2,1}}{K_{2,1}} + \frac{\Delta \bar{c}_{3,1}}{\bar{c}_{3,0}} = - \frac{\Delta \bar{c}_{3,2}}{\bar{c}_{3,0}} \left[1 + \frac{\bar{c}_{2,0}}{K_{2,1}} (1 + K_{3,4}) \left(1 + \frac{\bar{c}_{1,0}}{\bar{c}_{2,0}} \right) \right] \qquad (6\text{-}92)$$

The third relationship is directly given by (6-90) and $\Delta \bar{c}_{3,1}/\bar{c}_{3,0}$ by (6-87).

a. $c_1^0 = c_2^0$, also giving $\bar{c}_{1,0} = \bar{c}_{2,0}$. The above two equations simplify to

$$\frac{\Delta \bar{c}_{1,2}}{\bar{c}_{1,0}} = \left[\frac{\Delta K_{2,1}}{K_{2,1}} + \frac{\Delta K_{4,3}}{K_{4,3}} (1 + K_{4,3})^{-1} \right] \left[2 + \frac{K_{2,1}}{\bar{c}_{1,0}} (1 + K_{3,4})^{-1} \right]^{-1} \qquad (6\text{-}93)$$

$$\frac{\Delta \bar{c}_{3,2}}{\bar{c}_{3,0}} = \left[\frac{\Delta K_{2,1}}{K_{2,1}} + \frac{\Delta K_{4,3}}{K_{4,3}} (1 + K_{4,3})^{-1} \right] \left[1 + \frac{2\bar{c}_{1,0}}{K_{2,1}} (1 + K_{3,4}) \right]^{-1} \qquad (6\text{-}94)$$

The relationship between $\bar{c}_{1,0}$ and c_1^0 is given by one-half the value of (5-47).

b. $c_1^0 \ll c_2^0$, also giving $\bar{c}_{1,0} \ll \bar{c}_{2,0} \doteq c_2^0$. Equations (6-91) and (6-92) now become

$$\frac{\Delta\bar{c}_{1,2}}{\bar{c}_{1,0}} = \left[\frac{\Delta K_{2,1}}{K_{2,1}} + \frac{\Delta K_{4,3}}{K_{4,3}}(1 + K_{4,3})^{-1}\right]\left[1 + \frac{K_{2,1}}{c_2^0}(1 + K_{3,4})^{-1}\right]^{-1} \quad (6\text{-}95)$$

$$\frac{\Delta\bar{c}_{3,2}}{\bar{c}_{3,0}} = \left[\frac{\Delta K_{2,1}}{K_{2,1}} + \frac{\Delta K_{4,3}}{K_{4,3}}(1 + K_{4,3})^{-1}\right]\left[1 + \frac{c_2^0}{K_{2,1}}(1 + K_{3,4})\right]^{-1} \quad (6\text{-}96)$$

The limits of these equations are easily derived.

3. An association reaction, preceded by a monomolecular interconversion, as presented by (3-54). Because of the unsymmetry of this reaction sequence, a much larger number of equations would result than in the type where an association reaction is followed by a monomolecular interconversion. The necessary equations may be derived according to the principles outlined in the previous section, so they will not be derived here.

6–3. THREE-STEP MECHANISMS

A. Four Equilibrium Components Participate

The reaction system is described by (3-171). Thermodynamics will be treated as outlined previously in Section 6-2A1. As was already mentioned in the kinetic treatment of (3-171), there are two different ways in which the reaction steps could follow each other: The slowest step may be in the middle or at the side.

1. The natural sequence of relaxation processes prevails: Fastest is the reaction involving $K_{2,1}$ and slowest is the reaction involving $K_{6,5}$. The equilibrium constants are given by (1-4), (4-141), and (4-142).

a. For the fastest relaxation process, (6-38) is valid, which has to be combined with (6-46). Also inserting (1-4) (with zero as the second index for the equilibrium concentrations) gives (6-49). An expression obtained from (4-144) may be substituted for the concentration $\bar{c}_{1,0}$ leading to

$$\frac{\Delta\bar{c}_{1,1}}{c_1^0} = (1 + K_{2,1})^{-1}[1 + K_{1,2}(1 + K_{3,4}\langle 1 + K_{5/6}\rangle)]^{-1}\frac{\Delta K_{2,1}}{K_{2,1}} \quad (6\text{-}97)$$

The amount of the reaction enthalpy $\Delta H_{2,1}$, transferred to the relative concentration change, depends highly upon the size of the individual equilibrium constants.

b. For the second-fastest relaxation process, (6-41) and (6-42) have to be considered. The first equation is again reduced to (6-51) by subtracting (6-38). Solving for the previous concentration change leads to (6-53), completely in line with the more elementary derivation for a restricted two-step mechanism. But $\bar{c}_{1,0}$ of (6-53) has to be substituted for by (4-144), giving

$$\frac{\Delta\bar{c}_{1,2}}{c_1^0} = \frac{(\Delta K_{4,3}/K_{4,3}) + (\Delta K_{2,1}/K_{2,1})(1 + K_{1,2})^{-1}}{[1 + K_{4,3}(1 + K_{2,1})][1 + K_{1,2}(1 + K_{3,4}\langle 1 + K_{5,6}\rangle)]} \qquad (6\text{-}98)$$

No concentration terms appear on the right side of (6-98).

c. For the slowest relaxation process, one has to write the following three equations:

$$\frac{\Delta K_{2,1}}{K_{2,1}} = \frac{\Delta\bar{c}_{1,1} + \Delta\bar{c}_{1,2} + \Delta\bar{c}_{1,3}}{\bar{c}_{1,0}} - \frac{\Delta\bar{c}_{2,1} + \Delta\bar{c}_{2,2} + \Delta\bar{c}_{2,3}}{\bar{c}_{2,0}} \qquad (6\text{-}99)$$

$$\frac{\Delta K_{4,3}}{K_{4,3}} = \frac{\Delta\bar{c}_{2,1} + \Delta\bar{c}_{2,2} + \Delta\bar{c}_{2,3}}{\bar{c}_{2,0}} - \frac{\Delta\bar{c}_{3,2} + \Delta\bar{c}_{3,3}}{\bar{c}_{3,0}} \qquad (6\text{-}100)$$

$$\frac{\Delta K_{6,5}}{K_{6,5}} = \frac{\Delta\bar{c}_{3,2} + \Delta\bar{c}_{3,3}}{\bar{c}_{3,0}} - \frac{\Delta\bar{c}_{4,3}}{\bar{c}_{4,0}} \qquad (6\text{-}101)$$

One now subtracts (6-41) from (6-99) and (6-42) from (6-100), leading to the equilibrium relations

$$0 = \frac{\Delta\bar{c}_{1,3}}{\bar{c}_{1,0}} - \frac{\Delta\bar{c}_{2,3}}{\bar{c}_{2,0}} \qquad (6\text{-}102)$$

$$0 = \frac{\Delta\bar{c}_{2,3}}{\bar{c}_{2,0}} - \frac{\Delta\bar{c}_{3,3}}{\bar{c}_{3,0}} \qquad (6\text{-}103)$$

In addition, there is the law of conservation of mass for the slow process, giving

$$\Delta\bar{c}_{1,3} + \Delta\bar{c}_{2,3} + \Delta\bar{c}_{3,3} + \Delta\bar{c}_{4,3} = 0 \qquad (6\text{-}104)$$

There are then four equations for the four unknowns of the slowest process, giving, initially, with the (refined) equations (1-4), (4-141), and (4-142),

$$\frac{\Delta K_{6,5}}{K_{6,5}} = \frac{\Delta\bar{c}_{3,2}}{\bar{c}_{3,0}} + \frac{\Delta\bar{c}_{1,3}}{\bar{c}_{1,0}} [1 + K_{6,5}(1 + K_{4,3}\langle 1 + K_{2,1}\rangle)] \qquad (6\text{-}105)$$

The relative concentration change $\Delta\bar{c}_{3,2}/\bar{c}_{3,0}$ is not yet available but may be computed from (6-42), (6-51), and associated conditions, leading to

$$-\left[\frac{\Delta K_{4,3}}{K_{4,3}} + \frac{\Delta K_{2,1}}{K_{2,1}} (1 + K_{1,2})^{-1}\right] = \frac{\Delta\bar{c}_{3,2}}{\bar{c}_{3,0}}\left(1 + \frac{K_{3,4}}{1 + K_{2,1}}\right) \qquad (6\text{-}106)$$

Combining these last two equations gives

$$\frac{\Delta\bar{c}_{1,3}}{\bar{c}_{1,0}} = \frac{\dfrac{\Delta K_{6,5}}{K_{6,5}} + \dfrac{\Delta K_{4,3}}{K_{4,3}}\left(1 + \dfrac{K_{3,4}}{1 + K_{2,1}}\right)^{-1} + \dfrac{\Delta K_{2,1}}{K_{2,1}}\dfrac{1}{1 + K_{1,2}(1 + K_{3,4})}}{1 + K_{6,5}(1 + K_{4,3}\langle 1 + K_{2,1}\rangle)}$$

$$(6\text{-}107)$$

Equation (4-144) may again be inserted for $\bar{c}_{1,0}$, leading to an equation for $\Delta\bar{c}_{1,3}/c_1^0$ which is completely independent of concentration. But the various equilibrium constants have substantial effect on the actual size of the relative concentration change.

2. The left step is fastest and the middle step is slowest, thus causing a separation of two faster steps. As the two faster steps cannot be detected via the same component, they may even proceed at equal speed without kinetic interference.

a. The fastest step is determined by (6-49). In case $\Delta\bar{c}_{1,1}/c_1^0$ is desired, (6-97) has to be used.

b. The "second fastest" step (no absolute requirement!) is determined by an equation which is symmetric to (6-49),

$$\frac{\Delta\bar{c}_{4,2}}{\bar{c}_{4,0}} = \frac{\Delta K_{5,6}}{K_{5,6}}(1 + K_{5,6})^{-1} \tag{6-108}$$

The remaining equilibrium concentration may easily be substituted.

c. The slowest step is associated with the following three equations:

$$\frac{\Delta K_{2,1}}{K_{2,1}} = \frac{\Delta\bar{c}_{1,1} + \Delta\bar{c}_{1,3}}{\Delta\bar{c}_{1,0}} - \frac{\Delta\bar{c}_{2,1} + \Delta\bar{c}_{2,3}}{\bar{c}_{2,0}} \tag{6-109}$$

$$\frac{\Delta K_{4,3}}{K_{4,3}} = \frac{\Delta c_{2,1} + \Delta c_{2,3}}{\bar{c}_{2,0}} - \frac{\Delta\bar{c}_{3,2} + \Delta\bar{c}_{3,3}}{\bar{c}_{3,0}} \tag{6-110}$$

$$\frac{\Delta K_{6,5}}{K_{6,5}} = \frac{\Delta\bar{c}_{3,2} + \Delta\bar{c}_{3,3}}{\bar{c}_{3,0}} - \frac{\Delta\bar{c}_{4,2} + \Delta\bar{c}_{4,3}}{\bar{c}_{4,0}} \tag{6-111}$$

One may now subtract (6-38) from (6-109) and a similar equation from (6-111). This "similar equation" represents the initial equation for the "second step":

$$\frac{\Delta K_{6,5}}{K_{6,5}} = \frac{\Delta\bar{c}_{3,2}}{\bar{c}_{3,0}} - \frac{\Delta\bar{c}_{4,2}}{\bar{c}_{4,0}} \tag{6-112}$$

One then obtains the two equilibrium relations

$$0 = \frac{\Delta\bar{c}_{1,3}}{\bar{c}_{1,0}} - \frac{\Delta\bar{c}_{2,3}}{\bar{c}_{2,0}} \tag{6-113}$$

$$0 = \frac{\Delta\bar{c}_{3,3}}{\bar{c}_{3,0}} - \frac{\Delta\bar{c}_{4,3}}{\bar{c}_{4,0}} \tag{6-114}$$

The slowest step can certainly be observed via any component. For better comparison with former equations, the concentration change $\Delta\bar{c}_{1,3}$ will be considered. One obtains initially

$$\frac{\Delta K_{4,3}}{K_{4,3}} = \frac{\Delta\bar{c}_{2,1}}{\bar{c}_{2,0}} - \frac{\Delta\bar{c}_{3,2}}{\bar{c}_{3,2}} + \frac{\Delta\bar{c}_{1,3}}{\bar{c}_{1,0}}\left[1 + \frac{K_{4,3}K_{2,1}(1 + K_{1,2})}{1 + K_{5,6}}\right] \tag{6-115}$$

Upon substitution of the two faster relative concentration changes one obtains an equation, which may be solved for $\Delta \bar{c}_{1,3}/\bar{c}_{1,0}$:

$$\frac{\Delta \bar{c}_{1,3}}{\bar{c}_{1,0}} = \frac{\dfrac{\Delta K_{4,3}}{K_{4,3}} + \dfrac{\Delta K_{2,1}}{K_{2,1}}(1 + K_{1,2})^{-1} + \dfrac{\Delta K_{6,5}}{K_{6,5}}(1 + K_{6,5})^{-1}}{1 + K_{4,3}(1 + K_{2,1}(1 + K_{5,6})^{-1})} \tag{6-116}$$

This equation again shows no concentration parameter on the right side: The relative change $\Delta \bar{c}_{1,3}/\bar{c}_{1,0}$ (as well as $\Delta \bar{c}_{1,3}/c_1^0$) is independent of concentration.

3. There actually exists a third possibility, which has not yet been discussed: The step with $K_{6,5}$ is again the slowest, while the step with $K_{4,3}$ is now the fastest. One may proceed as outlined above, but the derivation of this case is omitted here, as no new aspects develop.

B. Five Equilibrium Components Participate

Again, only one case will be considered, that of (3-186), which was also thoroughly treated in Chapters 4 and 5. As has already been developed, there are three major cases, each one belonging to a special sequence of reaction steps. One may differentiate them according to the slowest step determined by the three different possibilities of longest relaxation times according to (3-188), (3-189), and (3-190).

1. The middle step is slowest, corresponding to $a_{22} \ll a_{11}, a_{33}$. This is a reaction sequence, which is quite similar to the one which was discussed in the Section (6-3A2). It makes no difference whether the step with $K_{2,1}$ or the step with $K_{6,5}$ is faster.

a. The step with $K_{2,1}$ will be treated first. One may either choose (6-49) or (6-97), depending upon whether the reference concentration should be an equilibrium or an analytical concentration.

b. The step with $K_{6,5}$ will be derived because of index labeling. The equilibrium constant of this fast and isolated step is given by (4-145); then

$$\frac{\Delta K_{6,5}}{K_{6,5}} = \frac{\Delta \bar{c}_{3,2}}{\bar{c}_{3,0}} - \frac{\Delta \bar{c}_{4,2}}{\bar{c}_{5,0}} - \frac{\Delta \bar{c}_{5,2}}{\bar{c}_{5,0}} \tag{6-117}$$

There are two relations among the $\Delta \bar{c}_{i,2}$,

$$-\Delta \bar{c}_{3,2} = \Delta \bar{c}_{4,2} = \Delta \bar{c}_{5,2} \tag{6-118}$$

Two relative concentration changes are of interest, the one with $\Delta \bar{c}_{3,2}$ and the one with $\Delta \bar{c}_{4,2}$. They are easily obtained from (6-117) and (6-118), leading to

$$\frac{\Delta \bar{c}_{3,2}}{\bar{c}_{3,0}} = \frac{\Delta K_{6,5}}{K_{6,5}}[1 + K_{6,5}(\bar{c}_{4,0} + \bar{c}_{5,0})]^{-1} \tag{6-119}$$

$$\frac{\Delta \bar{c}_{4,2}}{\bar{c}_{4,0}} = -\frac{\Delta K_{6,5}}{K_{6,5}}[1 + K_{6,5}\bar{c}_{4,0} + \langle K_{6,5}\bar{c}_{5,0} \rangle^{-1}]^{-1} \tag{6-120}$$

The two equilibrium concentrations on the right side have to be substituted for by (4-149) and its "index-inverted" expression for $\bar{c}_{5,0}$. Both equations would become quite complicated upon substitution in the general case, but they may be considerably simplified for $c_5^0 \gg c_4^0$. Equation (6-119) becomes

$$\frac{\Delta \bar{c}_{3,2}}{\bar{c}_{3,0}} = \frac{\Delta K_{6,5}}{K_{6,5}} [1 + K_{6,5} c_5^0]^{-1} \tag{6-121}$$

Equation (6-120) may be simplified easily, as long as $c_4^0 \ll K_{5,6}$, which is generally the case for this analytical condition; one obtains

$$\frac{\Delta \bar{c}_{4,2}}{\bar{c}_{4,0}} = -\frac{\Delta K_{6,5}}{K_{6,5}} \frac{c_5^0}{K_{5,6} + c_5^0} \tag{6-122}$$

As $K_{5,6}$ is the dissociation constant, one may rewrite (6-122) as

$$\frac{\Delta \bar{c}_{4,2}}{\bar{c}_{4,0}} = \frac{\Delta K_{5,6}}{K_{5,6}} \frac{c_5^0}{K_{5,6} + c_5^0} \tag{6-123}$$

This equation is structurally identical to (6-10), treating the same reaction as an isolated case. Also inserting the simplified equation (4-149) alters (6-123) to

$$\frac{\Delta \bar{c}_{4,2}}{c_4^0} = \frac{\Delta K_{5,6}}{K_{5,6}} \frac{c_5^0}{K_{5,6} + c_5^0} \frac{K_0}{K_0 + c_5^0} \tag{6-124}$$

The overall dissociation constant K_0 is defined according to (4-150) and may also be expressed by (4-151).

If $c_4^0 = c_5^0$, (6-119) may be combined with the properly simplified equation (4-149) as

$$\frac{\Delta \bar{c}_{3,2}}{\bar{c}_{3,0}} = \frac{\Delta K_{6,5}}{K_{6,5}} \left[1 + K_{6,5} K_0 \left(\left\langle 1 + \frac{4c_4^0}{K_0} \right\rangle^{1/2} - 1 \right) \right]^{-1} \tag{6-125}$$

One obtains full transfer of the driving parameter $\Delta K_{6,5}/K_{6,5}$ for $c_4^0 \to 0$. At $c_4^0 = 2K_0$, the effect of the driving parameter is reduced to $1/(1 + 2K_{6,5}K_0)$ of the total amount; this effect vanishes for $c_4^0 \to \infty$. Equation (6-121) demonstrates similar behavior for c_5^0 as the independent parameter and the relative concentration change $\Delta \bar{c}_{3,2}/\bar{c}_{3,0}$ as the dependent variable. These are relations for concentration changes relative to an equilibrium concentration. If the concentration change refers to an analytical concentration, one realizes from (6-124) that the relative change may proceed through some maximum for c_5^0 as the independent variable.

c. For the slowest step the conditions are described by (6-109), (6-110), and

$$\frac{\Delta K_{6,5}}{K_{6,5}} = \frac{\Delta \bar{c}_{3,2} + \Delta \bar{c}_{3,3}}{\bar{c}_{3,0}} - \frac{\Delta \bar{c}_{4,2} + \Delta \bar{c}_{4,3}}{\bar{c}_{4,0}} - \frac{\Delta \bar{c}_{5,2} + \Delta \bar{c}_{5,3}}{\bar{c}_{5,0}} \tag{6-126}$$

Subtracting (6-117) from (6-126) gives the pre-equilibration condition

$$0 = \frac{\Delta \bar{c}_{3,3}}{\bar{c}_{3,0}} - \frac{\Delta \bar{c}_{4,3}}{\bar{c}_{4,0}} - \frac{\Delta \bar{c}_{5,3}}{\bar{c}_{5,0}} \qquad (6\text{-}127)$$

The second pre-equilibration condition is given by (6-113). This leaves (6-110) and the relations among the $\Delta \bar{c}_{i,3}$:

$$\Delta \bar{c}_{4,3} = \Delta \bar{c}_{5,3} \qquad (6\text{-}128)$$

$$\Delta \bar{c}_{1,3} + \Delta \bar{c}_{2,3} + \Delta \bar{c}_{3,3} + \Delta \bar{c}_{4,3} = 0 \qquad (6\text{-}129)$$

One may now solve for any one of the five unknown $\Delta \bar{c}_{i,3}$ by employing (6-110), (6-113), (6-127), (6-128), and (6-129).

The concentration change $\Delta \bar{c}_{4,3}$ is selected here. One obtains

$$\frac{\Delta K_{4,3}}{K_{4,3}} = \frac{\Delta \bar{c}_{2,1}}{\bar{c}_{2,0}} - \frac{\Delta \bar{c}_{3,2}}{\bar{c}_{3,0}} - \frac{\Delta \bar{c}_{4,3}}{\bar{c}_{4,0}} \left[1 + \frac{\bar{c}_{4,0}}{\bar{c}_{5,0}} + \frac{K_{3,4}}{1 + K_{2,1}} \left(1 + \frac{K_{5,6} + \bar{c}_{4,0}}{\bar{c}_{5,0}} \right) \right] \qquad (6\text{-}130)$$

One obtains from (2-51), together with (1-4) and (2-50), an expression for $\Delta \bar{c}_{2,1} / \bar{c}_{2,0}$ [also used above for converting (6-115) to (6-116)], which is

$$\frac{\Delta \bar{c}_{2,1}}{\bar{c}_{2,1}} = - \frac{\Delta K_{2,1}}{K_{2,1}} (1 + K_{1,2})^{-1} \qquad (6\text{-}131)$$

One may now substitute (6-119) and (6-131) in (6-130) and solve for $\Delta \bar{c}_{4,3} / \bar{c}_{4,0}$, resulting in

$$-\frac{\Delta \bar{c}_{4,3}}{\bar{c}_{4,0}} = \frac{\dfrac{\Delta K_{4,3}}{K_{4,3}} + \dfrac{\Delta K_{2,1}}{K_{2,1}}(1 + K_{1,2})^{-1} + \dfrac{\Delta K_{6,5}}{K_{6,5}}[1 + K_{6,5}(\bar{c}_{4,0} + \bar{c}_{5,0})]^{-1}}{1 + \dfrac{\bar{c}_{4,0}}{\bar{c}_{5,0}} + \dfrac{K_{3,4}}{1 + K_{2,1}} \left(1 + \dfrac{K_{5,6} + \bar{c}_{4,0}}{\bar{c}_{5,0}} \right)} \qquad (6\text{-}132)$$

This complete equation may be further simplified by introducing suitable analytical conditions.

One obtains for $c_4^0 = c_5^0$, with $\bar{c}_4 = \bar{c}_5$,

$$\frac{\Delta \bar{c}_{4,3}}{\bar{c}_{4,0}} =$$

$$-\frac{\dfrac{\Delta K_{4,3}}{K_{4,3}} + \dfrac{\Delta K_{2,1}}{K_{2,1}}(1 + K_{1,2})^{-1} + \dfrac{\Delta K_{6,5}}{K_{6,5}} \left[1 + K_{6,5}K_0 \left(\left\langle 1 + \dfrac{4c_4^0}{K_0} \right\rangle^{1/2} - 1 \right) \right]^{-1}}{2 + \dfrac{K_{3,4}}{1 + K_{2,1}} \left(2 + \dfrac{K_{5,6}}{K_0} \left[\left\langle 1 + \dfrac{4\bar{c}_4^0}{K_0} \right\rangle^{1/2} - 1 \right]^{-1} \right)} \qquad (6\text{-}133)$$

Although this equation is quite complex, it is still useful for evaluations.

One obtains for $c_4^0 \ll c_5^0$ the considerably simplified equation

$$\frac{\Delta \bar{c}_{4,3}}{\bar{c}_{4,0}} = -\frac{\Delta K_{4,3}/K_{4,3} + \dfrac{\Delta K_{2,1}}{K_{2,1}}(1 + K_{1,2}) + \dfrac{\Delta K_{6,5}}{K_{6,5}}(1 + K_{6,5}c_5^0)^{-1}}{1 + \dfrac{K_{3,4}}{1 + K_{2,1}}\dfrac{c_5^0 + K_{5,6}}{c_5^0}}$$

(6-134)

The limits of this equation are easily realized. One may also substitute for $\bar{c}_{4,0}$ the simplified equation (4-149).

2. The left step is slowest, and thus the terminal monomolecular interconversion. There are then two choices left concerning the fastest one of the two remaining steps.

a. The right, bimolecular step is fastest.

1. Equation (6-117) is valid after change of the second index 2 to 1. One then obtains relative concentration changes, which are given by (6-119) and (6-120) with the correction of the second index: $\Delta \bar{c}_{i,2}$ becomes $\Delta \bar{c}_{i,1}$; it is otherwise referred to the discussion of these two equations.

2. For the second relaxation process, the following two equations are valid:

$$\frac{\Delta K_{6,5}}{K_{6,5}} = \frac{\Delta \bar{c}_{3,1} + \Delta \bar{c}_{3,2}}{\bar{c}_{3,0}} - \frac{\Delta \bar{c}_{4,1} + \Delta \bar{c}_{4,2}}{\bar{c}_{4,0}} - \frac{\Delta \bar{c}_{5,1} + \Delta \bar{c}_{5,2}}{\bar{c}_{5,0}}$$

(6-135)

$$\frac{\Delta K_{4,3}}{K_{4,3}} = \frac{\Delta \bar{c}_{2,2}}{\bar{c}_{2,0}} - \frac{\Delta \bar{c}_{3,1} + \Delta \bar{c}_{3,2}}{\bar{c}_{3,0}}$$

(6-136)

The properly re-indexed equation (6-117) has to be subtracted from (6-135), giving the equilibrium condition

$$0 = \frac{\Delta \bar{c}_{3,2}}{\bar{c}_{3,0}} - \frac{\Delta \bar{c}_{4,2}}{\bar{c}_{4,0}} - \frac{\Delta \bar{c}_{5,2}}{\bar{c}_{5,0}}$$

(6-137)

Equation (6-128) with $j = 2$ holds again, and as an independent fourth equation one has available

$$\Delta \bar{c}_{2,2} + \Delta \bar{c}_{3,2} + \Delta \bar{c}_{4,2} = 0$$

(6-138)

For comparison with two other derivations, the four equations are now solved for two different $\Delta \bar{c}_{i,2}$.

a. If $\Delta \bar{c}_{4,2}$ is chosen, one initially obtains from (6-136), (6-137), (6-128), and (6-138),

$$\frac{\Delta K_{4,3}}{K_{4,3}} = -\frac{\Delta \bar{c}_{3,1}}{\bar{c}_{3,0}} - \frac{\Delta \bar{c}_{4,2}}{\bar{c}_{4,0}}\left[1 + \frac{\bar{c}_{4,0}}{\bar{c}_{5,0}} + K_{3,4}\left(1 + \frac{\bar{c}_{4,0}}{\bar{c}_{5,0}} + \frac{K_{5,6}}{\bar{c}_{5,0}}\right)\right]$$

(6-139)

One may now substitute (6-119) for $\Delta\bar{c}_{3,1}/\bar{c}_{3,0}$ and solve (6-139) for $\Delta\bar{c}_{4,2}/\bar{c}_{4,0}$, which gives

$$\frac{\Delta\bar{c}_{4,2}}{\bar{c}_{4,0}} = -\frac{\dfrac{\Delta K_{4,3}}{K_{4,3}} + \dfrac{\Delta K_{6,5}}{K_{6,5}}[1 + K_{6,5}(\bar{c}_{4,0} + \bar{c}_{5,0})]^{-1}}{1 + \dfrac{\bar{c}_{4,0}}{\bar{c}_{5,0}} + K_{3,4}\left(1 + \dfrac{\bar{c}_{4,0}}{\bar{c}_{5,0}} + \dfrac{K_{5,6}}{\bar{c}_{5,0}}\right)} \tag{6-140}$$

The analytical conditions $c_4^0 = c_5^0$ and $c_4^0 \ll c_5^0$ lead easily [by employing the properly simplified equation (4.149)] to expressions which carry only analytical concentrations on the right side.

   b.   If $\Delta\bar{c}_{2,2}$ is chosen as indicating the concentration change, the above four equations initially give

$$\frac{\Delta K_{4,3}}{K_{4,3}} = -\frac{\Delta\bar{c}_{3,1}}{\bar{c}_{3,0}} + \frac{\Delta\bar{c}_{2,2}}{\bar{c}_{2,0}}\left(1 + K_{4,3}\left\langle 1 + \frac{K_{5,6}}{\bar{c}_{4,0} + \bar{c}_{5,0}}\right\rangle^{-1}\right) \tag{6-141}$$

One may now substitute the re-indexed equation (6-119) and solve for $\Delta\bar{c}_{2,2}/\bar{c}_{2,0}$, resulting in

$$\frac{\Delta\bar{c}_{2,2}}{\bar{c}_{2,0}} = \frac{\dfrac{\Delta K_{4,3}}{K_{4,3}} + \dfrac{\Delta K_{6,5}}{K_{6,5}}[1 + K_{6,5}(\bar{c}_{4,0} + \bar{c}_{5,0})]^{-1}}{1 + K_{4,3}\left[1 + \dfrac{K_{5,6}}{\bar{c}_{4,0} + \bar{c}_{5,0}}\right]} \tag{6-142}$$

One may again employ (4-149) and its alternative for $\bar{c}_{5,0}$ or the properly simplified equations according to the analytical conditions.

   3.   For the third relaxation process, the following three equations hold:

$$\frac{\Delta K_{2,1}}{K_{2,1}} = \frac{\Delta\bar{c}_{1,3}}{\bar{c}_{1,0}} - \frac{\Delta\bar{c}_{2,3} + \Delta\bar{c}_{2,2}}{\bar{c}_{2,0}} \tag{6-143}$$

$$\frac{\Delta K_{4,3}}{K_{4,3}} = \frac{\Delta\bar{c}_{2,2} + \Delta\bar{c}_{2,3}}{\bar{c}_{2,0}} - \frac{\Delta\bar{c}_{3,1} + \Delta\bar{c}_{3,2} + \Delta\bar{c}_{3,3}}{\bar{c}_{3,0}} \tag{6-144}$$

$$\frac{\Delta K_{6,5}}{K_{6,5}} = \frac{\Delta\bar{c}_{3,1} + \Delta\bar{c}_{3,2} + \Delta\bar{c}_{3,3}}{\bar{c}_{3,0}} - \frac{\Delta\bar{c}_{4,1} + \Delta\bar{c}_{4,2} + \Delta\bar{c}_{4,3}}{\bar{c}_{4,0}} - \frac{\Delta\bar{c}_{5,1} + \Delta\bar{c}_{5,2} + \Delta\bar{c}_{5,3}}{\bar{c}_{5,0}} \tag{6-145}$$

Subtracting (6-136) from (6-144) gives

$$0 = \frac{\Delta\bar{c}_{2,3}}{\bar{c}_{2,0}} - \frac{\Delta\bar{c}_{3,3}}{\bar{c}_{3,0}} \tag{6-146}$$

Subtracting (6-135) from (6-145) gives another relation for pre-equilibration,

$$0 = \frac{\Delta\bar{c}_{3,3}}{\bar{c}_{3,0}} - \frac{\Delta\bar{c}_{4,3}}{\bar{c}_{4,0}} - \frac{\Delta\bar{c}_{5,3}}{\bar{c}_{5,0}} \tag{6-147}$$

Equations (6-128) and (6-129) are again valid, to give together with (6-143), (6-146), and (6-147) the five equations necessary to solve for any $\Delta \bar{c}_{i,3}$.

    a.   Selecting Y_4 as the indicating component gives

$$\frac{\Delta K_{2,1}}{K_{2,1}} = -\frac{\Delta \bar{c}_{2,2}}{\bar{c}_{2,0}} - \frac{\Delta \bar{c}_{4,3}}{\bar{c}_{4,0}}\left[\left(1 + \frac{\bar{c}_{4,0}}{\bar{c}_{5,0}}\right)\left(1 + K_{1,2} + K_{1,2}K_{3,4}\right) + \frac{K_{1,2}K_{3,4}K_{5,6}}{\bar{c}_{5,0}}\right]$$

$$(6\text{-}148)$$

One may then substitute (6-142) in (6-148), which is avoided here because of the complexity of the expression for $\Delta \bar{c}_{2,2}/\bar{c}_{2,0}$.

    b.   Selecting Y_2 as the indicating component initially gives, with (6-128), (6-129), (6-143), (6-146), and (6-147),

$$\frac{\Delta K_{2,1}}{K_{2,1}} = -\frac{\Delta \bar{c}_{2,2}}{\bar{c}_{2,0}} - \frac{\Delta \bar{c}_{2,3}}{\bar{c}_{2,0}}\left\{1 + K_{1,2}\left[1 + K_{3,4}\left(1 + \frac{K_{5,6}}{\bar{c}_{4,0} + \bar{c}_{5,0}}\right)\right]\right\} \quad (6\text{-}149)$$

Again one may substitute (6-142). The difference in the structure of (6-148) and (6-149) is quite striking, being contained in the term of $\Delta \bar{c}_{i,3}/\bar{c}_{i,0}$.

    b.   The middle step is fastest, representing the other monomolecular inter-conversion. The question is how far the individual equations differ from the ones just derived in Section 6-3B2a.

    1.   The basic equation for the fastest step is given by

$$\frac{\Delta K_{4,3}}{K_{4,3}} = \frac{\Delta \bar{c}_{2,1}}{\bar{c}_{2,0}} - \frac{\Delta \bar{c}_{3,1}}{\bar{c}_{3,0}} \quad\quad (6\text{-}150)$$

The only other equation necessary for solution is

$$\Delta \bar{c}_{2,1} + \Delta \bar{c}_{3,1} = 0 \quad\quad (6\text{-}151)$$

Combining these two equations results in one, which is quite similar in structure to (6-108) and (2-51), namely

$$\frac{\Delta \bar{c}_{2,1}}{\bar{c}_{2,0}} = \frac{\Delta K_{4,3}}{K_{4,3}}(1 + K_{4,3})^{-1} \quad\quad (6\text{-}152)$$

One may then substitute an equation for $\bar{c}_{2,0}$. Considering the two simplifying experimental conditions results in two different solutions.

    a. $c_4^0 = c_5^0$. One obtains, with (4-152),

$$\Delta \bar{c}_{2,1} = \frac{\Delta K_{4,3}}{K_{4,3}} \frac{c_5^0 + \frac{1}{2}K_0}{(1 + K_{4,3})(1 + K_{3,4} + K_{2,1})}\left\{1 - \left\langle 1 - \left(\frac{c_5^0}{c_5^0 + \frac{1}{2}K_0}\right)^2\right\rangle^{1/2}\right\}$$

$$(6\text{-}153)$$

The concentration dependence of this equation is that of (4-152).

b. $c_4^0 \ll c_5^0$. One obtains from (6-152) with (4-153) the relatively simple relationship

$$\frac{\Delta \bar{c}_{2,1}}{c_4^0} = \frac{\Delta K_{4,3}}{K_{4,3}} \frac{1}{(1+K_{4,3})(1+K_{3,4}+K_{2,1})} \frac{c_5^0}{K_0 + c_5^0} \qquad (6\text{-}154)$$

An *S*-shaped dependence upon c_5^0 is directly evident.

2. The basic equations for the intermediate step are given by

$$\frac{\Delta K_{4,3}}{K_{4,3}} = \frac{\Delta \bar{c}_{2,1} + \Delta \bar{c}_{2,2}}{\bar{c}_{2,0}} - \frac{\Delta \bar{c}_{3,1} + \Delta \bar{c}_{3,2}}{\bar{c}_{3,0}} \qquad (6\text{-}155)$$

$$\frac{\Delta K_{6,5}}{K_{6,5}} = \frac{\Delta \bar{c}_{3,1} + \Delta \bar{c}_{3,2}}{\bar{c}_{3,0}} - \frac{\Delta \bar{c}_{4,2}}{\bar{c}_{4,0}} - \frac{\Delta \bar{c}_{5,2}}{\bar{c}_{5,0}} \qquad (6\text{-}156)$$

The relation for pre-equilibration is obtained by subtracting (6-150) from (6-155), giving

$$0 = \frac{\Delta \bar{c}_{2,2}}{\bar{c}_{2,0}} - \frac{\Delta \bar{c}_{3,2}}{\bar{c}_{3,0}} \qquad (6\text{-}157)$$

Except for (6-128) with $j = 2$, (6-138) is valid. One may now again solve for any available $\Delta \bar{c}_{l,2}$. Here it is only solved for $\Delta \bar{c}_{2,2}$, because of its relation to an investigated biochemical system (*4*).

One initially obtains from (6-128), (6-138), (6-156), and (6-157),

$$\frac{\Delta K_{6,5}}{K_{6,5}} = \frac{\Delta \bar{c}_{3,1}}{\bar{c}_{3,0}} + \frac{\Delta \bar{c}_{2,2}}{\bar{c}_{2,0}} [1 + (1 + K_{4,3})K_{6,5}(\bar{c}_{4,0} + \bar{c}_{5,0})] \qquad (6\text{-}158)$$

The necessary equation for $\Delta \bar{c}_{3,1}/\bar{c}_{3,0}$ is obtained from (6-152) with (6-151) and (4-141):

$$\frac{\Delta \bar{c}_{3,1}}{\bar{c}_{3,0}} = - \frac{\Delta K_{4,3}}{K_{4,3}} (1 + K_{3,4})^{-1} \qquad (6\text{-}159)$$

One may now combine (6-159) with (6-158) and solve for $\Delta \bar{c}_{2,2}/\bar{c}_{2,0}$:

$$\frac{\Delta \bar{c}_{2,2}}{\bar{c}_{2,0}} = \frac{(\Delta K_{6,5}/K_{6,5}) + (\Delta K_{4,3}/K_{4,3})(1 + K_{3,4})^{-1}}{1 + (1 + K_{4,3})K_{6,5}(\bar{c}_{4,0} + \bar{c}_{5,0})} \qquad (6\text{-}160)$$

One may again employ (4-149) and its alternative for $\bar{c}_{5,0}$. The analytical condition $c_5^0 \gg c_4^0$ gives directly

$$\frac{\Delta \bar{c}_{2,2}}{\bar{c}_{2,0}} = \frac{(\Delta K_{6,5}/K_{6,5}) + (\Delta K_{4,3}/K_{4,3})(1 + K_{3,4})^{-1}}{1 + (1 + K_{4,3})K_{6,5}c_5^0} \qquad (6\text{-}161)$$

Also employing (4-153) leads to

$$\frac{\Delta \bar{c}_{2,2}}{c_4^0} = \frac{(\Delta K_{6,5}/K_{6,5}) + (\Delta K_{4,3}/K_{4,3})(1 + K_{3,4})^{-1}}{1 + (1 + K_{4,3})K_{6,5}c_5^0} \frac{c_5^0}{K_0 + c_5^0} \qquad (6\text{-}162)$$

As c_5^0 becomes very large, the right side of (6-162) vanishes. As c_5^0 becomes very small, the right side of (6-162) vanishes also. Upon determining the extremum of (6-162), one obtains at the maximum relative signal change $\Delta \bar{c}_{2,2}/c_4^0$ a value for c_5^0 of

$$(c_5^0)_{\Delta\max} = \left(\frac{K_{5,6}K_0}{1 + K_{4,3}} \right)^{1/2} \tag{6-163}$$

If $K_{2,1} \ll 1$, (6-163) may be simplified to $c_5^0 = K_{5,6}(1 + K_{4,3})^{-1}$, as one realizes upon inspection of (4-151).

3. The basic equations for the slowest relaxation process are

$$\frac{\Delta K_{2,1}}{K_{2,1}} = \frac{\Delta \bar{c}_{1,3}}{\bar{c}_{1,0}} - \frac{\Delta \bar{c}_{2,1} + \Delta \bar{c}_{2,2} + \Delta \bar{c}_{2,3}}{\bar{c}_{2,0}} \tag{6-164}$$

$$\frac{\Delta K_{4,3}}{K_{4,3}} = \frac{\Delta \bar{c}_{2,1} + \Delta \bar{c}_{2,2} + \Delta \bar{c}_{2,3}}{\bar{c}_{2,0}} - \frac{\Delta \bar{c}_{3,1} + \Delta \bar{c}_{3,2} + \Delta \bar{c}_{3,3}}{\bar{c}_{3,0}} \tag{6-165}$$

$$\frac{\Delta K_{6,5}}{K_{6,5}} = \frac{\Delta \bar{c}_{3,1} + \Delta \bar{c}_{3,2} + \Delta \bar{c}_{3,3}}{\bar{c}_{3,0}} - \frac{\Delta \bar{c}_{4,2} + \Delta \bar{c}_{4,3}}{\bar{c}_{4,0}} - \frac{\Delta \bar{c}_{5,2} + \Delta \bar{c}_{5,3}}{\bar{c}_{5,0}} \tag{6-166}$$

Subtracting (6-155) and (6-150) from (6-165) and (6-166), respectively, yields the condition of pre-equilibration:

$$0 = \frac{\Delta \bar{c}_{2,3}}{\bar{c}_{2,0}} - \frac{\Delta \bar{c}_{3,3}}{\bar{c}_{3,0}} \tag{6-167}$$

$$0 = \frac{\Delta \bar{c}_{3,3}}{\bar{c}_{3,0}} - \frac{\Delta \bar{c}_{4,3}}{\bar{c}_{4,0}} - \frac{\Delta \bar{c}_{5,3}}{\bar{c}_{5,0}} \tag{6-168}$$

Equations (6-128) and (6-129), in conjunction with (6-164), (6-167), and (6-168), may then be used to solve for any $\Delta \bar{c}_{i,3}$. Here $\Delta \bar{c}_{2,3}$ is used again, giving

$$\frac{\Delta K_{2,1}}{K_{2,1}} = - \frac{\Delta \bar{c}_{2,1}}{\bar{c}_{2,0}} - \frac{\Delta \bar{c}_{2,2}}{\bar{c}_{2,0}} - \frac{\Delta \bar{c}_{2,3}}{\bar{c}_{2,0}} \left[1 + K_{1,2}\left(1 + K_{3,4}\left\langle 1 + \frac{K_{5,6}}{\bar{c}_4 + \bar{c}_5} \right\rangle \right) \right] \tag{6-169}$$

One may now employ (6-152) and (6-160) to obtain only the relative concentration change attributable to the third relaxation process and observed via component Y_2. One may then solve for $\Delta \bar{c}_{2,3}/\bar{c}_{2,0}$, which is avoided here because of the complexity of the expression. The analytical conditions $c_4^0 = c_5^0$ and $c_4^0 \ll c_5^0$ allow some simplification.

3. There is a third possibility, with the right (bimolecular) step being the slowest one. Also, for this case, one may employ two conditions: Either the step involving $K_{2,1}$ is fastest or the step involving $K_{4,3}$ is fastest. The extensive set of computations, proceeding quite along the lines of Section 6-3B2a and b, is avoided here. If $K_{2,1}$ represents the equilibrium constant of the fastest step, the conservation law of the step gives

$$\Delta \bar{c}_{1,1} + \Delta \bar{c}_{2,1} = 0 \qquad (6\text{-}170)$$

If, on the other hand, the equilibrium constant of the fastest step is given by $K_{4,3}$, its conservation law gives

$$\Delta \bar{c}_{2,1} + \Delta \bar{c}_{3,1} = 0 \qquad (6\text{-}171)$$

These equations, in conjunction with the $\Delta K_{i+1,i}/K_{i+1,i}$, lead to the relative concentration change for the fastest steps.

PROBLEMS

1. Derive (6-5) and establish the intermediary steps to reach (6-4).
2. If $y = [1 + 4(c_1^0 + c_3^0)K_{2,1}{}^{-1}]^{-1/2}$, determine $\partial^2 y / \partial (c_1^0 + c_3^0)^2$; set this second derivative equal to zero and solve for $(c_1^0 + c_3^0)$. Discuss the result [compare with (6-8)].
3. Derive (6-19) in detail.
4. Derive (6-24) in detail.
5. Set up the requirements for a system with $K_{2,1} = 1000$ and employment of (6-22).
6. Similar to 5, but employ (6-25); compare the two results and discuss feasibility.
7. Derive the equation for $\Delta \bar{c}_D / \bar{c}_D$ from (6-29) plus (6-26) and starting directly with (6-26) and (6-27).
8. Derive (6-74), (6-76), and (6-77) directly from (6-70) to (6-73).
9. Derive (6-76) from (6-74) with (6-73), and (6-77) from (6-76) with (6-70).
10. Plot (6-78), (6-81), and (6-82), with $c_2^0 / K_{2,1}$ as the independent variable, $K_{4,3} = 2$, and $\Delta K_{4,3}/K_{4,3} = \Delta K_{2,1}/K_{2,1} = 0.10$.
11. Plot (6-83) and (6-84) with $c_2^0 / K_{2,1}$ as the independent variable, $K_{4,3} = 2$, and $\Delta K_{4,3}/K_{4,3} = \Delta K_{2,1}/K_{2,1} = 0.10$.
12. Plot (6-93), (6-94), and (6-95), and (6-96) with $c_2^0 / K_{2,1}$ as the independent variable, $K_{4,3} = 2$, and $\Delta K_{4,3}/K_{4,3} = \Delta K_{2,1}/K_{2,1} = 0.10$. Compare these curves with the corresponding ones from Problems 10 and 11.
13. Derive an expression similar to (6-106) and (6-116) for the case that the right step in system (3-171) is slowest and the middle one is fastest.
14. Obtain $\Delta \bar{c}_{4,2}/\bar{c}_{4,0}$ from (6-128), (6-138), (6-156), and (6-157). Then derive and discuss $\Delta \bar{c}_{4,3}/c_4^0$ for $c_4^0 = c_5^0$ and for $c_4^0 \ll c_5^0$.
15. Employ (6-155), (6-156), (6-165), and (6-166) to solve for $\Delta \bar{c}_{4,3}/\bar{c}_{4,0}$.
16. Determine all three relative concentration changes $\Delta \bar{c}_{2,j}/\bar{c}_{2,0}$ for the case with the bimolecular step as the slowest one and (6-170), giving the conservation law of the fastest step.
17. Determine the three $\Delta \bar{c}_{2,j}/\bar{c}_{2,0}$ for the case with the bimolecular step the slowest one and (6-171) giving the conservation law of the fastest step.

REFERENCES

1. G. Czerlinski, *J. Theoret. Biol.*, **7**, 435 (1964).
2. G. Czerlinski, *J. Theoret. Biol.*, **7**, 463 (1964), specifically by Eq. (8-9).
3. G. Czerlinski, *J. Theoret. Biol.*, **7**, 478 (1964).
4. G. Czerlinski and J. Malkewitz, *Biochemistry*, **4**, 1127 (1965).

CHAPTER 7

SELECTED SYSTEMS

7-1. MEASURED SIGNAL CHANGES (EXTENDED THERMO-DYNAMICS)

A. General Aspects

In Chapter 2 the total measured signal change of an isolated relaxation process was defined by (2-48). If there are two or more relaxation processes involved, one has to introduce a second index j, referring to the jth relaxation process. Equation (2-48) then has to be extended to

$$\Delta \bar{S}_T = \sum_j \sum_i \eta_i \, \Delta \bar{c}_{i,j} \qquad (7\text{-}1)$$

This equation contains a number of restrictions. $\Delta \bar{S}_T$ represents the *total* equilibrium signal change of the system. The right side is positive only for concentration changes, which are observed in fluorescence. The right side becomes negative, if changes in transmission are observed. This sign is contained in the definition of η_i [and therefore does not appear in (7.1)], as was shown in Chapter 4, especially by (4-6). Equation (4-6) also shows another very important feature of η_i: that value of η_i has to be chosen which corresponds to $\bar{c}_{i,0} = $ the equilibrium concentration of the ith component present in solution just before the onset of the relaxation processes. The "specific signal" η_i becomes only concentration-independent for sufficiently low values of $\bar{c}_{i,0}$, where (4-7) is valid. There is a linearization contained in (7-1) which will be discussed later. Here only optical detection is considered, and $\Delta \bar{S}_T$ therefore refers only to detection of changes in transmission or in fluorescence. The means to perform such a detection (efficiently) are discussed in detail in Chapter 9. Equation (7-1) also contains conditions (2-10) and (2-21), although the latter equation does not need to be fulfilled, if *only* total equilibrium signal changes are considered.

However, (2-21) must be fulfilled [in the neighborhood (within about a factor of 30 up and down) of the time range under observation], if the total signal change *at a particular instant* $= \Delta S_T$ is considered. For this time-dependent change, (7-1) has to be extended to

$$\Delta S_T = \sum_j \sum_i \eta_i \, \Delta \bar{c}_{i,j} \exp(-t/\tau_j) \qquad (7\text{-}2)$$

The time-dependent ΔS_T would then describe the whole time course of the signal change [requiring also fulfillment of condition (2-21) over the same wide time range]. The expanded form of (7-2) with an upper limit of $j = 2$ was given previously as (8-1) of Ref. *1*. Equation (7-2) may also be considered the generalized form of a combination of (1) with (8') of Ref. *2*.

One may also consider an individual relaxation step, say, the *j*th with its time-dependent signal change ΔS_j :

$$\Delta S_j = \sum_i \eta_i \, \Delta \bar{c}_{i,j} \exp(-t/\tau_j) \qquad (7\text{-}3)$$

For this individual equation to be fulfilled, it is only necessary that

$$\tau_{j-1} \ll \tau_j \ll \tau_{j+1} \qquad (7\text{-}4)$$

The relations among any $\tau_p < \tau_{j-1}$ and any $\tau_q > \tau_{j+1}$ are unimportant for the validity of (7-3) (with the understanding that a relaxation time with a smaller index is always smaller than a relaxation time with a larger index). Largest is the *equilibrium* signal change of the *j*th relaxation process $(|\Delta S_j| < |\Delta \bar{S}_j|)$, given by

$$\Delta \bar{S}_j = \sum_i \eta_i \, \Delta \bar{c}_{i,j} \qquad (7\text{-}5)$$

One directly sees that (7-1) may be rewritten

$$\Delta \bar{S}_T = \sum \Delta \bar{S}_j \qquad (7\text{-}6)$$

The individual $\Delta \bar{S}_j$ may be large or small, positive or negative, resulting in a $\Delta \bar{S}_T$ which may be larger or smaller than individual $\Delta \bar{S}_j$ (in absolute amount). But $\Delta \bar{S}_T$ should still be small compared to the signal $S_0 - S_T$, which is fulfilled for small perturbations of the system.

Equation (7-5) will now be used to demonstrate a linearization which is contained in its presented form. At the beginning we set $j = 1$ and rewrite (4-5) as

$$\frac{\bar{S}_T - S_0}{S_0} = \exp[-l \sum \varepsilon_i \bar{c}_{i,0}] - 1 \qquad (7\text{-}7)$$

After the first relaxation process, (7-7) becomes

$$\frac{\bar{S}_T + \Delta\bar{S}_1 - S_0}{S_0} = \exp[-l \sum \varepsilon_i(\bar{c}_{i,0} + \Delta\bar{c}_{i,1})] - 1 \qquad (7\text{-}8)$$

One may easily solve for $\Delta\bar{S}_1$, by writing the difference

$$(\bar{S}_T + \Delta\bar{S}_1) - \bar{S}_T = S_0\left\{\exp\left[-l \sum \varepsilon_i\bar{c}_{i,0}\left(1 + \frac{\Delta\bar{c}_{i,1}}{\bar{c}_{i,0}}\right)\right] - \exp[-l \sum \varepsilon_i\bar{c}_{i,0}]\right\}$$
$$(7\text{-}9)$$

This equation may easily be simplified to give

$$\Delta\bar{S}_1 = \bar{S}_T\{\exp[-l \sum \varepsilon_i \, \Delta\bar{c}_{i,1}] - 1\} \qquad (7\text{-}10)$$

The exponential may now be expanded, and, upon doing so, one has to consider two cases.

1. The exponent is much smaller than unity, $l\sum \varepsilon_i \, \Delta\bar{c}_{i,1} \ll 1$. Under such conditions, one may omit any terms in the expansion which are higher than the linear ones. This simplification results in

$$\Delta\bar{S}_1 = -\bar{S}_T l \sum \varepsilon_i \, \Delta\bar{c}_{i,1} \qquad (7\text{-}11)$$

Comparison of (7-5) and (7-11) gives

$$\eta_i = -\bar{S}_T l\varepsilon_i \qquad (7\text{-}12)$$

The signal $\bar{S}_T$ in (7-12) does not need to carry a second index i. This omission becomes quite evident also by a comparison of (7-12) with (4-6), which is based on definition (4-4).

2. The exponent in (7-10) is *not* much smaller than unity. As an evaluation under such circumstances is much more difficult than in the previous case, it is advisable to investigate the probability of its occurrence.

Detection devices for chemical relaxation experiments are now capable of measuring on a background optical density of 3. A maximum concentration change of 10 per cent would then lead to an optical density change of 0.3, which corresponds to a change of the transmitted signal of 50 per cent! Certainly such a change can no longer be considered small. A signal change of about 10 per cent could be considered small which allows one to measure safely on background optical densities of 1.

Experimentally the principal point of concern is that the first term in (7-10) is still reasonably close to unity, say, within about 10 per cent. One realizes then from (7-10) that the condition for its linearization is given by

$$\Delta\bar{S}_j \ll \bar{S}_T \qquad (7\text{-}13)$$

with $j = 1$ to apply to (7-10). Condition (7-13) means that any $\Delta \bar{S}_j$ should not exceed 10 per cent of S_T. But, certainly, also, ΔS_T should at no time exceed 10 per cent of S_T.

If the fundamental condition (7-13) is not fulfilled, one has to form the logarithm to obtain proportionality. One obtains from (7-10), upon proper conversion,

$$\log \frac{\bar{S}_T}{\bar{S}_T + \Delta \bar{S}_1} = \sum \eta_i' \, \Delta \bar{c}_{i,1} \tag{7-14}$$

The relation between η_i and η_i' is easily derived from the definition for η_i' :

$$\eta_i' = l \varepsilon_i / 2.3 \tag{7-15}$$

As ε_i is the natural extinction coefficient, $\varepsilon_i/2.3$ is the decadic extinction coefficient. One obtains from (7-12) and (7-15) the relationship for linearized conditions,

$$\eta_i = -2.3 S_T \eta_i' \tag{7-16}$$

Equation (7-16) is not applicable when (7-14) has to be used [as a result of the nonfulfillment of condition (7-13)].

Nonfulfillment of condition (7-13) has quite an impact on the way in which the chemical relaxation time constants are evaluated. As long as condition (7-13) is fulfilled, ΔS_j is proportional to some concentration change (assuming for the moment that one η_i is much larger than any other one). One may then directly evaluate τ_j from the oscilloscope trace of the transmitted signal change. If condition (7-13) is not fulfilled, one has to convert the oscilloscope trace into a trace, which represents the time change in optical density. This means for the time change of the first relaxation process a slight modification of (7-14), assuming again that

$$\eta_i \gg \eta_{k \neq i} \tag{7-17}$$

The time-dependent form is then

$$\log \frac{\bar{S}_T}{\bar{S}_T + \Delta S_1} = \eta_i' \, \Delta c_{i,1} \tag{7-18}$$

A plot of $\Delta c_{i,1}$ versus t would then allow direct evaluation of τ_1.

Considering now that jth relaxation process, one may alter (7-10) to the more general form

$$\Delta \bar{S}_j = \bar{S}_T' \{ \exp[-l \sum \varepsilon_i \, \Delta \bar{c}_{i,j}] - 1 \} \tag{7-19}$$

The more generalized S_T' is defined by

$$\bar{S}_T' = \bar{S}_T + \sum_{k=1}^{j-1} \Delta \bar{S}_k \tag{7-20}$$

The more generalized S'_T would then also have to be used in (7-11), (7-12), (7-14), and (7-18). The difference between S_T and S'_T would have a particularly large effect on the evaluation of (7-14) and (7-18), whereas the correction is generally negligible for the other equations. As (7-18) is particularly important for an exact experimental evaluation, its generalized form will be repeated:

$$\log \frac{\overline{S'_T}}{\overline{S'_T} + \Delta S_j} = \eta'_i \, \Delta c_{i,j} \qquad (7-21)$$

Equation (7-20) defines $\overline{S'_T}$ = the actual (total) equilibrium signal reached, just before the jth relaxation process enters its time course.

B. Specific Aspects

Section 7-1A dealt primarily with those aspects which deal with the individual relaxation processes [and thus with index j]. In this section, differences among the individual η_i will be investigated.

1. ONLY ONE INDICATING SPECIES. This is the ideal case, which one should always attempt to approach as closely as possible. The condition is expressed in mathematical form by relation (7-17). Any summation over i is then no longer necessary; one obtains thus from the refined equation (4-3),

$$\bar{S}_T - S_0 = \eta_i \bar{c}_{i,0} \qquad (7-22)$$

The ratio of the simplified equation (7-5) and of (7-22) gives directly

$$\frac{\Delta \bar{S}_j}{\bar{S}_T - S_0} = \frac{\Delta \bar{c}_{i,j}}{\bar{c}_{i,0}} \qquad (7-23)$$

This equation then relates directly to the individual quotients of Chapter 6.

Equation (7-23) is only valid in its full sense if $\bar{S}_T$ is near S_0 (for transmission experiments, this linearity problem is somewhat less severe if detection of fluorescence is used and the solution is always poorly absorbing the exciting light). A "linearized" form of (7-23) may still be used for $\bar{S}_T \geqslant 0.1 S_0$. If $\bar{S}_T \geqslant 0.1 S_0$, one may employ the following substitution for (7-23):

$$(\bar{S}_T - S_0)_{\text{lin}} = \eta_i \bar{c}_{i,0} \qquad (7-24)$$

with η_i defined *only* by (4-7). Equation (7-24) requires a knowledge of η_i according to (4-7) and the knowledge of the value for $\bar{c}_{i,0}$. This knowledge is generally available after the kinetics has been fully resolved (Chapters 1 through 5).

If linearization is not possible or not wanted, one has to employ the generalized form of (7-14), which is

$$\log \frac{\overline{S_T'}}{\overline{S_T'} + \Delta \overline{S}_j} = \eta_i' \Delta \bar{c}_{i,j} \tag{7-25}$$

In addition, one has to employ the decadic logarithm of the refined equation (4-5), which is

$$\log \frac{S_0}{\overline{S}_T} = \eta_i' \bar{c}_{i,0} \tag{7-26}$$

One realizes immediately that the quotient of (7-25) and (7-26) results in the right side of (7-23), again permitting direct access to the equations of Chapter 6.

There exists one problem if only one species is indicating. The indicating species should be a component which participates in the fastest step and is kinetically connected to all other reaction steps. This condition is certainly not always met. This condition can actually never be fulfilled, when a slow step separates two (or more) fast steps. Under such circumstances there is no possibility of determining the reaction enthalpies of all individual steps (for the temperature-jump method, as an example). This is directly visible from the expressions of Section 6-3. It is then desirable to have more than one η_i much larger than all others. In optical detection one fortunately has the wavelength as an additional parameter. One should then attempt to approach condition (7-17) for each component at a particular wavelength.

2. TWO INDICATING SPECIES WITH OVERLAP. The overlap refers to the properties at a particular wavelength. If one could find wavelength regions where one η_i is much larger than any other $\eta_{k \neq i}$, one should follow the treatment of the previous section. It is assumed for this treatment that there will be overlap at any reasonable wavelength. To complicate the problem further, it is also assumed that the two indicating components participate in the same reaction. One may then differentiate among the following cases with only linearized conditions treated.

a. The monomolecular interconversion. Equation (7-5) becomes with (2-50) and $j = 1$,

$$\Delta \overline{S}_i = (\eta_1 - \eta_2) \Delta \bar{c}_{1,1} \tag{7-27}$$

The measurable signal change $\Delta \overline{S}_1$ is the smaller the more η_2 approaches η_1. If this monomolecular reaction would be connected to a bimolecular step, the equality $\eta_1 = \eta_2$ would not need to make measurements impossible. One has to distinguish two conditions.

1. The Monomolecular Step is Much Faster than the Bimolecular One: The monomolecular interconversion could not be detected, but the bimolecular one could.

2. The Bimolecular Step is much Faster than the Monomolecular One: The bimolecular step could always be detected, the monomolecular one only in a limited concentration range; under equilibrium conditions, where (2-50) is fulfilled for practical purposes (the third $\Delta\bar{c}$ is negligibly small compared to $\Delta\bar{c}_1$ and $\Delta\bar{c}_2$), Eq. (7-27) would give the equilibrium signal change (with $j = 1 \to j = 2$) and $\eta_1 = \eta_2$ would make detection impossible.

b. The bimolecular reaction. With $j = 1$ it is assumed that $\eta_2 = 0$. One then obtains with the equilibrium version of (3-5), together with (7-5),

$$\Delta\bar{S}_1 = (\eta_1 - \eta_3)\Delta\bar{c}_{1,1} \tag{7-28}$$

This equation us quite similar to (7-27), and quite similar considerations as there are also valid here.

c. The "transfer" reaction. This is the four-component reaction with $j = 1$ and originally defined according to (1-30). The two components with overlapping characteristics for indication are generally on opposite sides of the reaction; Y_1 and Y_4 are here chosen as these components. This condition was already chosen behind (4-37) by setting $\eta_2 = \eta_3 = 0$. The equilibrium versions of (2-13) and (2-14) give

$$\Delta\bar{c}_{1,1} = -\Delta\bar{c}_{4,1} \tag{7-29}$$

Equation (7-5) thus becomes

$$\Delta\bar{S}_1 = (\eta_1 - \eta_4)\Delta\bar{c}_{1,1} \tag{7-30}$$

This equation is again quite similar to (7-27), and here quite similar considerations are valid as there.

3. Experimental cases of components with overlapping characteristics are reported in the literature (*3,4*). It is also shown there how to handle systems which show considerable similarity in the indicating characteristics of some components.

7-2. KINETICS OF BUFFERED CYCLIC SYSTEMS

A. Introduction

Historically, the workers in the field of chemical relaxation encountered cyclic systems quite early. The first system, investigated with the temperature-jump method, actually contained two cycles [Eq. (24) of Ref. *2*]. A system which possibly contains only a single cycle was investigated quite recently (5). In a related biochemical system, the presence of two cycles was also considered (6). These more complicated systems are considered here separately because of their biological importance. These systems were not treated in previous chapters, and they will only be treated here under the buffering condition.

B. One Cycle and Six Components

1. This chemical system was already treated for the unbuffered condition and is represented by (3-219). In the treatment of (3-219), the reactions involving component Y_5 were considered the much more rapid ones. They are now considered here as the buffered reactions. The slowest relaxation time is of interest here only, which is τ_3 for this system. This derivation will be compared to a considerable extent with that of Chapter 3, following (3-219).

Relations (3-220) and (3-222) are fully valid for a buffered system. However, relations (3-221) and (3-226) are no longer valid at all. Although $\Delta \bar{\bar{c}}_5 = 0$ for all practical purposes, stoichiometry is "violated," owing to the presence of the buffering component. The concentration change Δc_5, which in (3-221) would have to be replaced by Δc_{05}, indicated the amount of Y_5 transferred "onto the buffering component." Fortunately, such a stoichiometric equation is not necessary. Equation (3-226) is invalid for similar reasons.

The differential equations (3-223) and (3-224) are again zero by postulating rapid buffering. Under such circumstances it is certainly $\Delta \bar{\bar{c}}_5 = 0$, and these two equations give very simple relations among four concentration changes,

$$\Delta c_1 = K_{5,6}\bar{\bar{c}}_5 \, \Delta c_2 \tag{7-31}$$

$$\Delta c_4 = K_{3,4}\bar{\bar{c}}_5 \, \Delta c_3 \tag{7-32}$$

Two bars above a concentration symbol again indicate its proper buffering.

Now combining (7-31) and (7-32) with (3-220) and (3-222) gives

$$\Delta c_3 = -\Delta c_6 \, \frac{K_{4,3}}{K_{4,3} + \bar{\bar{c}}_5} \tag{7-33}$$

$$\Delta c_4 = -\Delta c_6 \, \frac{\bar{\bar{c}}_5}{K_{4,3} + \bar{\bar{c}}_5} \tag{7-34}$$

$$\Delta c_2 = \Delta c_6 \, \frac{K_{6,5}}{K_{6,5} + \bar{\bar{c}}_5} \tag{7-35}$$

$$\Delta c_1 = \Delta c_6 \, \frac{\bar{\bar{c}}_5}{K_{6,5} + \bar{\bar{c}}_5} \tag{7-36}$$

These four equations may now quite easily be combined with (3-225), resulting in the differential equation

$$\frac{d\Delta c_6}{dt} = -\frac{\Delta c_6}{\tau_3} \tag{7-37}$$

with

$$\tau_3^{-1} = k_2 \frac{K_{4,3}}{K_{4,3} + \bar{c}_5} + k_8 \frac{\bar{c}_5}{K_{4,3} + \bar{c}_5} + k_1\left(\bar{c}_2 + \bar{c}_6 \frac{K_{6,5}}{K_{6,5} + \bar{c}_5}\right)$$

$$+ k_7\left(\bar{c}_1 + \bar{c}_6 \frac{\bar{c}_5}{K_{6,5} + \bar{c}_5}\right) \tag{7-38}$$

A similarity between (7-38) and (3-261) is immediately apparent. But there is considerable difference between the coefficients in (7-38) and those in (3-261), represented by the four equations (3-244), (3-245), (3-252), and (3-253).

These coefficients α, β, α', and β' certainly would become considerably simplified under the condition of buffering, whereby the concentrations $\bar{c}_2$ and $\bar{c}_3$ are "made to become negligible." The impact of this "diminution" will now be shown stepwise for the individual coefficients.

Equation (3-244) may also be written

$$\alpha = \frac{K_{4,3}\bar{c}_2 + K_{6,5}(K_{4,3} + \bar{c}_3 + \bar{c}_5)}{(\bar{c}_2 + \bar{c}_5 + K_{6,5})(\bar{c}_3 + \bar{c}_5 + K_{4,3}) - \bar{c}_2\bar{c}_3} \tag{7-39}$$

The "first impact of buffering" leads to

$$\alpha \rightarrow \frac{(K_{4,3} + \bar{c}_5)K_{6,5} + K_{4,3}\bar{c}_2}{(K_{4,3} + \bar{c}_5)(K_{6,5} + \bar{c}_5) - \bar{c}_2\bar{c}_3} \tag{7-40}$$

Under "adequate" buffering conditions the second terms in the numerator and denominator of (7-40) become negligibly small, leading to further simplification and resulting in the coefficient of $k_1\bar{c}_6$ of (7-38).

The above argumentation concerning buffering may also follow another line: Strong buffering causes $\bar{c}_5$ to appear quite large, leading to a virtual disappearance of the first term in the numerator of (3-244) and of the second term in the denominator of (3-244). This virtual disappearance changes (3-244) initially to

$$\alpha \rightarrow \frac{K_{6,5}}{K_{6,5} + \bar{c}_5 + \bar{c}_2} \tag{7-41}$$

Remembering the effect of buffering upon $\bar{c}_2$ in (7-41) results again in the proper coefficient of $k_1\bar{c}_6$ in (7-38).

This second procedure of simplification seems more lucid and will therefore be employed further on. The second term in the numerator and the second term in the denominator of (3-245) become negligibly small, owing to the virtually quite large appearance of $\bar{c}_5$ by buffering. One obtains initially

$$\beta \to \frac{K_{4,3}}{K_{4,5} + \bar{c}_5 + \bar{c}_3} \tag{7-42}$$

Buffering leads to $\bar{c}_3 \to 0$ and to the coefficient of k_2 in (7-38).

Equation (3-252) will now be considered. The concentration $\bar{c}_5$ is quite large because of buffering. This causes the first term in the numerator to become effectively unity, while the second term becomes much larger than unity. Relatively large $\bar{c}_5$ causes the first term in the denominator to become much larger than unity, while the second term becomes much smaller than unity. Equation (3-252) thus reduces initially to

$$\alpha' \to \frac{\bar{c}_5}{K_{6,5} + \bar{c}_5 + \bar{c}_3} \tag{7-43}$$

If $\bar{c}_5 \to \bar{c}_5$, then also $\bar{c}_3 \to 0$, which gives the coefficient of $k_7\bar{c}_6$ of (7-38). This coefficient appears thus again (as it should and all four of them do) at the place where one would expect it according to (3-261).

The fourth coefficient is originally defined by (3-253). The virtually large magnitude of $\bar{c}_5$ causes the following relations in (3-253):

$$\frac{\bar{c}_5}{\bar{c}_3} \gg \frac{\bar{c}_5}{K_{6,5} + \bar{c}_5 + \bar{c}_2} \tag{7-44}$$

$$\frac{K_{4,3} + \bar{c}_5 + \bar{c}_3}{\bar{c}_3} \gg \frac{\bar{c}_2}{K_{6,5} + \bar{c}_5 + \bar{c}_2} \tag{7-45}$$

These relations simplify (3-253) to

$$\beta' \to \frac{\bar{c}_5}{K_{4,3} + \bar{c}_5 + \bar{c}_3} \tag{7-46}$$

One obtains $\bar{c}_3 \to 0$ for $\bar{c}_5 \to \bar{c}_5$ and thus results the coefficient of k_8 in (7-38).

Summarizing, one realizes then that the buffering condition for component Y_5 actually reduces the complex form of (3-261) to the relatively simple form of (7-38). On the other hand, (7-38) still contains equilibrium concentrations which should be replaced by analytical concentrations.

2. EMPLOYMENT OF ANALYTICAL CONCENTRATIONS.

a. Without further restriction. Equation (7-38) contains three equilibrium concentrations, and one has thus to find three different equations for them. These expressions for $\bar{c}_1$, $\bar{c}_2$, and $\bar{c}_6$ are obtainable from the definitions

$$K_{2,1} \equiv \frac{k_2}{k_1} = \frac{\bar{c}_2 \bar{c}_6}{\bar{c}_3} \tag{7-47}$$

$$K_{4,3} \equiv \frac{k_4}{k_3} = \frac{\bar{c}_3 \bar{c}_5}{\bar{c}_4} \tag{7-48}$$

$$K_{6,5} \equiv \frac{k_6}{k_5} = \frac{\bar{c}_2 \bar{c}_5}{\bar{c}_1} \tag{7-49}$$

$$c_6^0 = \bar{c}_6 + \bar{c}_3 + \bar{c}_4 \tag{7-50}$$

$$c_1^0 = \bar{c}_1 + \bar{c}_2 + \bar{c}_3 + \bar{c}_4 \tag{7-51}$$

The definition for $K_{8,7}$ cannot be used, as $K_{8,7}$ is a function of $K_{2,1}$, $K_{4,3}$, and $K_{6,5}$ and is fully determined by them. There are five unknown equilibrium concentrations and five equations. One may thus solve for any one of the equilibrium concentrations. The solution proceeds via a quadratic equation, and one obtains

$$\bar{c}_1 = -\frac{a_1}{2}\left\{1 \pm \left\langle 1 + \frac{4b_1}{a_1^2}\right\rangle^{1/2}\right\} \tag{7-52}$$

with

$$a_1 = K_{2,1} \frac{1 + \dfrac{\bar{c}_5}{K_{6,5}} + \dfrac{c_6^0 - c_1^0}{K_{2,1}}\left(1 + \dfrac{\bar{c}_5}{K_{4,3}}\right)}{\left(1 + \dfrac{K_{6,5}}{\bar{c}_5}\right)\left(1 + \dfrac{\bar{c}_5}{K_{4,3}}\right)} \tag{7-53}$$

and

$$b_1 = \frac{K_{2,1} c_1^0 \dfrac{\bar{c}_5}{K_{6,5}}}{\left(1 + \dfrac{\bar{c}_5}{K_{4,3}}\right)\left(1 + \dfrac{K_{6,5}}{\bar{c}_5}\right)} \tag{7-54}$$

$$\bar{c}_2 = -\frac{a_2}{2}\left(1 \pm \left\langle 1 + \frac{4b_2}{a_2^2}\right\rangle^{1/2}\right) \tag{7-55}$$

with

$$a_2 = K_{2,1} \frac{1 + \dfrac{\bar{c}_5}{K_{6,5}} + \dfrac{c_6^0 - c_1^0}{K_{2,1}}\left(1 + \dfrac{\bar{c}_5}{K_{4,3}}\right)}{\left(1 + \dfrac{\bar{c}_5}{K_{6,5}}\right)\left(1 + \dfrac{\bar{c}_5}{K_{4,3}}\right)} \tag{7-56}$$

and

$$b_2 = \frac{K_{2,1}c_1^0}{\left(1 + \dfrac{\bar{c}_5}{K_{6,5}}\right)\left(1 + \dfrac{\bar{c}_5}{K_{4,3}}\right)} \tag{7-57}$$

$$\bar{c}_6 = c_6^0 - c_1^0 + \bar{c}_1\left(1 + \frac{K_{6,5}}{\bar{c}_5}\right) \tag{7-58}$$

These expressions for the three equilibrium concentrations may now be inserted. They would lead to an expression for τ_3^{-1} which is quite impractical to handle.

One way to avoid complex expressions is to employ the analytical condition $c_1^0 = c_6^0$. With this condition, one obtains the following simplifications:

$$a_1 \rightarrow \frac{K_{2,1}\bar{c}_5/K_{6,5}}{1 + \bar{c}_5/K_{4,3}} \tag{7-59}$$

$$a_2 \rightarrow \frac{K_{2,1}}{1 + \bar{c}_5/K_{4,3}} \tag{7-60}$$

$$\bar{c}_6 \rightarrow \bar{c}_1(1 + K_{6,5}/\bar{c}_5) \tag{7-61}$$

$$\bar{c}_6 \rightarrow \bar{c}_2(1 + \bar{c}_5/K_{6,5}) \tag{7-62}$$

This latter relation is obtained from (7-61) together with (7-49). Relations (7-61) and (7-62) simplify two terms in (7-38):

$$k_1\left(\bar{c}_2 + \bar{c}_6 \frac{K_{6,5}}{K_{6,5} + \bar{c}_5}\right) \rightarrow 2k_1\bar{c}_2 \tag{7-63}$$

$$k_7\left(\bar{c}_1 + \bar{c}_6 \frac{\bar{c}_5}{K_{6,5} + \bar{c}_5}\right) \rightarrow 2k_7\bar{c}_1 \tag{7-64}$$

In spite of these simplifications, the final result will contain two square roots, which cannot be eliminated (negative root valid for $c_1^0 = c_6^0$).

b. **With further restriction.** This further restriction is that of buffering component Y_6. Buffering alters (7-38) immediately to an expression in which $\bar{c}_1$ and $\bar{c}_2$ are eliminated,

$$\tau_3^{-1} = k_2 \frac{K_{4,3}}{K_{4,3} + \bar{c}_5} + k_8 \frac{\bar{c}_5}{K_{4,3} + \bar{c}_5} + \frac{\bar{c}_6}{K_{6,5} + \bar{c}_5}(k_1 K_{6,5} + k_7 \bar{c}_5) \quad (7\text{-}65)$$

This equation can be handled quite easily, but contains one problem, which was already mentioned in Chapter 5 when discussing the buffering of multistep reactions: Buffering of components which are directly involved in the reaction step under investigation obscures the actual mechanism. The buffering components themselves may enter into the mechanism. One would have to write, for instance, the following (alternative) mechanism for the reaction step involving Y_2 and Y_3:

$$Y_2 \underset{k_2}{\overset{k_1}{\rightleftharpoons}} Y_3 \atop \dot{Y}_7 \quad Y_8 \qquad (7\text{-}66)$$

The reaction step involving Y_1 and Y_4, would have to be changed correspondingly.

There is one approach left, which allows a simplified treatment of the mechanism. To use this approach, certain "internal conditions" of the system must be fulfilled. The basic condition actually follows from the discussions of (7-63) and (7-64), where only $c_1^0 = c_6^0$ was considered. The other possible experimental condition is $c_6^0 \gg c_1^0$. This condition simplifies (7-52) slightly to (7-58). But the investigation of the magnitude of certain ratios is important:

$$\frac{b_1}{a_1} \rightarrow \frac{c_1^0 \bar{c}_5 / K_{6,5}}{1 + \dfrac{\bar{c}_5}{K_{6,5}} + \dfrac{c_6^0}{K_{2,1}}\left(1 + \dfrac{\bar{c}_5}{K_{4,3}}\right)} \qquad (7\text{-}67)$$

$$\frac{b_2}{a_2} \rightarrow \frac{c_1^0}{1 + \dfrac{\bar{c}_5}{K_{6,5}} + \dfrac{c_6^0}{K_{2,1}}\left(1 + \dfrac{\bar{c}_5}{K_{4,3}}\right)} \qquad (7\text{-}68)$$

No further fundamental simplification is visible. Considerable further simplification is possible, however, if $c_1^0 \ll K_{2,1}$ leading to

$$\frac{b_1}{a_1^2} \ll 1 \quad \text{and} \quad \frac{b_2}{a_2^2} \ll 1 \qquad (7\text{-}69)$$

Conditions (7-69) allow expansion of both square roots and omission of terms higher than linear ones, leading to

$$\bar{c}_1 = \frac{b_1}{a_1} \quad \text{and} \quad \bar{c}_2 = \frac{b_2}{a_2} \tag{7-70}$$

The ratios are those of (7-67) and (7-68). It is evident from these equations that $\bar{c}_1$, $\bar{c}_2 < c_1^0$, which is to be expected from (7-51). Certainly the relation $\bar{c}_1$, $\bar{c}_2 < c_1^0$ is also valid for any size c_1^0 in relation to $K_{2,1}$. Equation (7-58) therefore simplifies to $\bar{c}_6 \to c_6^0$. And (7-38) thus becomes

$$\tau_3^{-1} = k_2 \frac{K_{4,3}}{K_{4,3} + \bar{c}_5} + k_8 \frac{\bar{c}_5}{K_{4,3} + \bar{c}_5} + k_1 c_6^0 \frac{K_{6,5}}{K_{6,5} + \bar{c}_5} + k_7 c_6^0 \frac{\bar{c}_5}{K_{6,5} + \bar{c}_5} \tag{7-71}$$

This equation is "almost identical" with (7-65). The major advantage of (7-71) over (7-65) is that (7-71) would give direct information in the mechanism. In the use of (7-65) as representing scheme (3-219), one would have to make sure that the mechanism does not contain any buffer catalysis [steps like those corresponding to (7.66)]. Equation (7-71) and its condition $c_6^0 \gg c_1^0$ is therefore of high importance for the evaluation of rate constants, belonging to mechanism (3-219).

C. Two Cycles and Eight Components

The system is represented by the scheme

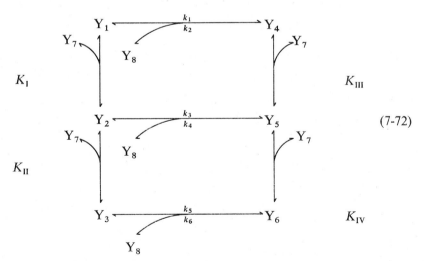

$$\tag{7-72}$$

The constants K_I, K_II, K_III, and K_IV are the dissociation constants of the rapid steps involving Y_7. The steps involving Y_8 are considered quite slow and are of major interest. This system contains five relaxation times. The first four relaxation times refer to reaction steps with Y_7 and are quite fast. The fifth relaxation time contains all remaining steps and thus all rate constants k_1 to k_6. But only two of these constants may actually be operative at a certain level of $\bar{c}_7$. As only the slowest step is of interest here, the component Y_7 may be buffered, denoted by $\bar{\bar{c}}_7$.

At this time it is advisable to discuss the deeper meaning of (7-31) and (7-32). These equations give the transfer relationships between the two coupled concentration changes. In (3-219), for instance, a certain amount of Y_2 may be generated. Equation (7-31) then gives the relationship with which this generated amount distributes among the two components. The buffered concentration $\bar{\bar{c}}_5$ offers there an "infinite" supply (or sink) of reactant. Such relations as in (7-31) exist certainly only in buffered pre-equilibria. There are four such pre-equilibria in (7-72), and one should therefore find four interrelations among the Δc_i.

One fast equilibrium is established by

$$\frac{d\Delta c_1}{dt} = -k_7(\bar{c}_1 \Delta c_7 + \bar{c}_7 \Delta c_1) + k_7 K_I \Delta c_2 \equiv 0 \qquad (7\text{-}73)$$

with $k_7 \equiv$ bimolecular rate constant in the conversion of Y_1 to Y_2. As $\Delta c_7 \equiv 0$ for practical purposes (which corresponds to adequate buffering), one obtains the interrelationship

$$\Delta c_2 = \frac{\bar{\bar{c}}_7}{K_I} \Delta c_1 \qquad (7\text{-}74)$$

In an analogous manner, one obtains the following additional inter-relationships:

$$\Delta c_3 = \frac{\bar{\bar{c}}_7}{K_{II}} \Delta c_2 \qquad (7\text{-}75)$$

$$\Delta c_5 = \frac{\bar{\bar{c}}_7}{K_{III}} \Delta c_4 \qquad (7\text{-}76)$$

$$\Delta c_6 = \frac{\bar{\bar{c}}_7}{K_{IV}} \Delta c_5 \qquad (7\text{-}77)$$

The concentration $\bar{\bar{c}}_7$ is determined by the buffer ratio. The system of (7-72) may then be established by mixing two components, which is formulated by

$$c_8^0 = \bar{c}_8 + \bar{c}_4 + \bar{c}_5 + \bar{c}_6 \qquad (7\text{-}78)$$

$$c_1^0 = \bar{c}_1 + \bar{c}_2 + \bar{c}_3 + \bar{c}_4 + \bar{c}_5 + \bar{c}_6 \qquad (7\text{-}79)$$

These two equations lead to the following relations among the concentration changes:

$$\Delta c_8 + \Delta c_4 + \Delta c_5 + \Delta c_6 = 0 \tag{7-80}$$

$$\Delta c_1 + \Delta c_2 + \Delta c_3 + \Delta c_4 + \Delta c_5 + \Delta c_6 = 0 \tag{7-81}$$

One differential equation may be written involving only those rate constants which are written out in system (7-72),

$$\frac{d\Delta c_8}{dt} = k_2\,\Delta c_4 + k_4\,\Delta c_5 + k_8\,\Delta c_6 - k_1(\bar{c}_1\,\Delta c_8 + \bar{c}_8\,\Delta c_1)$$

$$- k_3(\bar{c}_2\,\Delta c_8 + \bar{c}_8\,\Delta c_2) - k_5(\bar{c}_3\,\Delta c_8 + \bar{c}_8\,\Delta c_3) \tag{7-82}$$

There are seven Δc_i in (7-82), and seven independent equations among the Δc_i are available through (7-74), (7-75), (7-76), (7-77), (7-80), (7-81), and (7-82). One may thus solve for Δc_8, the variable of the differential equation. One then obtains

$$\frac{d\Delta c_8}{dt} = - \frac{\Delta c_8}{\tau_5} \tag{7-83}$$

with

$$\tau_5^{-1} = \left(k_6 + k_4\,\frac{K_{IV}}{\bar{c}_7} + k_2\,\frac{K_{III}K_{IV}}{(\bar{c}_7)^2}\right)\left(1 + \frac{K_{IV}}{\bar{c}_7} + \frac{K_{III}K_{IV}}{(\bar{c}_7)^2}\right)^{-1}$$

$$+ k_1\left[\bar{c}_1 + \bar{c}_8\left(1 + \frac{\bar{c}_7}{K_I} + \frac{(\bar{c}_7)^2}{K_I K_{II}}\right)^{-1}\right] + k_3\left[\bar{c}_2 + \bar{c}_8\left(1 + \frac{\bar{c}_7}{K_{II}} + \frac{K_I}{\bar{c}_7}\right)^{-1}\right]$$

$$+ k_5\left[\bar{c}_3 + \bar{c}_8\left(1 + \frac{K_{II}}{\bar{c}_7} + \frac{K_I K_{II}}{(\bar{c}_7)^2}\right)^{-1}\right] \tag{7-84}$$

The first term of this equation may also be divided into three individua terms. In the last three terms of (7-84) one important feature is immediately apparent: strong (enough, which means: overriding all unfavorable Y_7 effects) buffering of Y_8 would "wipe out" the other equilibrium concentrations, leading to

$$\tau_5^{-1} = k_6\left(1 + \frac{K_{IV}}{\bar{c}_7} + \frac{K_{III}K_{IV}}{(\bar{c}_7)^2}\right)^{-1} + k_2\left(1 + \frac{\bar{c}_7}{K_{III}} + \frac{(\bar{c}_7)^2}{K_{III}K_{IV}}\right)^{-1}$$

$$+ k_4\left(1 + \frac{\bar{c}_7}{K_{IV}} + \frac{K_{III}}{\bar{c}_7}\right)^{-1} + \left[k_1\left(1 + \frac{\bar{c}_7}{K_I} + \frac{(\bar{c}_7)^2}{K_I K_{II}}\right)^{-1}\right.$$

$$+ k_3\left(1 + \frac{\bar{c}_7}{K_{II}} + \frac{K_I}{\bar{c}_7}\right)^{-1} + \left. k_5\left(1 + \frac{K_{II}}{\bar{c}_7} + \frac{K_I K_{II}}{(\bar{c}_7)^2}\right)^{-1}\right]\bar{c}_8 \tag{7-85}$$

Equation (7-85) may be rewritten with $\bar{c}_8 \to c_8^0$, if $c_8^0 \gg c_1^0$, one of the analytical conditions for simplification, which *also* gives true kinetic results. If buffering is used as shown in (7-85), the problem of parallel reactions by the components of the buffer exists [any one of the reaction steps with Y_8 in (7-72) may have such a parallel reaction with buffer components]. Equation (7-85) is practically identical with Eq. (II.1.35) of Eigen (7).

One may also substitute analytical concentrations for $\bar{c}_1$, $\bar{c}_2$, $\bar{c}_3$, and $\bar{c}_8$ in (7-84), which is avoided here because of the complexity of the resulting equations. To find the expression for any $\bar{c}_i$, which contains only analytical concentrations, one has to use the definitions of the four dissociation constants involving $\bar{c}_7$, one equilibrium constant with $\bar{c}_8$ (the remaining two equilibrium constants with $\bar{c}_8$ are no longer independent!) and the two equations (7-78) and (7-79).

D. An Asymmetric Bicyclic System

This system also contains eight components and two cycles, but is asymmetric according to

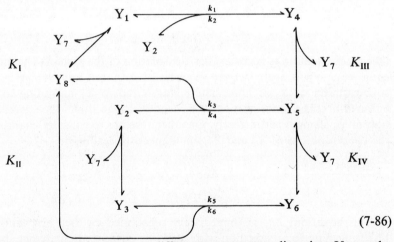

$$(7\text{-}86)$$

This system assumes that two different components dissociate Y_7 on the left side and quite fast, leading to the dissociation constants K_I and K_{II}. A two-step dissociation of Y_7 occurs on the right side, and these reactions are also considered quite rapid, leading to the dissociation constants K_{III} and K_{IV}. All steps appearing with rate constants are considered slow and thus determine the fifth relaxation time τ_5.

The four pre-equilibria, together with buffering of Y_7, lead to the following relations among the Δc_i :

$$\Delta c_1 = \frac{\bar{\bar{c}}_7}{K_{\mathrm{I}}} \Delta c_8 \tag{7-87}$$

$$\Delta c_2 = \frac{\bar{\bar{c}}_7}{K_{\mathrm{II}}} \Delta c_3 \tag{7-88}$$

$$\Delta c_4 = \frac{\bar{\bar{c}}_7}{K_{\mathrm{III}}} \Delta c_5 \tag{7-89}$$

$$\Delta c_5 = \frac{\bar{\bar{c}}_7}{K_{\mathrm{IV}}} \Delta c_6 \tag{7-90}$$

There are again two analytical concentrations, defined by

$$c_1^0 = \bar{c}_1 + \bar{c}_8 + \bar{c}_4 + \bar{c}_5 + \bar{c}_6 \tag{7-91}$$

$$c_2^0 = \bar{c}_2 + \bar{c}_3 + \bar{c}_4 + \bar{c}_5 + \bar{c}_6 \tag{7-92}$$

These two equations result in two relations among the Δc_i,

$$\Delta c_1 + \Delta c_8 + \Delta c_4 + \Delta c_5 + \Delta c_6 = 0 \tag{7-93}$$

$$\Delta c_2 + \Delta c_3 + \Delta c_4 + \Delta c_5 + \Delta c_6 = 0 \tag{7-94}$$

One more equation is necessary for the solution of the system. The differential equation is again derived in terms of Δc_8. But any change in the concentration of Y_8 is immediately transferred to Y_1 according to relation (7-87). The concentration of Y_8 cannot change alone; the concentration of Y_1 changes concurrently. One therefore has to consider changes in the concentrations of Y_1 and Y_8 simultaneously, leading to

$$\frac{d(\Delta c_1 + \Delta c_8)}{dt} = k_2 \, \Delta c_4 + k_4 \, \Delta c_5 + k_6 \Delta c_6 - k_1(\bar{c}_1 \, \Delta c_2 + \bar{c}_2 \, \Delta c_1)$$
$$- k_3(\bar{c}_2 \, \Delta c_8 + \bar{c}_8 \, \Delta c_2) - k_5(\bar{c}_3 \, \Delta c_8 + \bar{c}_8 \, \Delta c_3) \tag{7-95}$$

In this equation, Δc_1 is immediately substituted by Δc_8 according to (7-87), leading to an equation with only one concentration change in the differential. One may thereafter employ equations (7-88), (7-89), (7-90), (7-93), and (7-94) to obtain a differential equation with Δc_8 as the only variable. This equation is

$$\frac{d\Delta c_8}{dt} = -\frac{\Delta c_8}{\tau_5} \tag{7-96}$$

with

$$\tau_5^{-1} = \left(k_6 + k_4 \frac{\bar{c}_7}{K_{IV}} + k_2 \frac{(\bar{c}_7)^2}{K_{III}K_{IV}} \right) \left(1 + \frac{\bar{c}_7}{K_{IV}} + \frac{(\bar{c}_7)^2}{K_{III}K_{IV}} \right)^{-1}$$

$$+ k_1 \left(\bar{c}_2 \frac{\bar{c}_7}{K_I + \bar{c}_7} + \bar{c}_8 \frac{\bar{c}_7}{K_{II} + \bar{c}_7} \frac{\bar{c}_7}{K_I} \right) + k_3 \left(\bar{c}_2 \frac{K_I}{K_I + \bar{c}_7} + \bar{c}_8 \frac{\bar{c}_7}{K_{II} + \bar{c}_7} \right)$$

$$+ k_5 \left(\bar{c}_3 \frac{K_I}{K_I + \bar{c}_7} + \bar{c}_8 \frac{K_{II}}{K_{II} + \bar{c}_7} \right) \tag{7-97}$$

If one establishes sufficiently strong buffering (thereby also overriding any unfavorable Y_7 effects), (7-97) may be simplified to

$$\tau_5^{-1} = k_2 \left(1 + \frac{K_{III}}{\bar{c}_7} + \frac{K_{III}K_{IV}}{(\bar{c}_7)^2} \right)^{-1} + k_4 \left(1 + \frac{K_{IV}}{\bar{c}_7} + \frac{\bar{c}_7}{K_{III}} \right)^{-1}$$

$$+ k_6 \left(1 + \frac{\bar{c}_7}{K_{IV}} + \frac{(\bar{c}_7)^2}{K_{III}K_{IV}} \right)^{-1} + \left[k_1 \frac{\bar{c}_7/K_I}{1 + K_{II}/\bar{c}_7} \right.$$

$$\left. + k_3 \left(1 + \frac{\bar{c}_7}{K_I} \right)^{-1} + k_5 \left(1 + \frac{\bar{c}_7}{K_{II}} \right)^{-1} \right] \bar{c}_8 \tag{7-98}$$

This equation again may not give the true kinetic picture, as the components for buffering Y_8 may enter into the reaction. One may therefore choose $c_1^0 \gg c_2^0$, whereby $\bar{c}_8 \to c_1^0$ and no competing reactions are possible. Certainly, the equilibrium concentrations in (7-97) may also be substituted by expressions which contain only analytical concentrations. To arrive at these expressions, one has to combine the equations for the fast equilibria with (7-93), (7-94), and one equilibrium constant of a slow step. These equations are quite complex for the general case.

Diven, Goldsack, and Alberty (6) recently described a system which they represented by (7-86). Their final equation may be represented in the terminology of this section by

$$\tau_5^{-1} = k'_{app} + k''_{app}(\bar{c}_2 + \bar{c}_3 + \bar{c}_1 + \bar{c}_8) \tag{7-99}$$

$$k'_{app} = \left(k_2 \frac{\bar{c}_7}{K_{III}} + k_4 + k_6 \frac{K_{IV}}{\bar{c}_7} \right) \left(1 + \frac{\bar{c}_7}{K_{III}} + \frac{K_{IV}}{\bar{c}_7} \right)^{-1} \tag{7-100}$$

$$k''_{app} = \frac{k_1 \dfrac{\bar{c}_7}{K_I} + k_3 + k_5 \dfrac{K_{II}}{\bar{c}_7}}{1 + \dfrac{\bar{c}_7}{K_I} + \dfrac{K_{II}}{\bar{c}_7} + \dfrac{K_{II}}{K_I}} \tag{7-101}$$

Equation (7-100) is easily obtained from the *first* term of (7-97). The *second* term of (7-97) may also be written

$$k_1\left(1 + \frac{K_I}{\bar{c}_7}\right)^{-1}\left(1 + \frac{K_{II}}{\bar{c}_7}\right)^{-1}\left[\bar{c}_2\left(1 + \frac{K_{II}}{\bar{c}_7}\right) + \bar{c}_8\left(1 + \frac{K_I}{\bar{c}_7}\right)\frac{\bar{c}_7}{K_I}\right] \tag{7-102}$$

The expression in the brackets is identical with the sum of the equilibrium concentrations in (7-99). The factor in front of the brackets is identical to

$$k_1\frac{\bar{c}_7}{K_I}\left(1 + \frac{\bar{c}_7}{K_I} + \frac{K_{II}}{\bar{c}_7} + \frac{K_{II}}{K_I}\right)^{-1} \tag{7-103}$$

which appears as the first term of k''_{app} in (7-101). The other two terms in (7-101) are obtained in an analogous manner from the last two terms of (7-97).

Equation (7-99) looks simpler than (7-97), but there are still four equilibrium concentrations of a total of seven unknown ones ($\bar{c}_7$ is given by the buffer ratio). Fundamentally, (7-99) therefore has no advantage over (7-97).

There is actually a somewhat different problem with reference to multicyclic systems. The problem is associated with the precision to which relaxation times and their concentration dependence can be measured. The error of the data may allow one to fit a scheme to them which has one or two (or even three) reactions less than given in a multicyclic system. The more complex a system, the more effort should be placed on the precision of the measurements. And this emphasis on precision is stressed here by devoting a whole chapter to the observation of relaxation phenomena (Chapter 9).

PROBLEMS

1. Derive (7-84) according to the method given prior to (7-84).
2. Rewrite (7-84) in terms of analytical concentrations using (7-78), (7-79), and the necessary dissociation constants for the derivation of the functions $\bar{c}_i = f(c_i^0)$.

REFERENCES

1. G. Czerlinski, *J. Theoret. Biol.*, **7**, 463 (1964).
2. G. Czerlinski and M. Eigen, *Z. Elektrochem.*, **63**, 652 (1959).
3. G. Czerlinski and G. Schreck, *Biochemistry*, **3**, 89 (1964).

4. G. Czerlinski and G. Schreck, *J. Biol. Chem.*, **239**, 913 (1964).

5. D. Duffey, B. Chance and G. Czerlinski, *Biochem. Biophys. Res. Commun.*, **19**, 423 (1965).

6. W. F. Diven, D. E. Goldsack and R. A. Alberty, *J. Biol. Chem.*, **240**, 2437 (1965).

7. M. Eigen and L. DeMaeyer, *in* A. Weissberger (ed.), *Technique of Organic Chemistry*, Vol. VIII, Pt. II, p. 895, Wiley (Interscience), New York, 1963.

CHAPTER 8

REVIEW OF THEORETICAL SECTION

8–1. INTRODUCTION

In the previous chapters the theory of chemical relaxation was mainly treated. In this chapter a different approach will be pursued, being much more oriented toward experimental conditions. We shall attempt to unwrap the mechanism, starting with the functional dependence of the inverse chemical relaxation time upon analytical concentrations. Other experimental parameters will be considered as required by the experiments. The guiding line will be the number of (initial) analytical concentrations employed in the particular system. Supporting electrolytes are generally not considered as entering into the reaction, but in certain biological systems one might have to consider the possibility of their interference.

Any reaction buffered in H^+ or OH^- will be considered as if the reaction is proceeding via the buffered components. The two components providing for this buffering are then not considered as analytical entities separate from the proton or hydroxyl concentration. Buffering of any one component of a reaction system is considered similarly. If, for instance, the concentration of a metal ion is buffered, the concentrations of the metal-buffer complex and of the metal-free buffer will then not be considered (but only the buffered concentration of the metal ion). This buffering was extensively discussed in Chapter 5.

After the main division into the number of (initial) analytical concentrations has been established, subdivisions will be introduced considering the number of relaxation times. Other aspects will then have to be added in a systematic manner to establish individual minimal mechanisms. The equations describing the reaction system are repeated below for increased clarity.

8-2. ONE (INITIAL) ANALYTICAL CONCENTRATION ONLY

A. One Relaxation Process

1. The reciprocal relaxation time is *independent* of the analytical concentration of the only component added to the solution. A monomolecular interconversion of two species of the initial component determines the relaxation process. The system is given by

$$Y_1 \xrightleftharpoons[k_2]{k_1} Y_2 \tag{1-1}$$

and the inverse time constant by (3-3). The equation for the signal is given by (4-9) with c_2^0 omitted (this concentration is contained in c_1^0). The equilibrium signal change has to follow (2-64) together with (2-63). If the stated equation is suitably combined with (4-9) under the simplifying conditions, the resulting relative signal change is independent of c_1^0.

2. The inverse time constant is *dependent* upon the analytical concentration.

$$2Y_1 \xrightleftharpoons[k_2]{k_1} D \tag{8-1}$$

The relaxation time of this concentration-dependent process is then given by (5-27). The relative signal change is also dependent upon concentration and its equation may be derived from (6-29).

B. Two Relaxation Processes Are Determined

1. Both relaxation processes are concentration-independent. The mechanism is given by

$$Y_1 \xrightleftharpoons[k_2]{k_1} Y_2 \xrightleftharpoons[k_4]{k_3} Y_3 \tag{3-10}$$

Equations (3.41) and (3.42) give the two relaxation processes (which are both concentration-independent).

2. Concentration dependence of at least one relaxation process: These processes may be dimerizations coupled to monomolecular interconversions or dimerizations associated with trimerizations or tetramerizations. The latter may be considered as proceeding according to

$$4Y_1 \longrightarrow 2D \longrightarrow D_2 \tag{8-2}$$

A dimerization, followed by a monomolecular interconversion may have four different types of relaxation times, given by (3-52), (3-90), (3-122), and (3-123). As polymerizations are infrequent otherwise, they are not considered further here.

C. Survey of Derivations

At this point it appears quite desirable to give a general survey of all equations derived in the various chapters. This is best done in the form of a table. As quite a number of mechanisms has been investigated, use of a single table was not sufficient. Table 8-1 therefore gives only the simpler equations for mechanisms with one or two steps, resulting in not more than two relaxation times. The symbolic equations for each step are extremely abbreviated to the extent that only the "backbone of the double arrows" remained. Dashed lines are used when an equilibrium component appears at more than one point. If two reaction steps are shown, the left one is assumed to be much faster than the right one. If the opposite speed relationship does not lead to an equation, which is identical with the previous one, an extra (second) line is inserted without giving a separate mechanism, but containing the references to the appropriate equations. This is always the case where the mechanism of two consecutive steps is unsymmetrical to the "center" of the reaction scheme.

A rather narrow column is labeled n^0, giving with n^0 the smallest number of analytically different substances which then permit any relation between different c_i^0. The index i in c_i^0 may thus appear with n^0 different values. An asterisk is added in this column whenever buffering can be employed for a fast step in detecting a slow step. Only three species must then *originally* be participating in the fast step. For the slow step the equilibrium concentration of one of the rapidly associating components is buffered. Single-step mechanisms should not be buffered—except if the kinetics of this buffering is to be investigated: a system with four species in equilibrium. Wherever n^0 has the value 3, one should attempt to buffer at least one of the concentrations, to maintain it at fixed values, while the other two concentrations are varied to find the exact relationship.

The column following n^0 describes the relations between equilibrium concentrations and analytical concentrations. Only two different c_i^0 are considered as variables. If $n^0 > 2$, special conditions have been assumed to allow the simple analytical derivation, with only two different c_i^0, denoted by c_i^0 and c_{i+1}^0. Reference to these equations is given for three cases: The most general case is represented by the first subcolumn: $c_i^0/c_{i+1}^0 = $ any; the second subcolumn represents the case of equality between the two analytical concentrations; the third subcolumn give reference to the condition where the analytical concentrations are *quite* different from each other (represented by #).

TABLE 8-1

MECHANISM	$\tau_j^{-1} = f(\bar{c}_i)$		n^0	$\bar{c}_i = f(c_i^0);\ c_i^0/c_{i+1}^0$			$\tau_j^{-1} = f(c_i^0);\ c_i^0/c_{i+1}^0$				$\dfrac{\Delta\bar{c}_i}{\bar{c}_i} = f(c_i^0);\ c_i^0/c_{i+1}^0$			
	$j=1$	$j=2$		$=$any	$=1$	$\#1$[a]	$\backslash j=1/_\#$	$=1/_\#$	$\backslash j=2/_\#$	$=_\#$	$\backslash j=1/_\#$	$=1/_\#$	$\backslash j=2/_\#$	$=_\#$
—— 2 species	3.3	—	1	4.2	—	—	3.3	3.3	—	—	2.61	—	—	
—— 3 species	3.7	—	2	4.12	4.15	4.16	5.3	5.5	—	—	6.5	6.10	—	
—— 4 species	3.9	—	2	4.22	4.24	4.29	5.24	5.23	—	—	6.26	6.24	—	
—— dimerization	3.90	—	1	5.27	—	—	5.28	5.28	—	—	6.30	—	—	
	3.90	3.122	1											
	3.52	3.123												
	3.41	3.42	1	4.42	—		3.41	3.41	3.42	3.42	6.50	—	6.53	
	3.50	3.51	2*	4.48			5.48	5.53	5.49	5.54	6.67	6.68	6.79	6.83 + 4
	3.52	3.53					3.52	3.52	5.52	5.55	6.87	—	6.93 + 4	6.95 + 6
	3.50	3.57	2*	4.53			5.58	5.62 + 6	5.59	5.63 + 7				
	3.52	3.58					3.52	3.52	5.60	5.64 + 8				
	3.9	3.73	2 }	4.120 }	4.122	4.126	} 5.69 + 77	5.73 + 9	5.76				
	3.52	3.74		4.132 }	4.134	4.136	} 3.52	5.82 + 5	5.83 + 6				

[a] Means that c_i^0/c_{i+1}^0 is quite different from (unity).

TABLE 8-1—*continued*

MECHANISM	$\tau_j^{-1} = f(\bar{c}_i)$			$\bar{c}_i = f(c_i^0);\ c_i^0/c_{i+1}^0$			$\tau_j^{-1} = f(c_i^0);\ c_i^0/c_{i+1}^0$				$\frac{\Delta \bar{c}_i}{\bar{c}_i} = f(c_i^0);\ c_i^0/c_{i+1}^0$	
	$j=1$	$j=2$	n^0	$=\text{any}$	$=1$	$\#1^a$	$=\vert j=1/\#$		$=\vert j=2/\#$		$=\vert j=1/\#$	$=\vert j=2/\#$
	3.7	3.66	3*	4.99	$4.101+2$	$4.103+4$	5.3	5.5	5.90	$5.92+4$		
	3.67	3.68		4.106	4.109	4.112	(5.3)	(5.5)	5.96	5.97		
	3.7	3.61	3*	~ 4.71	4.90	4.91				5.101		
	3.7	3.63	3*							5.103		
	3.9	3.82	3*					5.106				
	3.83	3.84										
	3.9	3.77	3*					5.104				
	3.78	3.79										
	3.9	3.86	3									

^{a} Means that c_i^0/c_{i+1}^0 is quite different from (unity).

Certainly, in "statics" there is only one line of equations for each mechanism; at equilibrium, all reaction steps are completed and their sequence is irrelevant. Static signals are not given in a separate column, as these equations depend strongly upon the indicative properties of the system. Appropriate equations are generally given in the text following the equations, referred to in the table, (see also Chapter 7).

The next column in Table 8-1 summarizes data, derived in Chapter 5. Index j in τ_j^{-1} can be 1 or 2, as in the second column. But for each value of j one generally may derive a number of equations, depending upon the relations among the c_i^0. Only two such relations have been selected for incorporation into the table: equality of two c_i^0 is indicated by $=$ in the heading of the subcolumn, and their strong unequality by $\#$. This leads to a total of four subcolumns for this section. And even that is not enough; some lines show dual equations. Such splitting occurs if the associating components are arranged such that the condition $c_i^0 \gg c_{i+1}^0$ leads to a quite different result from the condition $c_i^0 \ll c_{i+1}^0$. Which specific condition prevails is not specified in Table 8-1, and one would have to consult the text around the specific equations.

The last "section of columns" in Table 8-1 gives the relative concentration change, which is directly related to the relative signal change (under conditions developed in Chapter 7). There are again subdivisions, which are quite similar to the ones of the previous "section of columns." Only a few representative equations are given, because of the elaborate derivations and the consideration of various aspects.

Table 8-2 lists primarily two-step mechanisms with some kind of feedback, thereby complicating the derivation. Complex dimerization reactions are also listed. The symbolism is the same as for Table 8-1. Only the kinetics of these equations is given.

Table 8-3 summarizes the relationships for three-step mechanisms with the symbolism the same as in Table 8-1. The first line under each mechanism gives reference to the equations for the case that the left step is the fastest and the right one the slowest. The second line under each mechanism gives reference to the equations for the case that the left step is the fastest and the middle one the slowest. The third line under a mechanism gives reference to the equation for the case that the right step is the fastest and the left one the slowest.

Whenever the third line is missing one may obtain the third case by index exchange: the reaction is symmetric to the "center." Almost all equations in the first two columns under τ_2^{-1} are set in brackets for two reasons. The indices in these equations generally do not correspond to the

TABLE 8-2

MECHANISM	$\tau_j^{-1} = f(\bar{c}_i)$		n^0
	$j = 1$	$j = 2$	
	3.154	3.156	1
	3.147 3.151	3.148 3.152	2*
	3.90 3.98	3.96 3.100	1
	3.90 3.107	3.106 3.108	2*
	3.90 3.113	3.112 3.114	2*
	3.90 3.119	3.118 3.120	2
	3.52 3.90	3.128 3.129	1
	3.132 3.90	3.133 3.134	2*
	3.137 3.90	3.138 3.139	2*
	3.143 3.90	3.144 3.145	2
	3.147	3.158	2*
	3.163 3.164	3.164 3.165	2
	3.163 3.113	3.167 3.168	3*
	3.163	3.170	3

TABLE 8-3

MECHANISM	$\tau_j^{-1} = f(\bar{c}_i)$			n^0	$\bar{c}_i = f(c_i^0); c_i^0/c_{i+1}^0$			$\tau_j^{-1} = f(c_i^0); c_i^0/c_{i+1}^0$						$\dfrac{\Delta \bar{c}_i}{\bar{c}_{i,0}} = f(c_i^0)$
	$j=1$	$j=2$	$j=3$		$=$any	$=1$	$\neq 1$	$=\backslash j=1/\ \neq$		$=\backslash j=2/\ \neq$		$=\backslash j=3/\ \neq$		
(diagram)	[3.41]; 3.41	[3.42]; 3.172	3.183; 3.174	1	4.144	—	—					3.183; 3.174		6.107; 6.116
(diagram)	[3.50]; [3.7]; [3.41]	[3.51]; [3.3]; [3.42]	3.189; 3.188; 3.190	2*	4.189 + 9	4.152	4.153	5.108; 3.108; [3.3 + 52]	5.109; 5.109	5.116; [3.3]; 5.123	5.115 + 9; —	5.113; 5.111; 5.122	5.112; 5.110; 5.121	6.142; 6.132
(diagram)	[3.50]; [3.7]; [3.41]	[3.57]; [3.3]; [3.42]	3.193; 3.192; 3.194	2*										
(diagram)	[3.52]; [3.41]; [3.52]	[3.58]; [3.41]; [3.53]	3.198; 3.196; 3.199	2*										
(diagram)	[3.9]; [3.9]; [3.41]	[3.73]; [3.3]; [3.42]	3.208; 3.201; 3.207	2										
(diagram)	[3.50]; [3.7]; [3.52]	[3.57]; [3.71]; [3.53]	3.210; 3.203; 3.209	3*										

TABLE 8-3—*continued*

MECHANISM	$\tau_j^{-1} = f(\bar{c}_i)$				$\bar{c}_i = f(c_i^0); c_i^0/c_{i+1}^0$			$\tau_j^{-1} = f(c_i^0); c_i^0/c_{i+1}^0$			$\dfrac{\Delta \bar{c}_{i,j}}{\bar{c}_{i,0}} = f(c_i^0)$
	$j=1$	$j=2$	$j=3$	n^0	= any	= 1	#1	$\big\vert j=1/\#$	$\big\vert j=2/\#$	$\big\vert j=3/\#$	
	[3.52] [3.3] [3.7]	[3.53] [3.7] [3.66]	3.214 3.213 3.212	3*							
	[3.67] [3.7] [3.7]	[3.68] [3.7] [3.66]	3.218 3.217 3.216	4*							
	[3.7]	[3.63]	3.261	3*	7.52 + 5						7.71
	[3.7] [3.3]	[3.63] [3.52]	3.276 3.286	2*							

ones contained in the equations for $j = 3$. On the other hand, each mechanism, with three rows (and three " step "- relaxation times) should actually carry six: the time sequence of the two fast steps can also be opposite to the one referred to in the table. Concerning the $\tau_j^{-1} = f(\bar{c}_i)$ for the fast two steps, one should therefore consult Table 8-1 (and Table 8-2).

Two cyclic mechanisms are shown at the end of Table 8-3. One of them is so symmetric that only one τ_3 can be derived. The other cyclic mechanism permits just two τ_3. Although four reaction steps are contained in these cyclic mechanisms, the strong "internal feedback" together with symmetry characteristics allows only three relaxation times, as discussed in detail after (3-261) and (3-276).

The column with n^0 as the most suitable number of analytically different substances was introduced in Table 8-1. An asterisk indicates that a slow step may be followed with one reactant in the fast step being fixed by buffering. Only one system was given with $n^0 = 4$. In following its slowest step one should attempt to buffer the concentrations of *two* of the much faster associating steps. Actually, one may make these steps faster just by buffering.

Equations for statics, extended kinetics, and thermodynamics were only derived for the simplest systems (and a representative cyclic one). An exhaustive treatment of the more complex systems would require a considerable extension of the table. Some equations for thermodynamics are only very briefly indicated. Equations for signal changes, referring to the simplest mechanism, are given in Chapter 7.

8-3. TWO REACTANTS INITIALLY ADDED

A. One Relaxation Process Only

1. The relaxation process is independent of concentration for both conditions $c_i^0 = c_l^0$ and $c_i^0 \ll c_l^0$, where the index $i \neq l$ (i or l can only be 1 or 2, respectively, but an index fixation is avoided at this point). If any relaxation process is detectable with the isolated components, its reappearance in the form

$$Y_4 \xrightarrow[k_4]{k_3} Y_2 \underset{k_2}{\overset{k_1}{\rightleftharpoons}} Y_3 \qquad (3\text{-}54)$$
$$Y_1$$

is most probable. Y_2 is then the component, which previously showed a relaxation process, which must have occurred in the same time range as the one of the mixture (if not, see below). The relaxation time is then either given by (3-52) or by (3-57), with the following additional conditions.

For (3-52), Eq. (3-58) would have denoted the second (slower) relaxation time. This reaction step could be so slow that it is out of the range of detection for the ordinary time range of the apparatus for chemical relaxation. This problem could be overcome by the addition of a stopped-flow device to the relaxation apparatus. On the other hand, this bimolecular reaction step could be associated with such a large $K_{2,1}$ that is not even approached by any experimental value of c_I^0.

2. CONCENTRATION-DEPENDENT THREE-COMPONENT PROCESS.   The simplest case is represented by

$$Y_1 + Y_2 \xrightarrow[k_2]{k_1} Y_3 \qquad\qquad (1\text{-}12)$$

The relaxation time as a function of analytical concentrations is given by (5-2). It is advisable to establish special analytical conditions to simplify this rather complex equation. A very simple relationship is, for example, given by (5-5). It is certainly possible that fast monomolecular inter-conversions are connected to either one of the components but are not appearing as detectable relaxation times (for kinetic, thermodynamic, or [mostly] indicative reasons). Relaxation times of this type are given, for instance, by (3-53), (3-58), (3-190), (3-194), and (3-196). Equation (3-286) is a special representative of an equation, where two fast steps may not be detectable.

3. CONCENTRATION-DEPENDENT FOUR-COMPONENT PROCESS.   The simplest case is represented by

$$Y_1 + Y_2 \xrightarrow[k_2]{k_1} Y_3 + Y_4 \qquad\qquad (1\text{-}30)$$

The appropriate relaxation time as a function of analytical concentrations is given by (5-21). Simplifications are easily possible with $c_i^0 = c_I^0$ and $c_i^0 \ll c_I^0$. Also, undetectable fast monomolecular interconversions may be coupled in here, leading, for instance, to (3-74) and (3-207).

B. Two Relaxation Processes

The complexity of possible reactions becomes considerable and one should inspect Tables 8-1 and 8-2 for possible mechanisms with $n^0 = 2$. One generally has some additional information (such as a concentration-independent fast step, or a strongly concentration-dependent fast step and a slow step with one rate constant concentration-dependent over a limited range), which allows us to restrict the number of possible mechanisms.

C. Three Relaxation Processes

Buffering for some of the steps is almost unavoidable for any elucidation and simplification of the equations. Table 8-3 may be helpful, but gives only a limited number of mechanisms. On the other hand, one rarely obtains three relaxation processes with only two analytical components.

8–4. THREE REACTANTS INITIALLY ADDED

A. One Relaxation Process

Equation (1-30) is about the only one that represents such a case; this was discussed in Section 8-3. It is rare, otherwise, to obtain only one relaxation process with three substances added initially.

B. Two Relaxation Processes

Several possibilities are given in Tables 8-1 and 8-2. But one should remember that there may exist " hidden " monomolecular interconversions. One would then have to consult the (incomplete) Table 8-3.

C. Three Relaxation Processes

A small selection of such reactions is given in Table 8-3. It is difficult to assemble all possible mechanisms which fall under this type of three analytical components and three (measurable) relaxation processes.

8–5. SPECIFIC CHEMICAL SYSTEMS

Many systems have already been investigated with chemical relaxation methods. A quite-thorough review of available data was given in 1963 by Eigen and DeMaeyer (1), as was already mentioned in the Introduction. Two other reviews on specific chemical systems which have been investigated by relaxation methods were given there also, one on the more biochemical applications by Eigen and Hammes (2), and a more general one by Hammes (3). Because of these relatively recent reviews, a table compiling the various data obtained by relaxation techniques is avoided here. The reader is referred to the cited literature.

REFERENCES

1. M. Eigen and L. DeMaeyer, in A. Weissberger (ed.), Technique of Organic Chemistry, Vol. VIII, Pt. II, p. 895, Wiley (Interscience), New York, 1963.
2. M. Eigen and G. G. Hammes, in F. F. Nord (ed.), Advances in Enzymology, Vol. XXV, p. 1, Wiley (Interscience), New York, 1963.
3. G. G. Hammes, Ann. Rev. Phys. Chem., 15, 13 (1964).

CHAPTER 9

LIMITATIONS IN DETECTION

9-1. THE SHOT-NOISE LIMITATION

In this treatment only optical-detection systems will be considered, as they seem to be most useful for the detection of very rapid and small changes. These optical-detection methods refer to any type: observation of changes in absorption, changes in luminescence, changes in optical rotation, or changes in light scattering. Similar basic considerations are valid for all these methods.

Any optical-detection system may be considered to consist of the photon generator, the photon diminisher, and the photon detector. The system may also contain a photon converter (a photon of one wavelength is absorbed and re-emitted at another wavelength in fluorescence or phosphorescence detection). Detection generally may be directed toward information on the generator or on the diminisher. Here only the property of that specific part is of interest which diminishes the number of transmitted photons.

The limit in the detection of rapid and small changes in light intensity (as measured by changes in absorption, reflection, or luminescence) is given by the rms noise in the output of the detection system. (The most instructive definition of the rms noise is given later in conjunction with Figure 9-2.) This noise is generally determined by Johnson or by shot noise (*1*). Shot noise originates in the photon detector upon conversion of photons into electrons and cannot be avoided. In "good" optical-detection systems, shot noise is made predominant over any other kind of noise. If N is the rms noise level in the output signal S, the S/N ratio should be made as large as possible. Aside from a large signal-to-noise ratio, however, the electronic detection system should also have a large bandwidth B, so that small changes may be detected rapidly.

The simplest equation that combines all requirements for a shot-noise-limited optical detection system is given by (2):

$$\left(\frac{S}{N}\right)^2 = \frac{I_p}{2eB} \qquad (9\text{-}1)$$

where I_p is the photocurrent and e is the charge of the electron. Multiplier phototubes of amplification A per stage require (3) a correction factor $(A-1)A^{-1}$ (for $5 \geqslant A \geqslant 3$) at the right side of (9-1) to give the correct value of $(S/N)^2$.

If both S/N and B have to be made as large as possible, (9-1) shows that I_p should be increased to the utmost. The optical-detection system must, therefore, be designed in such a manner that a very large I_p results. The photocurrent I_p is largest for a given luminous flux P_p when every incident photon produces at least one electron. This maximum conversion factor is 360 mamp/watt at 440-mμ wavelength, which is considerably above that of commercial multiplier phototubes. This "cathode radiant sensitivity" σ is simply the ratio of photocurrent to incident light power and may go up to 100 mamp/watt for selected tubes. The cathode radiant sensitivity of commercially available tubes is generally adequate and needs no substantial further improvement.

To demonstrate the over-all efficiency of a "conventional" optical detection system, one may determine

$$\eta_0 = \frac{P_p}{P_0} \qquad (9\text{-}2)$$

where P_0 is the power which is fed into the photon generator. P_0 is, for instance, the power consumed by a tungsten lamp, which may be 100 watts in this example. P_p is not directly accessible and has to be computed from

$$P_p = \frac{V_a^2}{RM\sigma} \qquad (9\text{-}3)$$

where V_a is the voltage across the anode resistor R of a multiplier phototube with over-all amplification M. In a slow conventional design, one may have $V_a = 1$ volt, $R = 10^6$ ohms, $M = 10^6$, and $\sigma = 72$ mamp/watt (corresponding to 20 per cent conversion of photons into electrons at 440 mμ); it is then $P_p = 1.4 \times 10^{-11}$ watt, and thus $\eta_0 = 1.4 \times 10^{-13}$. This is a surprisingly small over-all efficiency, which will be further investigated with the aim of considerable improvement.

If the bandwidth B is 1 cps, and the above data are taken into account, (9-1) results in $(S/N) = 1500$, which may be considered satisfactory (dark noise and Johnson noise are always assumed to be small compared to shot noise). These conditions are no longer satisfactory, however, if high sensitivity *and* fast response are desired.

Although the agreement between the experimental S/N and its value computed with (9-1) would be a good demonstration that the optical detection system is shot-noise-limited, it is not actually a criterion for the performance of an optical-detection system. This performance may only be considered good if η_0 is relatively large. The photocurrent, on the other hand, can only be increased to a value where saturation effects start to become limiting.

9–2. OPTICAL EFFICIENCIES

A. General

The over-all efficiency η_0 may now be considered as functionally dependent upon the center wavelength of the light detected ($=\lambda$), the axis of the optical-detection system ($=z$), and the area in space actually used by irradiative flux of the detection system ($=a$) [with z normal to a]. In the idealized case of a photon generator with point source, one may then differentiate among

$$\eta(\lambda) = (\partial\eta_0/\partial\lambda)_{a,z} \qquad (9\text{-}4)$$

$$\eta(a) = (\partial\eta_0/\partial a)_{\lambda,z} \qquad (9\text{-}5)$$

$$\eta(z) = (\partial\eta_0/\partial z)_{\lambda,a} \qquad (9\text{-}6)$$

These three equations will be considered in detail in the next three sections.

B. The Transmissive Contribution

The most important variable in these equations is z, the spatial coordinate in the axis of the optical-detection system, with the origin of z in the "center of the point source" and with Z at the "middle of the photo-detective surface." $\eta(z)$ then is the "transmissive efficiency" at point z and at constant a and λ. For the over-all transmissive efficiency, one then has to integrate from 0 to Z.

One specific part of the "photon diminisher" was already mentioned as being of particular interest and is defined to extend in space along the z axis from z_0 to $z_0 + l$. The question immediately arises whether there is a particular value of $\eta(z)$ along a given length l which is optimal for the detection of small changes.

The definition most generally employed is

$$\log I_0 - \log I \equiv \text{optical density} = \varepsilon_i'\bar{c}_i l \qquad (9\text{-}7)$$

where I_0 is the light intensity at some reference z_0 (may contain "reference absorption"), I is the light intensity at $z_0 + l$, ε_i' is the decadic molar extinction coefficient of the (only) absorbing species, and $\bar{c}_i$ is the molar equilibrium concentration of this absorbing species. From (9-7) one obtains

$$\eta(z) = \int_{z_0}^{z_0+l} \eta(z)\, dz = \frac{I}{I_0} = \exp(-\varepsilon_i'\bar{c}_i l \ln 10) \qquad (9\text{-}8)$$

Since $\bar{c}_i$ is the concentration of the component to be investigated, any change in $\bar{c}_i$ should give the largest possible change in the value of the integral. Then the question is: How must the parameters in (9-8) be chosen to give the largest change in I (being ΔI) for any given concentration change $\Delta \bar{c}_i$? Equation (9-8) becomes

$$(I + \Delta I)/I_0 = \exp[-\varepsilon_i' l(\bar{c}_i + \Delta \bar{c}_i) \ln 10] \qquad (9\text{-}9)$$

Introducing $\Delta \bar{c}_i / \bar{c}_i = x \ll 1$, one may expand (9-9) and obtain, after simplification and use of (9-8),

$$\Delta I/I_0 = -(\ln 10)\varepsilon_i' l \bar{c}_i x \exp[-(\ln 10)\varepsilon_i'\bar{c}_i l] \qquad (9\text{-}10)$$

This is the equation for which a maximum may be found, where $d\, \Delta I/d\bar{c}_i = 0$. Differentiation of (9-10) is easily possible if x is considered a constant. The relation $x \neq f(\bar{c}_i)$ is rarely true to its full extent but may frequently be assumed in zero approximation. If a change in x cannot be neglected, its full equation has to be inserted in (9-10) before differentiation. Equations for the parameter x may become rather complex for multistep reactions and have previously been given in the literature (4). Expressions for x for a larger number of systems were derived in Chapter 6. One then obtains at the maximum,*

$$(\ln 10)\varepsilon_i' l \bar{c}_i = 1 \qquad (9\text{-}11)$$

For (9-11) to be useful, ΔI should be sufficiently above the rms noise-equivalent light intensity: For any relaxation process (see below), where the time constant should be determined with some precision, ΔI *is* substantially above the rms noise-equivalent intensity.

* Equation (9-11) is different from Eq. (III,1,17) of M. Eigen and L. DeMaeyer *in* A. Weissberger (ed.), *Technique of Organic Chemistry* 2nd ed., Vol. VIII, Pt. 2, p. 975, Wiley (Interscience), New York, 1963. Their value is different from the above by a factor of 2, apparently because of their use of the shot-noise equation, which should not enter into our derivation, being restricted to $\Delta I \gg$ the rms-noise-equivalent light intensity.

Equation (9-11) then determines the value of (9-8) for optimum "response" to small concentration changes: $(I/I_0)_{opt} = 1/e$. Outside the range of l, one should then attempt to obtain

$$\int_{z=0}^{z_0} \eta(z)\, dz \to 1, \qquad \int_{z=z_0+l}^{Z} \eta(z)\, dz \to 1 \qquad (9\text{-}12)$$

Equation (9-12) means that one should employ as little absorbing material and refracting interfaces as possible outside region l.

In fluorescence detection, the right side of (9-12) should not be valid; on the contrary, one should make it zero, since no detector is at Z. In addition one has to introduce a new axis z', which is the optical axis of fluorescence detection (5) with $z' = 0$ at the "origin" of fluorescence and $z' = Z'$ in the "middle of the photodetective surface," l' may be termed the "depth of fluorescence generation." For the z'-axis one has to write

$$\int_{z'=0}^{Z'} \eta(z')\, dz' \to 1 \qquad (9\text{-}12a)$$

(generally valid for some λ' which is different from λ used for fluorescence excitation).

As the transmitted light (in the axis and of wavelength λ) is not effective in fluorescence generation, but rather the total energy absorbed along l, (9-8) should be changed to

$$(I_0 - I)/I_0 = 1 - \exp[-(\ln 10)\varepsilon_i' \bar{c}_i l] \qquad (9\text{-}13)$$

Optimizing as described after (9-8) again leads to condition (9-11), which thus also becomes valid for fluorescence detection.

C. The Geometric Efficiency

Equation (9-5) introduces the geometric efficiency, although only for a point source. Real sources are extended, as the one in Figure 9-1. A cylindrical light source of height h is indicated, but only part of its surface, given by the entrance pupil (with radius r_0), is available for the detection system. The area of this entrance pupil is given by $a_0 \doteq \pi r_0^2$, if $r_0 \ll r$. The radiation intensity from a surface element da_0 decreases with b_1^{-2}, if b_1 is the distance between this surface element da_0 and some separated surface element da_1. Then $\eta(a)$ may be defined as b_1^{-2}. Upon integration one obtains the dimensionless efficiency

$$\int \eta(a)\, da_1 = \int \frac{da_1}{b_1^2} \approx \frac{\pi r_1^2}{b_1^2} \qquad (9\text{-}14)$$

The right-hand expression employs the radius r_1 of the exit pupil of Figure 9-1 and approximates the spherical surface of the plane.

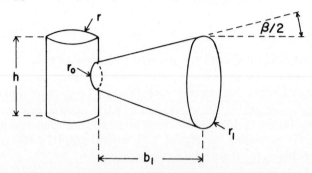

Figure 9-1. A light source of radius r and height h. The radius of the output pupil of this light source effective for the geometric flux is r_0. The radius in the imaging plane effective for the geometric flux is r_1. The distance between these two planes is given by b_1. The angular opening of the light cone is β.

With the angle $\beta/2$ introduced in Figure 9-1, the right side of (9-14) may be written $\pi \tan^2 \beta/2$. This expression becomes π for $\beta/2 = 45°$, but the approximation of (9-14) then becomes so crude that it should no longer be used [an (equivalent) sine relationship is more appropriate then]. The element da_0 was implicitly treated as located along the z-axis, which simultaneously intersects the circle with the radius r_1 at its center. The same relationship (9-14) is approximately valid for any surface element near the z-axis. If r_d is the distance of such an element from the z-axis, "near" means fulfillment of $r_d \ll b_1$. The larger the deviation from this condition, the larger the error in the approximation. The concept of radiance in a given direction is not introduced so as to simplify the treatment of this section.

So far only a point source has been considered. Integration over the whole useful area a_0 leads to a new concept, the geometric flux (6):

$$\Phi_1 = \frac{\pi^2 r_0^2 r_1^2}{b_1^2} \quad \text{or} \quad \Phi_i = \frac{\pi^2 r_{i-1}^2 r_i^2}{b_i^2} \qquad (9\text{-}15)$$

The right expression represents the generalized ith flux between the $(i - 1)$ and the ith pupil. Because of the simplifications mentioned in the previous paragraph, (9-15) represents the actual geometric flux best for $r_0, r_1 \ll b_1$. But (9-15) may still be used as an estimate, even when this condition is only poorly fulfilled. The geometric flux multiplied with the intensity of the light at $z(i)$ gives directly the power transferred in the system.

In a detection system there are generally more than two effective pupils, resulting in more than one geometric flux. It is, therefore, most advantageous to maintain the following condition throughout the optical detection system:

$$\Phi_i = \Phi_{i+1} \tag{9-16}$$

This relationship is only valid for uniaxial detection systems. In biaxial detection systems (such as in fluorescence, with a z- and z'-axis), one has two different geometric flux systems, each having its own condition (9-16).

The left equation in (9-15) contains the effective source area $a_0 = \pi r_0^2$. Since Φ_i also fulfills (9-16), the division of a_0 by the total source area $A_0[=2\pi r(r + h)$ according to Figure 9-1] would result in the over-all geometric efficiency $\eta_{0,a}$ (best fulfilled for $r_0 \ll r$):

$$\eta_{0,a} = \Phi_1/A_0 \tag{9-17}$$

D. Spectral Efficiency

The decadic molar extinction coefficient of the ith component, ε_i', introduced in (9-7), is strongly dependent upon wavelength. Generally, that wavelength is selected for detection where ε_i' is maximal. Ordinary light sources, unfortunately, have a broad spectral distribution. Optical masers, on the other hand, have quite narrow spectral bands and would be ideal for detection, but will not be considered here. For high spectral efficiency and conventional light sources one should integrate over as wide a wavelength range as possible. If g is the rms error in the determination of some change ΔI, relative to I, the wavelength band of the spectral filter may be as wide as the spectral width is for $\varepsilon_\lambda' \geqslant \varepsilon_{max}'(1 - 2g)$ without substantially affecting the results. This way one obtains a crude practical value for a rectangular spectral filter; such filters are closely approximated by the multilayer interference filters, now commercially available. The light source should be selected so that its maximum spectral emission is as close to the wavelength for ε_{max}' as possible. The photodetector should also have its maximum sensitivity at that same wavelength.

If $\Delta\lambda = \lambda_2 - \lambda_1$ is the wavelength band just introduced after defining g and if the spectral characteristics of other optical components can be neglected, the spectral efficiency of the light source is given by

$$\int_{\lambda_1}^{\lambda_2} \left(\frac{\partial \eta_0'}{\partial \lambda}\right)_{a_{0,0}} d\lambda = \frac{\int_{\lambda_1}^{\lambda_2} F(\lambda)\, d\lambda}{\int_0^\infty F(\lambda)\, d\lambda} \tag{9-18}$$

$F(\lambda)$ is the radiative flux at the wavelength λ of width $d\lambda$. Commercially available data giving the relative spectral distribution $F(\lambda)$ are generally adequate for the use of (9-18). An equation similar to (9-18) also holds for the detector, but the relative sensitivity curves are easily available and generally allow quick determination of this efficiency.

9–3. DETERMINATION OF SIGNAL-TO-NOISE RATIOS

A. Concept of Bandwidth

With reference to the radiative area, that design is optimal where the opening pupil coincides with the expansion of the source. This is that part of A_0 which is visible through the pupil with r_1; the area is $\frac{1}{2}A_0$ at best for a ribbon filament lamp. This optimum is used in systems for transmission, where one may employ General Electric's tungsten lamp type 6.6 A-T 21/2 Q-C 2-45 W. This lamp is not useful for fluorescence excitation around 360 mμ, if the electronic bandwidth B has to be large. General Electric's mercury-arc lamp BH 6 must then be used (several companies supply equivalent lamps). When an instrument has been constructed with an experimental photocurrent I_p, it is appropriate to check the performance by plotting the measured S/N as a function of B^{-1}. Before doing so, the various parameters of (9-1) have to be considered in more detail. Output signal and photocurrent are related by

$$S = RA^n I_p \qquad (9-19)$$

where R is the load resistor at the anode of the photodetector, A is the amplification per stage in multiplier phototubes, if all stages are considered with the same amplification (if not, one may define A as average amplification per stage as long as they do not differ much; in ordinary phototubes, A is unity), and n is the number of amplifying dynode stages in muliplier phototubes. The parameters I_0, I, and ΔI of (9-7) to (9-13) are light intensities and related to I_p by $I_p = Ia_p\sigma$ with $a_p =$ irradiated surface area of the photocathode, $\sigma =$ conversion factor.

The electronic bandwidth of the detection system is generally determined by a bandwidth-selecting filter, which is frequently variable, to allow greater flexibility in the detection. The frequency-response curve of such a filter depends upon its detailed structure. Only two different responses upon a unit step function will be considered here: the exponential rise and the sigmoid rise. If E_{in} is the input voltage and E_{out} the output voltage of a frequency-limiting network (or amplifier), the bandwidth B is that frequency where $(E_{out}/E_{in})^2 = \frac{1}{2}$ (corresponding to the " 3-db point "). This leads to $B = 0.16(RC)^{-1}$ for a plain RC filter. [If $\tau_0 = RC$, $(E_{out}/E_{in})^2 = \frac{1}{2} = [1 + (2\pi B\tau_0)^2]^{-1}$, and thus $B = (2\pi\tau_0)^{-1} = 0.16\tau_0^{-1}$]. In pulse circuits one considers the time rise θ, defined experimentally as the time necessary for a rise from 10 to 90 per cent of total pulse height. For such response, the bandwidth is defined as $B = 0.35\theta^{-1}$. This is the factor most generally used now. Many discussions on this subject have been published (see, for instance, Ref. 7). Equalizing the two relationships for B gives $\theta = 2.2RC$. One may obtain the same result with the definition of θ: $\theta = t_{0.9} - t_{0.1} = 2.3RC$ (log 0.1 − log 0.9) = 2.2RC.

B.   Graphical Determination of RMS Noise

The noise N is the rms noise in the signal. The linear instantaneous value* of this noise in the signal, δS, is defined such that its time average value is zero, i.e., $\overline{\delta S} = 0$; it determines the final value for signal S and is used here as the reference value for the noise. The rms noise is then given by $N = \left[\overline{(\delta S)^2}\right]^{1/2}$. One may now consider a constant value δS_0. Then there is a certain probability p that $\delta S \geqslant \delta S_0$. This expression for p, most accessible via tables on normal distribution (8), is

$$p = 0.5 - \frac{1}{(2\pi)^{1/2}} \int_0^{\delta S_0/N} \exp(-\tfrac{1}{2}x^2)\, dx \qquad (9\text{-}20)$$

For convenience one may plot $p = f(\delta S_0/N)$ (9).

Equation (9-20) may actually be used (9) to evaluate N from a trace of δS. This is especially advisable when very fast phenomena are observed (on an oscilloscope screen). Figure 9-2 demonstrates such a trace (without superposition of a time-dependent phenomenon). $\overline{\delta S}$ and some arbitrary δS_0 are marked on the figure. It is of importance to realize that the time course of δS can easily be traced. This is accomplished by maintaining $\dot{X} = \mathscr{H}RC$, where $\dot{X}$ is the horizontal deflection and $\mathscr{H} = 10\ \text{cm}^{-1}$ (approximately). The probability p is evaluated with the relation $p = \Delta t_0/t_0$, where t_0 is the total time during which the trace is on the screen and Δt_0 the amount of time during which $\delta S \geqslant \delta S_0$. To find the reference value $\overline{\delta S} = 0$, one uses the same Δt_0 for *negative* excursions of δS; Δt_0 is that amount of time during which $\delta S \leqslant \delta S_0$. Equation (9-20) or its graphical representation then leads to the corresponding $\delta S_0/N$ and to N.

It is immediately apparent from Figure 9-2 that δS_0 cannot be chosen freely: N cannot be evaluated for $\delta S_0 = 0$ and $\delta S = \delta S_{\text{peak}}$ (during t_0). The trace of any particular noise curve may be considered as having $2Bt_0$ "independent" values. These values are quoted as "independent" ones, owing to the sampling theorem in the time domain, which was derived by

---

* Its abbreviation LINIVA was introduced by S. Goldman in his book *Information Theory*, Prentice-Hall, Englewood Cliffs, N.J., 1953.

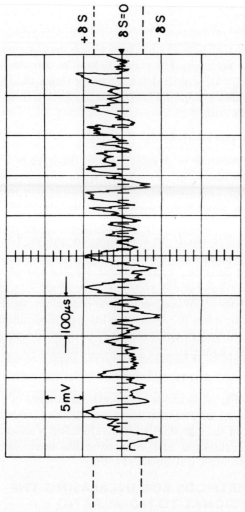

Figure 9-2. A trace of the shot noise as taken with a Tektronix oscilloscope 545. The linear instantaneous value of the voltage fluctuation around the zero position is given by δS.

C. E. Shannon, *Proc. IRE*, **37**, 10 (1949); see also the definition of θ. How far the above $2Bt_0$ values are really independent will not be discussed here. In the way it is employed further on, it can only be considered an estimation of an upper limit. Then one may immediately give a lower permissible limit for the probability p and, with it, an upper (theoretical) limit for $\delta S/N$. One should observe

$$p \geqslant (2Bt_0)^{-1} \tag{9-21}$$

This limit is only of theoretical interest; for purposes of practical evaluation it is important that δS_0 be chosen such that Δt_0 may be determined with adequate precision. The precision may be considered adequate when the error $\Delta(\Delta t_0)/\Delta t_0 < p$. But this certainly limits the usable range of p quite severely (also $p < 0.5$). This practical aspect will be considered further in the next section.

C. Nongraphical Determination

So far only the evaluation of N directly from the trace of δS has been considered. Since the length of this trace is quite limited, such a determination is associated with some error. A convenient way to measure N independently over a wider time range is possible with a true rms voltmeter, from which one obtains N directly. Keithley Model 121 is such a meter, in which δS is "squared" by dissipating the power. The large time constant of the meter, together with the conductive losses, provide for averaging. The heat-detecting thermocouple "takes the square root." The 3-db point at the *lower* end is approximately 10 $\sec^{-1}$, which may be equalized to $(5t_0)^{-1}$ $\sec^{-1}$. Whenever a time-dependent signal is superimposed upon the noise trace, this long-integrating method cannot be used.

A third independent way of determining N is via the original equation for shot noise (single channel):

$$I_N = (2eI_pB)^{1/2} \tag{9-22}$$

Since I_N in (9-22) is the noise in the photocathode current of a multiplier phototube, it has to be combined with an equation equivalent to (9-19) to give the noise N in the signal. All three values for N should agree. In performing actual evaluations and comparing the three values for N, reasonably good agreement was obtained (*10*).

9–4. METHODS FOR INCREASING THE SIGNAL-TO-NOISE RATIO

In chemical relaxation one frequently encounters the problem that an individual relaxation process is preceded by a much faster one. A clean separation of the two processes generally requires observation at much wider electronic bandwidth than would be necessary if only the specifically observed process were present. To demonstrate such a process, an example from the field of chemical relaxation is shown in Figure 9-3, which was taken from a biochemical paper (*11*). The fast change may not always be as small in height compared to the observed chemical change shown in Figure 9-3, but may even be 10 times as large (*12*).

There are various alternative ways in which the signal-to-noise ratio of observed phenomena like the one in Figure 9-3 could be improved. If the phenomenon can easily be repeated, one may employ noise reduction by any rapid sampling or storing device. If the number of repetitions is n, the improvement of the signal-to-noise ratio would be proportional to $n^{1/2}$ for full storage of individual traces and consequent averaging. Unfortunately, biological systems are frequently not associated with a high degree of reproducibility, so that one should attempt to obtain all information from a single experiment. It is therefore advisable to look for alternative approaches to noise reduction. The previous equation (9-1) may be considered, a precursor of which was originally derived by Schottkey (*13*). According to (9-1), it is possible to improve the signal-to-noise ratio by increasing the photocurrent. Unfortunately, some biological systems are rather sensitive to high light intensities, and multiplier phototubes eventually restrict the light level, owing to saturation effects at the photocathode. Equation (9-1) represents just one example, where S/N is proportional to the square root of the signal-determining parameter (here I_p) and inversely proportional to the square root of the electronic bandwidth B.

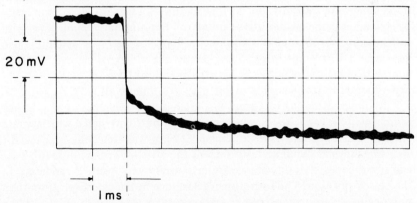

Figure 9-3. Oscilloscope trace of a relaxation process on a dehydrogenase system employing detection of fluorescence changes. The initial step is mainly due to the change of fluorescence upon temperature.

Equation (9-1) also shows that the signal-to-noise ratio could be increased by decreasing the electronic bandwidth B. B could be reduced to a value which corresponds to the time the oscilloscope beam requires to move 1 mm along the time axis; an error of less than 10 per cent is allowed in the measurement of a relaxation process with a time constant 10 to 20 times larger than the exponential rise time of the electronic circuit (*14*).

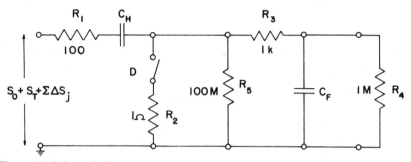

Figure 9-4. Schematic diagram of the electronic diode switch D to attenuate the incoming signal to the point when observation should start. C_H is the holding capacitance, C_F the filter capacitance. Both are changeable together and over a wide range.

Figure 9-4 demonstrates a simplified diagram of the switching circuit as relevant to the signal $S_0 + S_T + \sum \Delta S_j$ [for the relations between ΔS_j and the individual concentration changes $\Delta c_{i,j}$; see (7-3)]. S_0 represents the signal with the blank, S_T the (static) signal due to the biological system, and ΔS_j represents the equilibrium signal change of the jth process. $S_T > 0$ for fluorescence detection and $S_T < 0$ in the observation of absorption changes. In transmission, S_T is generally kept near 1 volt (S_0 similarly) by a load-selector switch at the anode of the multiplier phototube with resistances of 1, 10, and 100 kilohm; in fluorescence, S_T is generally also kept near 1 volt if possible. ΔS_j represents the jth signal change, the time course of which is of interest. For the mentioned values of S_0 and S_T, experimental ranges were 0.4 mvolt $\lesssim \Delta S_j \lesssim$ 100 mvolt (*15*).

The diode switch D in Figure 9-4 is closed at reference time t_0, thus discharging the capacitor C_F and " grounding out " any signal which comes via C_H. Experimentally the anticipated 1 ohm was not quite reached for R_2, the internal dynamic resistance of the switch (2 ohms instead). One can never expect to fabricate a very fast switch with " zero " resistance in the closed position. The operational resistance in the closed position then practically determines all other parameters of the circuit. If F_A is the attenuation factor desired for the " grounding out " of prior fast signal changes, F_A directly determines the resistor R_1 by $R_1 = F_A R_2$. An attenuation factor F_A of from 50 to 200 is generally adequate for investigating consecutive relaxation processes.

Figure 9-5 shows a timing diagram to be discussed later in more detail. At t_3 the diode switch D is opened and, by that time, the capacitor C_F is practically discharged. $R_3 C_F$ primarily determines the rise time of the oscilloscope at this point (for $R_1 \ll R_3$). In addition to a rise-time constant, there is a holding-time constant $R_4 C_H$. The holding time should be long enough not to affect the actual detection of the time course of the signal.

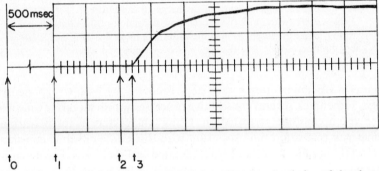

Figure 9-5. A trace of a relaxation process demonstrating the timing of the electronic circuit with the introduction of the various time constants; see Table 9-1 for the meaning of these delay times.

As is apparent from the diagram, $R_4 C_H = 1000 R_3 C_F$. This value is adequate if the oscilloscope deflection $dt/dx = 10 \text{ cm}^{-1} R_3 C_F$, as outlined above. The designer of a specific network would have to keep in mind that a capacitive voltage divider (C_H, C_F) attenuates the signal amplitude of relaxation processes.

R_5 must be large enough so that the signal change ΔS is practically not affected. For avoiding any attenuation of the signal, the condition $R_4 \gg R_1 + R_3$ must hold. Also, C_H and C_F must always have a leakage resistance which is sufficiently above R_4. Although R_F, the leakage resistor of the filtering capacitor C_F, need only be at least 100 times larger than R_4, the leakage resistor of the holding capacitor R_H has to be much larger. If $S_0 = 5$ volts (the upper limit) has to be attenuated at the input of the oscilloscope to "at least 0.5 mvolt," one obtains $R_H = 10^4 R_4$. This condition is actually limiting the upper value in the capacitors C_H.

Figure 9-5 shows the oscilloscope trace of a testing signal, introducing the individual trigger times. The ranges of the time delays are given in

Table 9-1. The first long delay time is necessary to ensure complete discharge of all the capacitors. The delay $t_2 - t_1$ provides a sufficiently long zero line for the evaluations. The delay $t_3 - t_2$ actually " grounds out " any signal which is much faster than the one under investigation. The chemical time constant itself should be in the range of $t_2 - t_1$; the electronic RC rise time is set near $t_3 - t_2$.

TABLE 9-1

DELAY TIMES

$t_1 - t_0 = 500$ msec fixed, sufficient time to discharge all capacitors
$t_2 - t_1 = 2$ cm $\times$ dt/dx (with dt/dx the chosen time deflection of the oscilloscope)
$t_3 - t_2 = 1$mm $\times$ dt/dx as closely as possible within the range 5×10^{-6} sec $< t_3 - t_2 <$
     5×10^{-2} sec

Figure 9-3 demonstrates a fast step, followed by a slow exponential change. Sometimes, several consecutive processes appear along the time axis as response upon some perturbation. Using temperature as the perturbing parameter, a relaxation time spectrum with three different time constants was recently obtained (16) and is represented in Figure 9-6. The equation of the curve is

$$\Delta S = \Delta S_1[1 - \exp(-t/\tau_1)] + \Delta S_2[1 - \exp(-t/\tau_2)]$$
$$+ \Delta S_3[1 - \exp(-t/\tau_3)] \quad (9\text{-}23)$$

with the constants given in Table 9-2. The constant τ_0 of Figure 9-6 is the time constant originating from the perturbing process which initiates the appearance of all ΔS_j (τ_0 is, for instance, the time constant of the temperature rise). The initial shape of the curve is not (markedly) affected as long as $\tau_0 \ll \tau_1$. Any influence of τ_0 upon τ_1 remained unconsidered in Figure 9-6.

TABLE 9-2

EXPERIMENTAL VALUES OF THE PARAMETERS FOR EQUATION (9-23)

INDEX j	ΔS_j, mvolts	τ_j, μsec
1	−9	50
2	2.5	4×10^3
3	−5.7	6×10^5

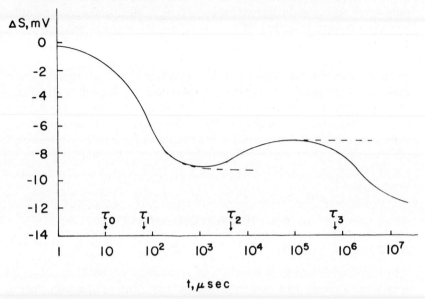

Figure 9-6. Sequence of three relaxation processes with heating time τ_0. The fastest relaxation process is determined by τ_1, a much slower one by τ_2, and the slowest by τ_3. Equation (9-23) leads to the curve in conjunction with Table 9-2.

The first relaxation process with τ_1 can generally be measured directly with $R_3 C_F \approx 0.1\tau_1$. When τ_2 is to be measured, one attenuates strongly any signal appearing before $0.1\tau_2$. "Instantaneous" release from attenuation at $0.1\tau_2$ permits one to follow the time course of the second relaxation process with adequate precision. τ_3 is then measured in the same way: The signal remains "grounded" until about $0.1\tau_3$, at which time grounding is released.

The dashed lines of Figure 9-6 represent the approach to that equilibrium value which would be present without another relaxation process following. The small differences between the actual curve and the dashed extrapolations indicate that the relaxation times τ_j and the associated equilibrium changes ΔS_i (individually determined from the curves of the actual system) are barely different from the ones determined from the curves of isolated reaction steps. This is only possible if the condition $\tau_j \ll \tau_{j+1}$ is sufficiently well fulfilled. Then, little further error is introduced by grounding out the jth process up to about $0.1\tau_{j+1}$. Figure 9-6 shows that the consecutive relaxation processes are associated with approximately equal changes in the signal. If consecutive signal changes are about equal, one only needs to maintain the condition $\tau_{j+1}/\tau_j > 30$. If there is some difference in the signal heights ΔS_j, a ratio of 100 becomes necessary. The experimental ratios may easily be derived from Table 9-2, averaging about 100.

The above discussion showed that an improvement in the signal-to-noise ratio of consecutive processes can be obtained by (lossfully) attenuating those processes which are much faster than the one under consideration and switching the attenuation off when the particular process of interest enters the (selected) time range of the recording (or displaying) system. If the phenomena show very poor reproducibility, one would have to employ a multichannel circuit, one channel each for the observation of a particular time range.

9–5. POLARIZED LIGHT

A. Brewster's Angle

For optical-detection methods it is sometimes advisable to cover all optical interphases with antireflection coating. This is the only way to reduce reflection on image-forming surfaces. With non-image-forming surfaces and linearly polarized light, an alternative approach is available, based on the application of Brewster's law:

$$\tan \phi_p = n \qquad (9\text{-}24)$$

where n is the refractive index referred to vacuum, ϕ_p is the angle for incidence with no reflection of light which is polarized in the plane of incidence. As sufficient understanding of Brewster's law is important for an efficient design of equipment employing polarized light, a brief discussion of some basic optical principles will follow.

Figure 9-7 shows schematically the plane of incidence for a light beam with $E_{\parallel}$ demonstrating the electric field vector of the light beam, *parallel* to the plane of incidence. $E_{\perp}$ represents the electric field vector *perpendicular* to the drawing plane of Figure 9-7. The law of refraction between the light beam incident under the angle ϕ and the light beam refracted with angle χ is then

$$\frac{\sin \phi}{\sin \chi} = n \qquad (9\text{-}25)$$

There are some special angles, one being the angle of "total reflection," which is only defined for a beam of direction, which is opposite to the one

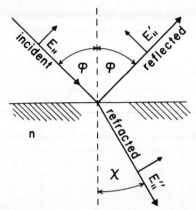

Figure 9-7. Reflection and refraction of a light beam shown in the plane of incidence with E as electric field vector and ϕ and χ the angles between beams.

shown in Figure 9-7 and thus propagating *from* the denser medium. This angle of total reflection, ϕ_T, is defined by

$$\sin \phi_T = \frac{1}{n} \qquad (9\text{-}26)$$

Another angle is given by Brewster's law, under which conditions the reflected beam is perpendicular to the refracted one. At this angle ϕ_p, it is by definition the reflected $E'_\parallel = 0$; the incident beam with $E_\parallel$ is fully refracted. An incident beam with $E_\perp$ is, on the other hand, still partially reflected.

B. Fresnel's Description

A plot of the ratios E'/E as a function of the angle ϕ is shown in Figure 9-8 for the transition air → crown glass with $n = 1.5$. Fresnel described the curves of Figure 9-8 by the two equations

$$\frac{E'_\perp}{E_\perp} = -\frac{\sin (\phi - \chi)}{\sin (\phi + \chi)} \qquad (9\text{-}27)$$

$$\frac{E'_\parallel}{E_\parallel} = \frac{n \cos \phi - \cos \chi}{n \cos \phi + \cos \chi} \qquad (9\text{-}28)$$

The reflected field vectors are denoted by the prime introduced in Figure 9-7. A *negative* right side in (9-27) simply means that there is a phase difference of 180° between incident and reflected field vector. A *positive* right side in (9-28) means that $E'_{||}$ and $E_{||}$ show a phase difference of $180°$ upon reflection. Aside from $E''/E = 1 - E'/E$, one may also directly derive trigonometric relations between the refracted field vector $E''_{\perp}$ (or $E''_{||}$) and the incident field vector.

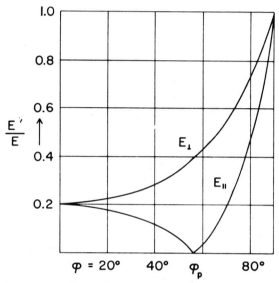

Figure 9-8. Ratio of the amplitudes between the reflected and the incident electric field vector as a function of the angle of incidence ϕ, shown for two perpendicular directions of polarization of the electric vector.

For the special case of normal incidence with $\phi = 0$, one obtains for the total reflection (without the possibility of distinguishing between $E_{||}$ and $E_{\perp}$):

$$\frac{E'}{E} = -\frac{n-1}{n+1} \tag{9-29}$$

The minus sign in this equation means that E and E' have opposite direction for $n > 1$ and the same direction for $n < 1$.

The reflectance R_λ per interphase (the wavelength dependence now being considered) is defined by the ratio of reflected radiative power to incident radiative power. As radiative power is proportional to the square of the electric field vector, one obtains

$$R_\lambda = (E'/E)^2 \tag{9-30}$$

Combining (9-30) and (9-29) results (for normal incidence!) in the important equation for the reflectance:

$$R_\lambda = \left(\frac{n-1}{n+1}\right)^2 \tag{9-31}$$

One obtains for crown glass with $n = 1.5$ (for visible light; see also Figure 9-8) a reflectance of $R_\lambda = 4$ per cent. For diamand with $n = 2.4$ (for visible light) one finds $R_\lambda = 17$ per cent.

C. Interrelationships

The field vector $E'_\parallel$ would have a phase difference of 90 per cent to $E_\parallel$ at ϕ_p, if $E'_\parallel$ would exist at this point. This nonexistence can easily be seen by rewriting (9-28)

$$\frac{E'_\parallel}{E_\parallel} = \frac{\tan(\phi - \chi)}{\tan(\phi + \chi)} \tag{9-32}$$

As Brewster's angle is defined as the one where the reflected and refracted beam are perpendicular to each other, it here becomes $\chi = 90° - \phi_p$. The numerator in (9-32) has then some finite value, while $\tan 90° = \infty$. One may now also easily derive Brewster's law by the sequence

$$\sin \phi_p = n \sin \chi = n \sin(90° - \phi_p) = n \cos \phi_p \tag{9-33}$$

If n is the refractive index of the denser medium with reference to vacuum, Brewster's angle for a light beam propagating toward the optical interphase from within the denser medium (from below in Figure 9-7) is defined by

$$\tan \phi_p = \frac{1}{n} \tag{9-34}$$

One thus obtains $\phi_p < 45°$, while (9-24) only allows $\phi_p > 45°$. For the case valid for (9-34) the curves in Figure 9-8 are also compressed together to the left with $E'/E \to 1$ for $\phi \to \phi_p$. The angle ϕ is defined throughout as the angle of incidence, without regard to whether incidence occurs from air to glass (or any "weakly absorbing" medium), from glass to air, or from one optical medium to some other. This strict definition was already used in (9-26).

As long as n is not substantially changing with the wavelength λ, one may use Brewster's angle windows also for spectropolarimeters. Much more effective are such windows for monochromatic light. Interphases oriented at ϕ_p are therefore extensively used for the highly monochromatic lasers, treated somewhat more extensively in Chapter 13. Brewster's angle surfaces can then also provide for pulsed laser light with a very high degree of linear polarization.

PROBLEM

A light-scattering apparatus is to be designed with very fast response, thus requiring very high geometric flux and incorporation of interference filters. A mercury arc of 20 mm length and 2 mm width represents the light source. The rectangular flow cell is about 4 mm × 4 mm × 25 mm. The head-on multiplier phototube has a circular active area of 22-mm diameter. Distances between the light source and the center of the flow cell and between the center of the flow cell and the photocathode cannot be made smaller than 10 cm. Compute the minimum geometric flux for the illuminating beam and for the scattering beam, and the diameters, positions, and lengths of the lenses to be employed.

REFERENCES

1. (a) A. J. Williams, Jr., R. E. Tarpley, and W. R. Clark, *Trans. AIEE*, **67**, 47 (1948); (b) B. Chance, *Rev. Sci. Instr.*, **22**, 619 (1951); (c) C. C. Yang, *Rev. Sci. Instr.*, **25**, 807 (1954); (d) M. Laikin, *Rev. Sci. Instr.*, **34**, 773 (1963).

2. (a) W. Schottkey, *Ann. Physik*, **57**, 541 (1918); (b) T. C. Fry, *J. Franklin Inst.*, **199**, 203 (1925); (c) V. K. Zworykin and E. G. Ramberg, *Photoelectricity and Its Application*, Wiley, New York, 1949; (d) R. C. Jones, *Advan. Electron.*, **5**, 1 (1953); (e) D. A. Bell, *Electrical Noise*, Van Nostrand, London, 1960.

3. (a) W. Schockley and J. R. Pierce, *Proc. IRE*, **26**, 321 (1938); (b) R. W. Engstron, R. G. Stoudenheimer and A. M. Glover, *Nucleonics*, **10**, 58 (1952).

4. (a) G. Czerlinski, *Biochim. Biophys. Acta*, **64**, 199 (1962); (b) G. Czerlinski and F. Hommes, *Biochim. Biophys. Acta*, **79**, 46 (1964); (c) G. Czerlinski and G. Schreck, *Biochemistry*, **3**, 89 (1964); (d) G. Czerlinski and G. Schreck, *J. Biol. Chem.*, **239**, 913 (1964); (e) G. Czerlinski, *J. Theoret. Biol.*, **7**, 463 (1964).

5. (a) W. H. Melhuish, *J. Phys. Chem.*, **65**, 229 (1961); (b) W. H. Melhuish, *J. Opt. Soc. Am.*, **51**, 278 (1961); (c) A. Shepp, *J. Chem. Phys.*, **25**, 579 (1956); (d) A. Shepp, *Opt. Spectry. USSR, English Transl.*, **8**, 43 (1960).

6. The concept of geometric flux was extensively used formerly by (a) K. Räntsch, *Die Optik in der Feinmesstechnik*, pp. 53, 68, C. Hanser Verlag, Munich, 1949; (b) see also G. Czerlinski, *Rev. Sci. Instr.*, **33**, 1184 (1962), Table II.

7. D. G. Tucker, *J. Inst. Elec. Engrs.*, **94(III)**, 218 (1947).

8. J. V. Uspensky, *Introduction to Mathematical Probability*, p. 407, McGraw-Hill, New York, 1937.

9. V. D. Landon, *Proc. IRE*, **29**, 50 (1941).

10. G. Czerlinski and A. Weiss, *Appl. Opt.*, **4**, 59 (1965).

11. G. Czerlinski and G. Schreck, *Biochemistry*, **3**, 89 (1964).

12. G. Czerlinski and F. Hommes, *Biochim. Biophys. Acta*, **79**, 46 (1964).
13. W. Schottkey, *Ann. Physik*, **57**, 541 (1918); see also Ref. *1*.
14. G. Czerlinski and M. Eigen, *Z. Elektrochem.*, **63**, 652 (1959), Eq. (20) and its discussion with $RC/2$ there $\to \tau_J$ here and $\tau \to R_3 C_F$ [where R_3 and C_F are as defined in Figure 9-4].
15. G. Czerlinski and W. Nadler, *J. Sci. Instr.*, **42**, 470 (1965).
16. G. Czerlinski and J. Malkewitz, *Biochemistry*, **4**, 1127 (1965).

CHAPTER 10

JOULE HEATING

Among the transient methods for chemical relaxation, the temperature-jump method clearly seems to become the most useful one, which is apparently due to the following factors:

1. Fast heating can easily be accomplished by high-voltage capacitator discharges (Joule heating). The discharge time is determined by the resistance of the solution R and by the capacitance C which is being charged up. The heating time constant τ_0 is then defined by

$$\tau_0 = \tfrac{1}{2} RC \qquad (10\text{-}1)$$

2. From the very beginning, optical detection of concentration changes was used which allows reasonably good decoupling between the perturbing circuit and the detecting device. Optical detection also gives much larger flexibility in the number of systems which can be followed, including systems of higher complexity.

3. Perturbation by temperature jumps is based upon the thermodynamically important quantity enthalpy. Enthalpies have been considered for many decades as important parameters of chemical systems, and extensive information on them is available in the literature. Chemical relaxation by temperature jumps produces as a by-product information on the enthalpy changes of individual reaction steps.

4. After a temperature-jump apparatus has been constructed, very few crucial adjustments are necessary for the operation of the instrument. The use of such an instrument does therefore not require technically sophisticated personnel.

5. Temperature jumps can be generated in quite small volumes, which is of great importance if the kinetics of valuable materials (such as enzyme systems) is to be investigated.

6. Only relatively few experiments are needed to give the desired kinetic information derivable from the concentration dependence of the chemical relaxation time constants.

The temperature-jump method was originally proposed by Eigen in 1954, suggesting conductometric detection (*1*). But in the first operational instrument, optical detection was used (*2*). From there on the instrumenta development followed two different lines. In one of them a design was developed (*3*), which is shown in Figure 10-1. The inner square in the right (cross-sectional) view is perpendicular to the axis of the cell and about 1 cm × 1 cm. A comparatively large volume for this discharge cell is required by the employment of "floating" electrodes (the discharge area of the electrodes has to be surrounded by water to avoid direct arc over, when up to 100 kv are employed).

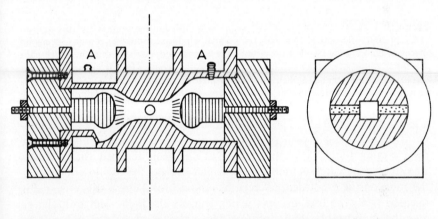

Figure 10-1. Sample cell of Eigen and DeMaeyer, redrawn from M. Eigen and L. DeMaeyer *in* A. Weissberger (ed.), *Technique of Organic Chemistry*, Vol. VIII, Pt. II, p. 895, Wiley (Interscience), New York, 1963. Axial view on the left side, cross-sectional view in the optical axis on the right side; *A* are stoppers for filling the cell.

A considerably different design was developed in the other line (*4*). Further modifications led to a design shown in Figure 10-2. The distance of the inner plane surfaces of the conical lenses is 1 cm, while the electrode distance is about 0.5 cm. The sample cells employ conical lenses for high performance in optical detection (*5*). The tube for filling the cell is normal to the plane of the drawing.

A block diagram of the actual instrumental arrangement is shown in Figure 10-3. The detection circuit employs a special filtering network with

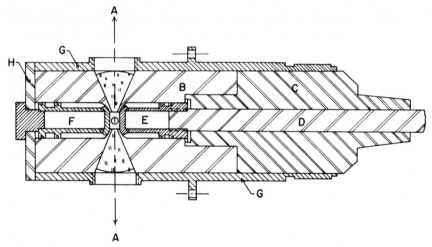

Figure 10-2. Axial view of the latest design of a temperature-jump cell of the author. *AA* represents the optical axis with the conical windows of quartz; *B* and *C* are solid pieces of compounded Teflon or nylon; *D* is a brass rod, connected to the spark gap; *E* is the (thermostated) high-voltage electrode; *F* is the grounded electrode; *G* is the outer (grounded) brass tube; *H* is the (brass) cover plate (72 mm in diameter). The solution is heated where the cell axis and the optical axis cross; the electrodes are platinum-covered.

a grounding switch (*6*). The operation of the instrument for a single temperature jump starts with pushing the push button for the high voltage for charging the 10-kV capacitor. Full charge is reached within 4 sec. The small footswitch is then closed, which triggers the oscilloscope. After the trace on the oscilloscope screen has moved for 2 cm, a trigger signal is released from the oscilloscope, which triggers the high-voltage discharge and the monostable multivibrator. The pulse width of the monostable multivibrator is set such that it coincides with the time the oscilloscope trace requires for moving along 1 mm; a trigger is then released, which initiates the quick ungrounding of the signal. All processes are thus blanked out, which are much faster than appropriate for measurement at the selected time deflection. A rise-time filter provides in addition for the best signal-to-noise ratio. As the oscilloscope trace reaches the end of the deflection, a trigger is obtained which renews the grounding of the signal. An oscilloscope trace of a slow relaxation process with two faster ones grounded out is shown in Figure 10-4 (*7*). See also Section 9-4.

Although the temperature-jump method is generally applicable to any phase, the liquid phase is most suitable; of primary interest to biological systems are conducting aqueous solutions.

The temperature rise in a solution ΔT is given by

$$\Delta T = \frac{W}{Q}\frac{\kappa_T}{\kappa_S} \qquad (10\text{-}2)$$

where $\kappa_T = 0.239$ cal/joule, κ_S is the specific heat of system (in cal deg^{-1} cm^{-3}), Q is the volume (in cubic centimeters) actually heated by ΔT, and W is the energy dissipated in the system.

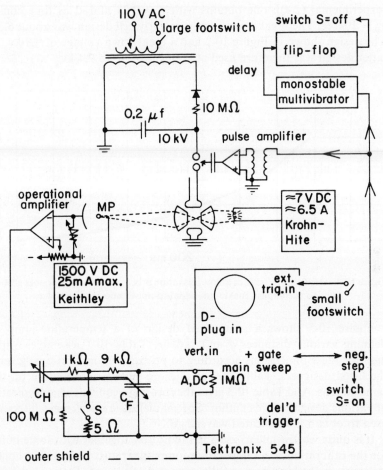

Figure 10-3. Over-all block diagram for the temperature-jump apparatus as used in 1964. Full wiring and grounding are not shown.

If the capacitance C is charged to a voltage V and discharged across the solution, it is the dissipated energy

$$W = \tfrac{1}{2} CV^2 \qquad (10\text{-}3)$$

The smaller the capacitance C [to obtain a short heating time, use (10-1)], the larger voltage V has to be applied. To avoid quite small capacitances, one therefore should attempt to keep the resistance of the solution R as low as possible. The electrolytic resistance may be measured at 10 kc in a bridge circuit. If an ohmic resistance of the solution of 80 ohms is measured [experimental (2,4)], one obtains with $C = 0.25$ μfarad as time constant $\tau_0 = 10\mu$sec. The breakdown voltage in early cell design was about 6.2 kv. The design shown in Figure 10-2 had a breakdown voltage of 9.8 kv. This latter design was therefore used at voltages of up to 9.4 kv.

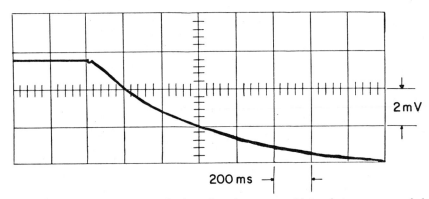

Figure 10-4. Oscilloscope trace of a slow relaxation process with two faster ones grounded out, to accomplish maximum signal-to-noise ratio for this process.

Figure 10-5 shows a generalized design of a temperature-jump cell, defining various distances d and radii r. Table 10-1 assembles various data for these dimensions according to private communications, given by the listed designers. Table 10-2 gives more general information on these same designs. And Table 10-3 gives the rms-noise equivalent concentrations of various designs of this author. Special dielectric interference filters were used to obtain the indicated wavelength.

It is quite worthwhile to use a pH indicator, together with some buffers, for the calibration of a temperature-jump apparatus. If the buffer concentration is high, kinetics normally cannot be followed. Static signals of a buffered system are generally given by (4-38). One should search for an

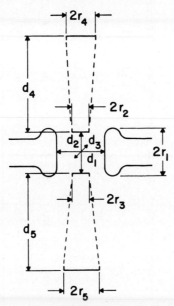

Figure 10-5. Definition of dimensional parameters around temperature-jump cells: electrode distance $= d_1$, distance of the two optical borders of the solution $= d_2$, while
$$d_3 \perp d_1 \perp d_2 \perp d_3.$$

indicator and conditions where η_4 can be neglected. For this omission, (4-38) may be simplified (also employing $c_4^0 = 0$) to

$$S_T - S_0 = \frac{K_{2,1}c_3^0/c_2^0}{K_{2,1}c_3^0/c_2^0 + 1}\, \eta_1 c_1^0 \tag{10-4}$$

If I^-, IH, and B^-, BH are the two different forms of indicator and of buffer, one may write the reaction scheme

$$I^- + BH \underset{k_2}{\overset{k_1}{\rightleftharpoons}} B^- + IH \tag{10-5}$$

If $K_{I,H} = \bar{c}_I \bar{c}_H/\bar{c}_{IH}$ and $K_{B,H} = \bar{c}_B \bar{c}_H/\bar{c}_{BH}$, then $K_{2,1} = K_{I,H}/K_{B,H}$ and $K_{2,1}c_3^0/c_2^0 = K_{I,H}/\bar{c}_H$ (the double bar again indicates buffering). Inserting this latter expression in (10-4) gives, after rearrangement, and with the assumption that *only* $\eta_1 = \eta_1 \neq 0$:

$$S_T - S_0 = \eta_1 c_1^0 \frac{1}{1 + \bar{c}_H/K_{I,H}} \tag{10-6}$$

η_1 for an absorbing indicator is derived via

$$S_T - S_0 = S_0[\exp(-\varepsilon_I' l \bar{c}_I \ln 10) - 1] \tag{10-7}$$

TABLE 10-1

DESIGN VALUES OF DIFFERENT TEMPERATURE-JUMP CELLS ACCORDING TO FIGURE 10-5

DESIGNER (ASSISTANT, YEAR)	$2r_1$, mm	πr_2^2, mm²	πr_3^2, mm²	πr_4^2, mm²	πr_5^2, mm²	d_1, mm	d_2, mm	d_3, mm	d_4, mm	d_5, mm
R. A. Alberty (A. H. Colen, 1961–1964)	20	20	20			10	10	5-10	20	20
R. Lumry (A. F. Yapel, Jr., 1962–1963)	20	20	20	20	20	15	11	11	20	20
H. Scheraga (G. Davenport, 1964)		12	12			15.7	10	10		
G. Czerlinski (Refs. 4, 7)[a]	10	20	20	400	400	10 ± 2	10	10	23 ± 2	23 ± 2
L. DeMaeyer and co-workers[b]	15.9	29	29	83	83	25	10	10	15	15

[a] Latest model manufactured by Science Products Corp., Route 46, Dover, N.J.
[b] Latest model designed and built in 1964–1965 by Messanlagen Studiengesellschaft m.b.H., Göttingen, Lange Geismarstrasse 75, West Germany.

TABLE 10-2

Further Characteristics of Temperature-Jump Instruments

DESIGNER (ASSISTANT, YEAR)	TOTAL PER FILLING, ml	VOLUMES ACTUALLY HEATED, ml	HEATING-TIME CONST., μsec	TEMP. RISE, °C	DISCH. VOLTS EMPL., kv	MEASURED RATE CONSTANTS			
						BIMOLECULAR		MONOMOLECULAR	
						LARGEST, M^{-1}	SMALLEST, sec^{-1}	LARGEST, sec^{-1}	SMALLEST, sec^{-1}
Alberty (Ref. 10)	10	1	10	3–10	15–30	10^5	10		
Lumry (Refs. 8, 9)	20	1	1–2	8–10	35–45	7×10^8	6×10^2		
Scheraga (Ref. 11)	2	1.4	4	≤5.2	≤25				
Czerlinski (Refs. 4, 7)	4	0.5	8	2–5	5–9	6.8×10^8	4×10^4	24,000	2.2
DeMaeyer (Ref. 13)	7	1.5	0.1	[a]	to 50 kv	[a]		[a]	

[a] See **Ref. 3** for ranges.

TABLE 10-3

RMS-Noise Equivalent Concentrations

RMS-NOISE-EQUIV. CONC., NO ABS. BACKGROUND AT 10^5 cps ELECTRONIC BANDWIDTH	OPTICAL CHARACTERISTICS				TYPE OF LIGHT SOURCE	DISTANCES		REFERENCE
	EXCITATION		EMISSION			LAMP ↔ CELL, cm	CELL ↔ PHOTOM., cm	
	λ, mμ	$\Delta\lambda$, mμ	λ, mμ	$\Delta\lambda$, mμ				
7×10^{-9} M phenol red-anion	564	16	—	—	W of G.E.	10.5 ± 0.4	6.5 ± 0.5	12
6×10^{-8} M tryptophane	280	16	—	—	B H 6	10.5 ± 0.4	6.5 ± 0.5	12
2×10^{-7} M tryptophane	280	25	350	40	B H 6	10.5 ± 0.4	10.0 ± 0.5	12
5×10^{-7} M DPNH[a]	350	40	440	60	B H 6	10.5 ± 0.4	10.0 ± 0.5	5, 12

[a] DPNH = reduced diphosphopyridinenucleotide, which is a coenzyme with only 3% fluorescence yield at room temperature. Generally: pH 7-buffer, ionic strength 0.1, 25°C.

where S_0 is the input signal without the absorbing indicator, appearing in volts (for instance, if detection of static signals is observed on the oscilloscope screen, where the kinetic results are observed afterward), ε_I' is the decadic molar extinction coefficient in $M^{-1}\,cm^{-1}$, l is the length of the light path in the solution, here 1 cm, and $\ln 10 = 2.303$ is the conversion factor between decadic and natural logarithms.

If $\varepsilon_I' \bar{c}_I l \ll 1$, one may expand the exponential term in the last equation and omit higher terms, giving

$$S_T - S_0 = -S_0 \varepsilon_I' l \bar{c}_I \ln 10 \tag{10-8}$$

One immediately derives that under such conditions

$$\eta_I = -S_0 \varepsilon_I' l \ln 10 \tag{10-9}$$

Since only one component is absorbing, (10-6) may be rewritten with the experimental parameter $S_I^0 = \eta_I c_I^0$. Then

$$S_I = -S_I^0 (1 + \bar{c}_H / K_{I,H})^{-1} \tag{10-10}$$

Figure 10-6 is a plot of (10-10) for three different pH buffers and also shows the corresponding experimental points. As $S_0 = 1.8 \pm 0.1$ volt, corrections for nonlinearity have been neglected.

For $\eta_4 = 0$, (7-23) represents the proper general form of the relative signal change. Thus (7-23) gives, together with (6-21) and further modifications,

$$\frac{\Delta S_T}{S_T - S_0} = \frac{\Delta H_{2,1}\, \Delta T}{RT^2}(1 + K_{I,H}/\bar{c}_H)^{-1} \tag{10-11}$$

One obtains an S-shaped curve as for (10-10), but with inverse inflection. Employing (10-10) and its definition, the last equation becomes

$$\Delta S_I = 4\,\Delta S_I^0\, \frac{\bar{c}_H / K_{I,H}}{(1 + \bar{c}_H / K_{I,H})^2} \tag{10-12}$$

where

$$4\,\Delta S_I^0 = \frac{\Delta H_{2,1}\, \Delta T}{RT^2}\, S_I^0 \tag{10-13}$$

The factor 4 has been introduced to define ΔS_I^0 as the maximum value in the experimentally determined curves. Figure 10-7 demonstrates a plot of (10-12) for three different buffers. Three different ΔS_I^0 are derivable experimentally, with their differences being solely due to differences among the $\Delta H_{2,1}$ of the systems.

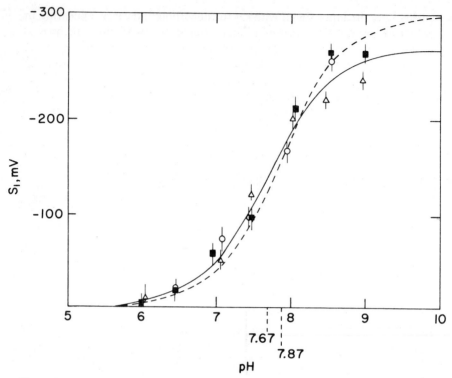

Figure 10-6. pH titration curve of phenol red in various buffers within a temperature-jump apparatus. Squares represent the most probable points for phosphate buffer, triangles those for glycylglycin, and circles those for histidin. The vertical lines represent experimental fluctuations. The solid line is drawn for pK = 7.67 and $S_I^0 = 274$ mvolts, the dashed line for pK = 7.87 and $S_I^0 = 310$ mvolts.

Looking at the definition of $K_{2,1}$ in terms of protonic dissociations [following (10-5)], one realizes then that

$$\Delta H_{2,1} = \Delta H_{I,H} - \Delta H_{B,H} \qquad (10\text{-}14)$$

If $\Delta \bar{S}_I^0$ denotes the maximum signal change in one buffer system and $\Delta \bar{\bar{S}}_I^0$ the maximum signal change in another buffer system, the quotient of two equations (10-12), also incorporating (10-14), gives

$$\frac{\Delta \bar{S}_I^0}{\Delta \bar{\bar{S}}_I^0} = \frac{\Delta H_{I,H} - \Delta \bar{H}_{B,H}}{\Delta H_{I,H} - \Delta \bar{\bar{H}}_{B,H}} \qquad (10\text{-}15)$$

If thus any two ΔH are known, the third one may be determined according to (10-15). This ratio is not restricted to the maximum of the curve. The ratio of signal changes may be formed at any *fixed* pH within the range of reasonable measurement of ΔS_I. After determination of the enthalpies of the individual reactions, one may then proceed to compute the temperature change according to (10-11) or (10-13).

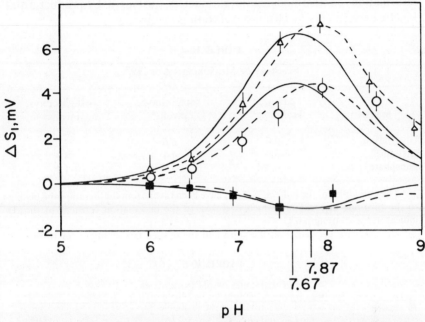

Figure 10-7. The "jump height," ΔS_1, as a function of pH in different buffers. Symbols and lines are denoted as in Figure 10-6, although here three solid and three dashed lines are necessary to account for the differences in the enthalpies of the buffers.

Table 10-4 gives the results from actual measurements, demonstrated in Figure 10-7. The pH indicator phenol red was used, and its enthalpy of proton dissociation may now be computed with (10-15). If one inserts pairs of the ΔS_I^0 in (10-15), one obtains for the solid curves and for the dashed curves an enthalpy, which is -2.2 ± 0.1 kcal/mole.

The fluorescence pH indicator 4-methylumbelliferon may be used in a similar manner as the absorbing indicator phenol red, leading to an enthalpy for the protonic dissociation of 4-methylumbelliferon of $\Delta H_{I,H} = -3$ kcal/mole. This enthalpy is associated with an error of about 20 per cent, as the precision in measuring fluorescence changes is somewhat less than that of measuring absorption changes. The experiments show that enthalpies of reactions can be determined from temperature-jump experiments, using either fluorescence or transmission. As the maxima of the equilibrium changes also give the protonic dissociation constants (or dissociation constants in general), and as one knows the temperature, one may also calculate entropies of reactions. Thus one obtains quite valuable information on thermodynamic parameters, just as a by-product from kinetic experiments by chemical relaxation methods.

TABLE 10-4

SUMMARY OF MEASUREMENTS OF ΔS_I^0

BUFFER	$\Delta H_{B,H}$, kcal/mole[a]	SOLID CURVE, mvolts[b]	DASHED CURVE, mvolts[b]
Glycylglycin	-10.0	6.6	7.0
Histidin	-6.9	4.4	4.3
Phosphate	-0.95	-1.1	-1.2

[a] The enthalpies of the buffers, $\Delta H_{B,H}$, have been taken from the literature and belong to the protonic dissociation, which is closest to the dissociation constant of the pH indicator, ionic strength 0.1.

[b] The ΔS_I^0 are derived from the solid and the dashed curves of Figure 10-7.

TABLE 10-5

ENTHALPIES OF pH INDICATORS

COMPOUND	pK_H	ΔH, kcal/mole	λ_I, mμ	λ_{IH}, mμ	$\varepsilon'_{\lambda I}$, M^{-1} cm^{-1}	$\varepsilon'_{\lambda IH}$, M^{-1} cm^{-1}
4-Methylumbelliferon	7.6	-3.0 ± 0.6	360[a]	320	1.9×10^4	1.4×10^4
Phenol red	7.9	-2.2 ± 0.1	563	430	5.4×10^4	3.0×10^4
Bromthymol blue	6.9	-2.1 ± 0.3	620	435	3.6×10^4	2.0×10^4
Bromcresol green	4.7	$+1.0 \pm 0.3$	610	450	4.2×10^4	2.0×10^4
Bromchlorphenol blue	4.0	$+1.2 \pm 0.5$	590	440	6.9×10^4	2.2×10^4

[a] Fluorescence excitation.

Table 10-5 summarizes enthalpies of pH indicators, determined by the temperature-jump method in the laboratory of the author. These pH indicators are frequently used in calibrations or in coupled reactions, so that knowledge of their enthalpies is rather important. 4-methylumbelliferon is the only fluorescent pH indicator used thus far with the temperature-jump apparatus. Some other physical parameters, which might be of interest, have also been incorporated in Table 10-5. The pK_H was obtained by spectrophotometric titration (ionic strength 0.1, 25°C), λ_I and λ_{IH} are the wavelengths of maximum absorption (in the visible) of components I and IH, respectively. The decadic molar extinction coefficient ε'_λ refers to the wavelength of maximum absorption of the component, indicated behind λ.

PROBLEMS

1. Assume there are no difficulties in using a very fine beam for detection (such as a continuous-wave laser), compute from the values given in the text [around (10-3)]: (a) the resistance of a heating cell of 1 mm $\times$ 1 mm $\times$ 1 mm; (b) capacitance, voltage, and field strength for such a small cell and $\Delta T = 5°C$, $\tau_0 = 10$ μsec; (c) capacitance, voltage, and field strength for this same cell and $\Delta T = 2°C$, $\tau_0 = 0.5$ μsec; (d) discuss the feasibility of arrangements (b) and (c).
2. Compute the design values for a 10-nanosec discharge circuit, neglecting distributed capacitances and inductances. What difficulties would one encounter in building and using such a discharge circuit for temperature-jump experiments?

REFERENCES

1. M. Eigen, *Discussions Faraday Soc.*, **17**, 194 (1954).
2. G. Czerlinski and M. Eigen, *Z. Elektrochem.*, **63**, 652 (1959).
3. M. Eigen and L. DeMaeyer, *in* A. Weissberger, (ed.), *Technique of Organic Chemistry*, Vol. VIII, Pt. II, p. 895, Wiley (Interscience), New York, 1963.
4. G. Czerlinski, *Rev. Sci. Instr.*, **33**, 1184 (1962).
5. G. Czerlinski and A. Weiss, *Appl. Opt.* **4**, 59 (1965).
6. G. Czerlinski and W. Nadler, *J. Sci. Instr.*, **42**, 470 (1965).
7. G. Czerlinski and J. Malkewitz, *Biochemistry*, **4**, 1127 (1965).
8. A. Yapel and R. Lumry, *J. Am. Chem. Soc.*, **86**, 4499 (1964).
9. R. Lumry and A. Yapel, personal communication.
10. R. A. Alberty and A. H. Colen, personal communication.
11. H. A. Scheraga and G. Davenport, personal communication.
12. G. Czerlinski, unpublished data.
13. L. DeMaeyer, personal communication (see footnote b of Table 10-1).

CHAPTER 11

DIELECTRIC HEATING

In Joule heating, a single aperiodically damped pulse is employed to heat the solution by frictional dissipation of the moving ions. The fundamental frequency of this discharge pulse corresponds to one which is somewhat below 1 Mcps (depending upon the individual design). One generally attempts to avoid (damped) oscillations in the discharges, as they would extend the heating over a longer time than desired. Joule heating, on the other hand, could certainly also be generated by any oscillatory process of a few microseconds duration as long as the ions can follow the change in the direction of the electric field. The movement of the ion has to proceed in one direction over a distance of at least about the diameter of the hydration sphere to generate reasonable frictional disturbance.

Although the distance of movement is dependent upon field strength, Joule heating generally loses importance above the kilomegacycle range. But the losses by the dipolar reorientations of water molecules then gain progressively in importance. Near 10 kMc water molecules demonstrate

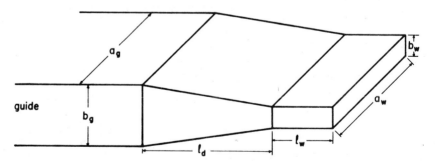

Figure 11-1. Termination of a wave guide for X-band heating in the terminating cavity (see the text as a guide to the labeling).

their largest dielectric absorption. This is in the X-band region of microwaves, which therefore may be used for heating. Ertl and Gerischer (1) employed this method originally in 1961. Figure 11-1 demonstrates a design for an absorption cavity originally considered by this author early in 1960 for construction. The various lengths are defined as follows: l_d is the length of the dielectric (a rectangular pyramid) within the axis of the wave guide; l_w is the length of the water-carrying cavity (flow system); a_w is the width of the water-carrying cavity; b_w is the height of the water-carrying cavity; a_g is the width of the wave guide, filled with air (or pressurized SF_6); b_g is the height of the gas-filled wave guide.

The dimensions of a wave guide are commercially given, and are largely determined by the microwave band. Thus the choice for the values of l_d, l_w, a_w, and b_w need only to be discussed. The choice of these four parameters is determined as follows: l_d is given by the H_{10} wavelength within the dielectric; l_w is given by the H_{10} wavelength within the aqueous solution; a_w is given by the H_{10} wavelength within the dielectric; b_w is determined by the power per pulse and the anticipated temperature rise ΔT. This latter dimension is the only one permitting flexibility. But certain lower limits in b_w are set by optical detectability and breakdown voltage. The latter could occur easily at heating speeds which are faster than the propagation of sound in water. As the X-band-microwave generating magnetrons mostly have pulse widths far below 10 microseconds, one should start to work around 4°C, where the temperature coefficient of the expansion of water is zero. The formulation in mathematical language requires some additional definitions and relationships. First, all equations will be reviewed, and then additional definitions will be introduced.

$$l_d \geqslant \frac{1}{2} \frac{\lambda}{[\varepsilon_d - (\lambda/\lambda_{\lim})^2]^{1/2}} = \tfrac{1}{2} \Lambda_d \tag{11-1}$$

where Λ_d is the wavelength in the guide with reference to dielectric (d as index) or water (w as index); ε_d is the adequate dielectric constant; $\lambda_{\lim}$ is the wavelength limit $= 2a_{\text{vaccum}} = 2a_g$ of the above definition; and λ is the wavelength of the microwave radiation in free vacuum.

$$l_w \geqslant \tfrac{1}{2} \Lambda_w = \frac{1}{2} \frac{\lambda}{[\varepsilon_w - (\lambda/\lambda_{\lim})^2]^{1/2}} \tag{11-2}$$

$$a_w \geqslant l_d \tag{11-3}$$

$$b_w = \frac{W \kappa_T}{\kappa_s a_w l_w \, \Delta T} \tag{11-4}$$

where $\kappa_T = 0.239$ cal/joule, a conversion constant; κ_s = specific heat of water $= 1.0$ cal $\deg^{-1}$ cm^{-3}; ΔT is the "desired" temperature rise (the "most dependent variable"); and W is the actually dissipated pulse energy $=$ (power N) $\times$ (time τ_0).

$$W = N\tau_0 = \frac{a_w b_w}{2} \left(\frac{\varepsilon_0}{\mu_0}\right)^{1/2} \frac{\lambda}{\Lambda_w} \left(\frac{V_{max}}{b_w}\right)^2 \Delta t \qquad (11\text{-}5)$$

where Δt is the pulse width in seconds; V_{max} is the peak voltage of the microwave pulse in the cell; $Z_0^* = (\varepsilon_0/\mu_0)^{1/2} = 377$ ohms in vacuo, while one finds in a dielectric of dielectric constant ε the impedance $Z^* = Z_0^* \varepsilon^{1/2}$. Now combining (11-4) with (11-5) and (11-2) gives with $\gamma = \kappa_T/\kappa_S$:

$$b_w = \left\{ Z_0^* \left[\varepsilon_w - \left(\frac{\lambda}{\lambda_{lim}}\right)^2 \right]^{1/2} \frac{\tau_0}{\Delta T} V_{max}^2 \frac{\gamma}{2l_w} \right\}^{1/2} \qquad (11\text{-}6)$$

or, by neglecting $(\lambda/\lambda_{lim})^2$,

$$b_w \doteq \left(\frac{Z^* \tau_0 \gamma}{2l_w \Delta T}\right)^{1/2} V_{max} \qquad (11\text{-}7)$$

One may also write this equation in the form [using the left term of (11-2)]:

$$b_w \doteq \left(\frac{Z^* \tau_0 \gamma}{\Lambda_w \Delta T}\right)^{1/2} V_{max} \qquad (11\text{-}8)$$

One realizes immediately that the parameter b_w is highly dependent upon matching. There is one possible point of adjusting a mismatch between wave guide and absorbing cavity. This mismatch should be as small as possible, to diminish (eventually destructable) reflection of pulse power back into the microwave generator. This matching is best accomplished before connection to the high-power pulse generator with a small auxiliary microwave generator set for the same wavelength. Adjustment of mismatch is possible at the joint of wave guide and pyramidal dielectric. At this place, wave-guide capacitors or inductors may be inserted (metal strips or pins).

The limiting wavelength was defined above as $\lambda_{lim} = 2a_g$, which is thereby defined for the gas phase. This relation needs to be revised for the tapered part and for the cavity, as one would have to consider the cutoff of the vacuum wavelength, which takes care also of the sections filled with dielectric. For any distance x along l_d, the length of the dielectric, one has to consider $\lambda_{lim} = \lambda_{lim}(x)$, or, more exactly, $\lambda_{lim} = 2a(x)$ with the two borders (x starting at the base of the pyramid): $\lambda_{lim}(x = 0) = 2a_g$ and $\lambda_{lim}(x = l_d) = 2a_w$. This latter value is also valid throughout the cavity.

Thus one recognizes easily the condition for cutoff in a wave guide filled with dielectric: The root becomes zero or imaginary; in other words, $\lambda/\lambda_{\lim} \geqslant \varepsilon^{1/2}$. In the actual design, one should stay safely outside this region to maintain a small range for tuning.

One important condition should be maintained, which then determines all constants:

$$\Lambda_d^w = \Lambda_w = \Lambda_g \tag{11-9}$$

with Λ_g the wavelength in the vacuum wave guide, Λ_w the wavelength within the water-filled part of the wave guide, and Λ_d^w the wavelength in that part of the wave guide which is filled with solid dielectric at the interphase toward water. With the former definitions one then obtains

$$\varepsilon_d - \left(\frac{\lambda}{2a_w}\right)^2 = \varepsilon_w - \left(\frac{\lambda}{2l_w}\right)^2 = 1 - \left(\frac{\lambda}{2a_g}\right)^2 \tag{11-10}$$

As the dimension a_g is given, one obtains

$$2a_w = \frac{\lambda}{[\varepsilon_d - 1 + (\lambda/2a_g)^2]^{1/2}} \tag{11-11}$$

and

$$2l_w = \frac{\lambda}{[\varepsilon_w - 1 + (\lambda/2a_g)^2]^{1/2}} \tag{11-12}$$

If one applies the above equations to the characteristics of commercial equipment, one obtains numerical results, which are assembled in Table 11-1. Table 11-2 gives comparative data for cavities, employing the same frequencies as in Table 11-1. The dimensions for cutoff in Table 11-2 have been computed according to the equations $2a_w = \lambda(\varepsilon_d)^{-1/2}$ and $2l_w = \lambda(\varepsilon_w)^{-1/2}$. Some cavity dimensions have also been proposed, resulting in the indicated volume of the cavity suggested later on.

One additional parameter will now be discussed very briefly. There is the relationship $\Lambda_d^w < \Lambda_d^{\mathrm{real}} < \Lambda_d^g$ with $\Lambda_d^{\mathrm{real}} =$ the actual wavelength within the conical part, $\Lambda_d^w =$ wavelength at the interphase dielectric/water, and $\Lambda_d^g =$ wavelength at interphase dielectric/vacuum. One obtains

$$\Lambda_d^w = 2a_w \tag{11-13}$$

and

$$\Lambda_d^g = \frac{\lambda}{[\varepsilon_d - (\lambda/2a_g)^2]^{1/2}} \doteq 2a_w \tag{11-14}$$

according to the actual value of $(\lambda/2a_g)^2$ (compare Table 11-1). Thus $l_d = a_w$ and is extremely small, requiring a cone of $l_d^g = (n/2)\Lambda_d^g$ with n uneven.

TABLE 11-1

SYSTEM PARAMETERS

FREQUENCY kMc	λ, mm	$2a_g$, mm	$\dfrac{\lambda}{2a_g}$	$\left(\dfrac{\lambda}{2a_g}\right)^2$	ε_w	$\varepsilon_w - 1 +$	$\left(\dfrac{\varepsilon_w - 1}{1 +}\right)^{1/2}$	$2l_w$, mm	$(\varepsilon_d^{\text{theoret}})$ $\varepsilon_d^{\text{exp}}$	$\varepsilon_d - 1 +$	$(\varepsilon_d -)^{1/2}$	$2a_w$, mm
2.9	103	144	0.715	0.512	75.5	75.0	8.68	11.9	(8.7) 8.0	7.51	2.74	37.6
9.2	32.5	44.8	0.724	0.525	54	54.5	7.3	4.45	(7.4) 7.9	7.42₅	2.72	12.0

TABLE 11-2

COMPARATIVE DATA

FREQUENCY, kMc	λ, mm	ε_d	$(\varepsilon_d)^{1/2}$	CUTOFF, $2a_w$ mm	ε_w	$(\varepsilon_w)^{1/2}$	CUTOFF, $2l_w$, mm	"PROPOSED" CAVITY DIMENSIONS, mm			CAVITY, V_{total}, ml
								l_w	a_w	b_w	
2.9	103	8.0	2.82	36.6	75.5	8.69	11.5	6.0	19.0	2.0	0.228
9.2	32.5	7.9	2.81	11.6	54	7.35	4.42	2.23	6.0	2.0	0.0268

One also realizes that the equations become highly simplified for practical purposes.

Although the design of such a cavity seemed quite feasible, it was not translated into reality for the following reasons:

1. High-voltage pulses would still be present and would cause breakdown problems comparable to those of the apparatus for Joule heating.

2. In Joule heating the total stored energy is converted into heating, while only a part of the energy, supplied to the magnetron, is converted to microwave radiation and absorbed in the cavity, thus leading to reduced efficiency.

3. Optical coupling to a detection system with high efficiency for the detection of changes produced by the heating seemed to be rather complicated. The difficulties originate from the requirement of high conductivity for the surface of the absorbing cavity. Ertl and Gerischer (*1*) therefore actually used conductive detection, which, on the other hand, is associated with the requirement that only systems with very few components can be investigated conductometrically. Most of the applications on the temperature-jump method are associated with systems which contain various kinds of ions so that detection of changes in conduction operate on a very large background.

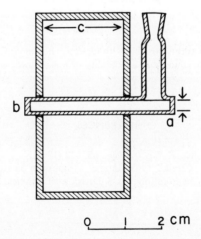

Figure 11-2. Wave-guide arrangement of Caldin and Crooks (*2*).

4. Infrared heating seemed to be much more effective than dielectric heating; infrared flash heating avoids many of the complications associated with heating by capacitor discharges or microwave pulses. The advent of

the optical maser led to the hope that very fast flash heating might soon be possible. The emphasis on microwave heating was therefore considerably reduced. Certainly, microwave heating has its place, but one cannot expect that it will reach the importance of Joule heating or infrared flash heating.

5. Instrumentation in microwave heating is much more complex and expensive than the equipment for heating by capacitor discharges.

In spite of the reasons just mentioned, Caldin and Crooks recently constructed an apparatus with optical detection (2). Figure 11-2 shows a cross section of their wave guide. They have a very small glass tube in the center of the cavity, where the field strength is largest. Because of the relatively small "lossy post," the disturbance of this cavity is not large and is compensated for by empirical tuning. The powerful light source with the heat filter is very close to the optical window a. The tube acts as a light pipe and the transmitted light leaves the tube through window b as a narrow cone. This light is then projected onto a photodetector after passing additional optical filter(s). Caldin and Crooks used chlorobenzene as the dipolar solvent for their experiments (2).

PROBLEM

Is the design of an apparatus possible with dielectric heating operating in the K-band region of microwaves, assuming that availability of pulse power is no problem?

REFERENCES

1. G. Ertl and H. Gerischer, *Z. Elektrochem.* **65**, 629 (1961).
2. E. F. Caldin and J. E. Crooks, 1965 Summer Symposium on Relaxation Techniques in Chemical Kinetics in Solution (ACS Division of Physical Chemistry) Buffalo, N.Y., Abstracts, p. 3.

CHAPTER 12

HEATING BY VIBRATIONAL EXCITATION

12-1. ADVANTAGES OF THIS MODE

As was already mentioned in Chapter 11, the most suitable mode of heating is accomplished by vibrational excitation of solvent molecules, as effected by giant-pulse laser flashes. Such a mode of heating was originally suggested by Czerlinski, Gibson, and Staerk in early 1964 (*1*). The broad applicability of this type of heating was more extensively discussed several months later (*2*). This mode of heating has the following advantages over the ordinary method of conductive heating:

1. Extensive electronic decoupling between the perturbing circuit and the electro-optical detection circuit, although optical filtering has to be highly perfected.

2. Aside from homogeneous systems, heterogeneous systems may also be investigated. In this respect, cellular and subcellular systems are of particular interest for biological investigations.

3. Much smaller volumes than with ordinary temperature-jump instruments may be heated within much shorter times by infrared laser flashes; dielectric breakdown shows up much later than with pulsed high-voltage discharges.

4. As heating is generated by vibrational excitation, no chemical side processes could occur; in Joule heating, the electrolysis products may slowly degenerate the chemical system.

The problem of inhomogeneously heating the solution during flash impact can be partly overcome by a slight collimation of the pulsed laser beam. Laser flash heating is much less efficient than Joule heating; 1 kjoule may have to be injected into the pumping flash lamps, to obtain only about

1 joule as flash out of the crystal (in the Q-switched mode for pulse widths of 10 to 50 nanosec). The advantages of this method nevertheless largely outweight this comparatively poor power-transfer efficiency for perturbing the system.

12–2. METHODOLOGICAL REVIEW

A. Along the Time Axis

Before vibrational heating will be considered in more detail, a quite general outline of fast chemical and physical processes should be considered. This way, methods for investigating fast reactions are also brought into proper perspective. The best criterion for dividing up the many chemical and physical processes is time, permitting distribution of these processes along the time axis. Figure 12-1 shows such a scheme with bimolecular processes below the time axis and monomolecular ones above. The definition of the time constant τ, used as a criterion, is given in the figure, the content of which is mainly based on work of Eigen and co-workers (3,4,5,6). In the upper part of the figure only one point has been selected for singlet excitation, corresponding to a wavelength in the near ultra-violet. The electronic transition times for excitation by visible light are slightly larger than the indicated " 1 femtosec."

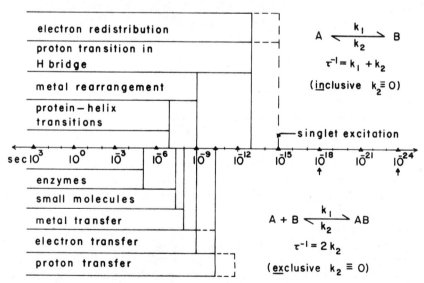

Figure 12-1. Elementary reactions in liquid systems, aligned along the time axis.

10^{-24} sec corresponds to the elementary time unit obtained by dividing the "diameter" of an elementary particle by the speed of light. 10^{-18} sec is the corresponding "elementary" unit for a small molecule of size 10^{-8} cm. In diffusion-determined reactions the fastest step for the bimolecular association is considered to be 10^{-10} sec. This value is derived from the high mobility of the proton in water. This process may be faster in liquid systems with a high content of hydrogen bridging, which is indicated in Figure 12-1 by the dashed extensions. Proton transitions in pure hydrogen-bridged systems were measured to be quite fast (5). As such proton transitions are necessarily associated with electron redistributions, electron rearrangements are at least that fast, but they may be considered as fast as the time for electron transitions in the excitation process.

The upper limit for bimolecular electron transfer is not quite known yet, but is expected to be faster than the transfer of metal ions. The associations of ionic species can be faster than that of small neutral molecules if the associating ions are oppositely charged and have a relatively high effective charge. Enzymes are representatives of large molecules of molecular weight of about 10,000 or above. Proteins are known to show transitions between a helix and a random coil. These transitions are expected to be as fast as about 10^{-7} sec (7). One would thus expect that enzyme reactions are frequently associated with much faster intramolecular interconversions, compared to bimolecular associations.

Figure 12-2 shows an expanded scale of the middle portion of the

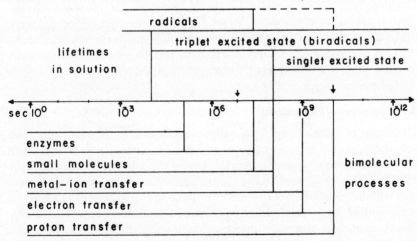

Figure 12-2. Alignment of lifetimes of electronically excited states in solution along the time axis.

previous figure, with the bimolecular processes again represented in the lower section of the figure. Only conversions which are *slower* than the fastest bimolecular step are considered as "chemical process." The upper part of Figure 12-2 demonstrates the range of lifetimes of various types of molecules in solution. Fluorescence emission is a direct indication of the presence of molecules with singlet excited states (*8*). It is apparent that only one type of chemical reaction is fast enough to compete successfully with fluorescence emission—proton transfer reactions. Proton transfer reactions have been followed via fluorescence detection by Weller for more than a decade (*9*).

George Porter extensively investigated the molecules with triplet excited states in solution (*10*). Lifetimes of up to about 100 μsec have been measured in solution. Triplets are also sometimes called "biradicals," although the latter ones may actually also be quite stable. Such molecules may dissociate into radicals. One actually could expect such radicals to be much shorter-lived. But one probably would not consider such radicals as chemical entities if their life is shorter than 10^{-10} sec, as they would not get sufficiently separated by diffusion to be treated as individual radicals even if they depart at rather high initial velocity, because of residual excitation energy. As stable radicals in solution have been obtained, there is no actual upper limit to their lifetime.

It is evident from Figure 12-2 that molecules with triplet excited states can actually enter into any one of the types of bimolecular processes shown. The time limit of monomolecular interconversions for the slowest type, that is, for enzyme reactions, is so far below the lifetime of ordinary triplet states that one could expect to eventually encounter complete conversions of triplet excited states into enzyme rearrangements. Any chemical reaction may thus occur as a consequence of the appearance of triplet excited states.

B. Electronic Excitation

Instead of going now into extensive discussions of reversible and irreversible photochemical reactions, it seems advisable to retreat to another platform. Figure 12-3 gives a general view of the singlet excitation process with the decay cycle back to the ground state. The *quantum* energy associated with laser radiation is so small that ionizing effects are not expected to occur with ordinary laser radiation. Among the effects *not* associated with singlet excitation processes, one may distinguish direct singlet-to-triplet transitions, vibrational excitation, and effects not based on the quantized nature of the radiation.

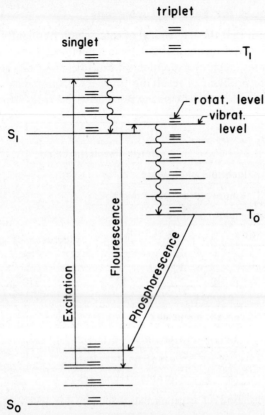

Figure 12-3. A highly abbreviated energy-level scheme of an isolated particle.

Singlet-to-triplet transitions have not as yet been observed. They are exceedingly improbable, but the available high-laser-power densities may permit the detection of such transitions. As the lifetime of the triplet state is expected to be rather short, the associated phosphorescence has to be measured quickly, generally in conjunction with special switching circuits.

Vibrational excitation of molecules offers the possibility of localized heating. But, vibrationally excited molecules generally lose their excitation energy too fast to be considered "hot spots" during the time *chemical* processes can occur. However, if vibrational excitation is produced in a sufficient number of *solvent* molecules, the solution will be homogeneously heated. Computations show that such vibrational excitations are possible with water molecules in conjunction with a neodynium laser operating near the wavelength 1.35 μ.

C. Techniques for Fast Perturbations

It is apparent that these chemical effects, which frequently proceed quite fast, require special techniques for their detection. If one could establish stationary states, such measurements would be easy; but generally one is faced with the problem of resolving transient phenomena. First, we shall consider how such transient phenomena have been investigated thus far.

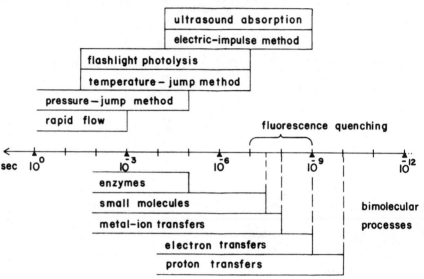

Figure 12-4. Alignment of experimental techniques for following rapid chemical processes.

Figure 12-4 shows a repetition of the lower part of Figure 12-2 and an array of perturbation methods for the investigation of rapid chemical reactions. In ultrasound absorption techniques the chemical system is situated in a variable resonant cavity and the energy absorption is measured as a function of frequency, showing a maximum at a frequency which is directly related to the chemical relaxation time of the system. Ultrasound absorption techniques are stationary methods, and they have recently been extensively discussed by Tamm (*11*). Electric impulse methods were originally introduced by Wien (*12*), who employed high-voltage discharge circuits. Shortly afterward Onsager developed the theory for these relaxation phenomena (*13*). Further extensive investigations of this method were not pursued until about two decades later, when Eigen entered the field (*14*). These two methods, together with the already mentioned fluorescence quenching techniques of Weller, are the fastest ones which are just about able to measure even the most rapid bimolecular reaction.

In flashlight photolysis, at least the initial stages of the perturbations are irreversible, and sometimes the complete photolytic sequence is irreversible (unidirectional). This irreversibility is not present with the temperature-jump method, where temperature jumps of only 2 to 10°C are generally employed. Although the principle of the temperature-jump method is quite simple, it was not thought of until about 10 years ago by Eigen (15). The first operative system was published 5 years later by Czerlinski and Eigen (16). A highly resolving pressure-jump apparatus was introduced by Strehlow and Becker (17).

Although most of the fast methods were developed within the last decade, rapid-flow systems have existed for about 40 years, originally introduced by Hartridge and Roughton (18). For flow systems the present lower limit in time resolution is about 1 msec, and it is presently thought that the major reason for this limitation is given by the design of current mixers (see also Chapter 17).

Perturbation of system by	Detection generally employed
electric field (-jump)	conductometrically in a hf-balanced bridge[*]
flash photolysis	optically by separate illumination
temperature jump	optically by separate illumination[*]
pressure jump	conductometrically in a hf-balanced bridge[*]

[*] theory of chemical relaxation directly applicable

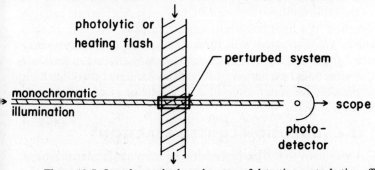

Figure 12-5. Impulse methods and means of detecting perturbation effects.

Figure 12-5 lists the methods based on impulse perturbation and the technique of detection generally employed. Three of the four methods allow direct application of the theory of chemical relaxation. The general principle of detection is outlined at the bottom of the figure. Certainly, the chemical changes initiated by the electric field or by a change in pressure could also be observed photometrically. A refined design intended to be used for detection of perturbations by high-laser-power densities is shown in Figure 13-3 (detailed description given there).

12–3. EFFECTS OF LASER PULSES

A few years ago Townes thought about possible application of optical masers to biological systems (19). Actually, very little of quantitative nature has been done since, which is probably largely because several phenomena appear simultaneously, requiring somewhat refined detection circuits to differentiate between the individual phenomena. Townes was aware of this problem.

The various ways in which laser light can affect chemical systems were discussed, as if most of the experiments had already been performed. This is not the case, and it seems therefore advisable to report now what actually has been done. Many photolytic investigations have been pursued for some time, and also prior to the discovery of the laser.

If an ion (such as Cu^{++}) absorbs a laser pulse (from a ruby crystal in this example), but loses this energy exceedingly fast (within about 10^{-13} sec), this energy becomes fully converted into heat (no re-emission of any light). As laser pulses can be made as short as 50 nanosec (and shorter), exceedingly rapid temperature rises may be generated. The temperature change may be observed photometrically, as shown in the lower section of Figure 12-5. A suitable combination of a pH buffer with a pH indicator [resulting in a large over-all $\Delta H_{2,1}$; see (10-11)] is then employed for the indication of the rapid temperature rise (20). Only very few ions are suitable for this conversion of a light pulse into a heat pulse, as very high photon densities, which are associated with these Q-switched laser pulses, may "photobleach" the absorbing dye (21). Such bleaching effects can certainly be avoided, if vibrational excitation of solvent molecules is used. Such an excitation is possible for water molecules, if a sideline of the neodynium laser is used (22).

12–4. DIFFUSION-LIMITED REACTIONS

Figure 12-1 was used to differentiate between monomolecular reactions and bimolecular reactions. As was implicitly stated in Section 12-2A, the scheme of Figure 12-1 may be used for dividing chemistry from physics with about 10^{-10} sec as the lower limit for the range of chemistry. This limit is given by the limit in diffusion-determined reactions. This is also the limit for bimolecular reactions. Although monomolecular reactions may eventually proceed faster, one may set 10^{-9} sec as the limit for *chemical* monomolecular interconversions. Certainly, these limits are chosen rather arbitrarily, as there is considerable overlap between chemical and physical processes. This overlap led to the new terms " chemical physics " and " physical chemistry." The dividing line (if any!) between the subjects of these two fields could probably be set at about 10^{-9} sec.

As the diffusion of ions toward each other so critically determines the range of chemistry, one may consider such reactions in more detail, which will be done here in conjunction with the discussion of Figure 12-1. The basic reaction scheme in more generalized terminology than in Figure 12-1 is given by

$$Y_1 + Y_2 \underset{k_2}{\overset{k_1}{\rightleftharpoons}} Y_3 \qquad (12\text{-}1)$$

The product Y_3 may be just the diffusion complex, or a "completely" new compound, resulting from the diffusion complex after considerable electronic and geometric rearrangement, which is assumed to be much faster than the diffusion step (to avoid complications due to multistep mechanisms).

A recent summary on the limitation of the rate of reactions by diffusion was given by Eigen and Hammes (23). A more elaborate recent treatment on this limitation also carefully considers the various approximations employed in the derivation of the equations (24). The discussion here will follow the latter treatment, although with some abbreviations. Debye gave the first detailed treatment of ionic recombination (25). He considered that the reacting partners have a finite radius and that the electrostatic potential of interaction is spherical. He obtained for the rate constant of diffusional encounter,

$$k_1 = 4\pi N_A a_D (D_1 + D_2)\Phi_D \qquad (12\text{-}2)$$

If cgs units are employed, (12-2) has to be multiplied by 10^{-3} to obtain k_1 in M^{-1} sec^{-1}. Furthermore, N_A is Avogadro's number, 6.02×10^{23} molecules per mole; a_D is Debye's reaction distance, which is the distance of closest approach of the (spherical) reaction partners Y_1 and Y_2, generally a few angstroms; and $D_1 + D_2$ is the sum of the two diffusion coefficients (of the order of 10^{-4} cm^2 sec^{-1}). Φ_D is Debye's function, given by

$$\Phi_D = \left[a_D \int_{a_D}^{\infty} \exp\left(\frac{z_1 z_2 e_0^2 \beta}{4\pi\varepsilon\varepsilon_0 rkT}\right) \frac{dr}{r^2} \right]^{-1} \qquad (12\text{-}3)$$

This function assumes a coulombic potential. In this equation, z_1 and z_2 are the valencies of the ions Y_1 and Y_2; e_0 is the charge of the electron (1.6×10^{-9} coulomb); $\varepsilon\varepsilon_0$ is the dielectric permittivity of the medium ($\varepsilon = 79$ for water at $T = 298°K$); r is the (variable) distance between the two ions; β is a "correction factor," normally considered unity. If $z_1 z_2 = 0$, one obtains $\Phi_D = 1$, which represents Smoluchowski's condition (26). The rate of coagulation of colloidal suspensions was calculated by Smoluchowski, whereby he arrived at the simplified equation. If $a_D = 10^{-7}$ cm, one computes with equation (12-2) for uncharged particles: $k_1 = 7.5 \times 10^{10}$ M^{-1} sec^{-1}. Generally, particles of the given size diffuse somewhat slower than given by $D_1 + D_2 = 10^{-4}$ cm^2 sec^{-1}; the resulting value of k_1 is therefore somewhat high.

This "correction factor" β becomes different from unity if concentrations of univalent ions extend beyond 10^{-3} M, which is generally prevalent in solutions, ordinarily employed. Screening of the ionic atmosphere enters in and one has to substitute according to Debye and Hückel:

$$\beta = \exp\left(-r/a_H\right) \tag{12-4}$$

where a_H is the "radius of the ionic atmosphere," given by

$$a_H \doteq 2 \times 10^{-10}(\varepsilon T/\mu)^{1/2} \tag{12-5}$$

with $\mu = \frac{1}{2}\sum_i c_i^0 z_i^2$ as the ionic strength of the solution. Equation (12-3) together with (12-4) could only be integrated numerically, unless if conditions are chosen whereby (12-4) may be expanded and its linear approximation used. The correction factor β will be set to unity later, as only the approximate value of k_1 is of interest.

The dielectric permittivity is a continuum concept. But its use may be restricted on the molecular level, expecially if a_D becomes comparatively small (that is: no [or nearly no] space left for solvent molecules to still separate Y_1 from Y_2). For a more detailed discussion of these aspects, the reader is referred to the literature (24).

If (12-3) is integrated with $\beta = 1$, one obtains

$$\Phi_D = \frac{\phi_D}{\exp\left(\phi_D\right) - 1} \tag{12-6}$$

with

$$\phi_D = \frac{z_1 z_2 e_0^2}{4\pi\varepsilon\varepsilon_0 a_D kT} \tag{12-7}$$

The value of Φ_D approaches unity for large a_D (and any $z_1 z_2$) and equals unity still within a factor of 3 at $a_D = 10$ A (and $3 \geqslant z_1 z_2 \geqslant -4$), but with progressively smaller a_D the value of Φ_D becomes much *smaller* than unity for $z_1 z_2 > 0$ and much *larger* than unity for $z_1 z_2 < D$.

One may also consider the limiting case of point charges. The resulting equation was originally derived by Onsager (27), who obtained

$$k_1 = 4\pi N_A a_B (D_1 + D_2) \tag{12-8}$$

The Bjerrum distance a_B may be considered as an effective range of the coulombic forces (28) and is defined by

$$a_B = -\frac{z_1 z_2 e_0^2}{4\pi \varepsilon \varepsilon_0 k T} \tag{12-9}$$

Formally, (12-8) is identical with Smoluchowski's equation for uncharged particles [(12-2) with $\Phi_D = 1$].

The rate of diffusional dissociation of an ion pair Y_3 into the individual ions Y_1 and Y_2 may be derived similarly to Debye's process for the inverse rate constant, except that a different set of boundary conditions is used. Eigen (29) obtained in this manner

$$k_2 = \frac{3(D_1 + D_2)}{a_D^2} \Phi_D' \tag{12-10}$$

with

$$\Phi_D' = \exp(\phi_D)\Phi_D \tag{12-11}$$

Debye's function Φ_D is originally given by (12-3), which may be integrated (under the restricting conditions) to yield (12-6). One may then also write

$$\Phi_D' = \frac{\phi_D}{1 - \exp(-\phi_D)} \tag{12-12}$$

The value of Φ_D' approaches also unity for large a_D. For smaller a_D the value of Φ_D' deviates from unity in a manner quite similar to Φ_D (inverted behavior with respect to the sign of $z_1 z_2$). For a value of $a_D = 10^{-7}$ cm, k_2 becomes quite large, around 3×10^{10} sec^{-1}, corresponding to a value for a strong acid (as an example, assuming again $D_1 + D_2 = 10^{-4}$ cm^2 sec^{-1}).

One may now easily form the dissociation constant:

$$K_{2,1} = \frac{\bar{c}_1 \bar{c}_2}{\bar{c}_3} = \frac{k_2}{k_1} = \frac{3 \exp(\phi_D)}{4\pi a_D^3 N_A} \tag{12-13}$$

If $|\phi_D| \ll 1$, one obtains with the previously mentioned values of a_D and N_A for $K_{2,1} = 0.4 \times 10^{-3}$ M, again somewhat low. One may generally assume a value of 1 mM as the lower limit for a diffusion-limited dissociation constant. But the presence of a dissociation constant $K_{2,1} \geqslant 1$ mM is certainly no indication that *only* one step, the diffusion limited step, is present in a two-component reaction system.

As long as small molecules are involved, (12-2) may easily be employed. Eigen (29) was particularly successful in this respect, deriving the reaction distance for protonic recombinations. As this distance was much larger than the "solid" ion-ion distance, he concluded that the proton was "instantly" recombining with the negative ion upon reaching the experimental value for a_D; the proton recombines through hydrogen bridges, offered by the water molecules.

But the more complex the interacting ions become, the more difficult is the use of (12-2). Its use actually becomes quite difficult, if enzymes are involved. Enzymes offer the following still unsolved problems:

1. 4π, the geometric factor for spherical approach, is certainly no longer valid. But very little can be said yet as to what fraction of 4π has to be inserted.

2. a_D; how should this distance be understood. Enzymes are generally thought of as being surrounded with layer(s) of hydration.

3. $D_1 + D_2$; diffusion constants may easily be determined. If components of rather different size are involved, the smaller component generally has the larger diffusion constant and governs $D_1 + D_2$.

4. z_1 and z_2 in Φ_D. It is rather difficult to assess the charge of a large enzyme molecule. Should its total charge be used or that of the highly restricted active site?

5. β, aside from the screening of the ionic atmosphere in the bulk of the solution, there may be quite specific screening effects in the neighborhood of the active site.

6. ε may be that of the bulk of the solution, but ε may also be altered near the active site.

Although the resolution of such a complex case seems rather difficult, some of the problems may have but little effect on the diffusion-limited rate constants and should therefore be neglected, namely $D_1 + D_2$, $z_1 z_2$, β, and ε. The factor β always causes reduction of charge. One may therefore assume as *effective* charge for the enzyme: $|z_1| \leqslant 1$. The charge of the substrate then gives z_2. The geometric factor and the Debye distance are then left. X-ray-crystallographic data may give indications on the former, leaving the Debye distance. Further data on hydration spheres of enzymes may be necessary in most cases, before (12-2) may be usefully applied to enzyme reactions.

PROBLEMS

1. A 1-mm. depth of water absorbs about 90 per cent of light at 1.4 μ. Devise a cell in which water can be heated with a homogeneity of ± 10 per cent.

2. Plot $\Phi_D = f(a_D)$ on a log-log paper with $T = 298°K$, $\varepsilon = 79$, and $z_1 z_2 = -4$, -1, $+1$, $+4$; employ $2A \leqslant a_D \leqslant 20A$.

REFERENCES

1. G. Czerlinski, Q. Gibson and H. Staerk, Eighth Annual Meeting, Biophysical Society, Chicago, Abstract WB2, 1964.

2. G. Czerlinski, *in* B. Chance, R. Eisenhardt, Q. Gibson, and K. Lonberg-Holm (eds.), *Rapid Mixing and Sampling Techniques in Biochemistry*, p. 183, Academic Press, New York, 1964.

3. M. Eigen and L. DeMaeyer, *Z. Elektrochem.*, **60**, 1037 (1956).

4. H. F. Eicke, Dissertation, Göttingen, 1961.

5. M. Eigen, *Ber. Bunsengesellschaft*, **67**, 753 (1963).

6. M. Eigen, L. DeMaeyer and H.-Ch. Spatz, *Ber. Bunsengesellschaft*, **68**, 19 (1964).

7. G. Schwarz, *J. Molec. Biol.*, **11**, 64 (1965).

8. T. Foerster, *Fluoreszenz Organischer Vergindungen*, Vandenhoeck and Ruprecht, Göttingen, 1951.

9. A. Weller, *Z. Elektrochem.*, **56**, 662 (1952).

10. G. Porter, *in* A. Weissberger (ed.), *Technique of Organic Chemistry*, Vol. VIII, Pt. 2, p. 1055, Wiley (Interscience), New York, 1963.

11. K. Tamm, *in* D. Sette (ed.), *Dispersion and Absorption of Sound by Molecular Processes* (Course XXVII of Proceedings of the International School of Physics, Enrico Fermi), p. 175, Academic Press, New York, 1963.

12. M. Wien, *Physik Z.*, **32**, 545 (1931).

13. L. Onsager, *J. Chem. Phys.*, **2**, 599 (1934).

14. M. Eigen and J. Schoen, *Z. Elektrochem.*, **59**, 483 (1955).

15. M. Eigen, *Discussions Faraday Soc.*, **17**, 194 (1954).

16. G. Czerlinski and M. Eigen, *Z. Elektrochem.*, **63**, 652 (1959).

17. H. Strehlow and M. Becker, *Z. Elektrochem.*, **63**, 457 (1959).

18. H. Hartridge and F. J. W. Roughton, *Proc. Roy. Soc.* (*London*), **A104**, 376 (1923).

19. C. H. Townes, *Biophys. J.*, **2**, 325 (1962).

20. H. Staerk and G. Czerlinski, *Nature*, **205**, 63 (1965).

21. H. Staerk and G. Czerlinski, *Nature*, **207**, 399 (1965).

22. G. Czerlinski et al, in preparation.

23. M. Eigen and G. G. Hammes, in F. F. Nord (ed.), *Advances in Enzymology*, Vol. XXV, p. 1, Wiley (Interscience), New York, 1963.

24. M. Eigen, W. Kruse, G. Maass and L. DeMaeyer, *in* G. Porter (ed.), *Progress in Reaction Kinetics*, Vol. 2, p. 287, Pergamon Press, London, 1964.

25. P. Debye, *Trans. Electrochem. Soc.*, **82**, 265 (1942).
26. M. v. Smoluchowski, *Z. Physik. Chem.*, **92**, 129 (1917).
27. L. Onsager, *J. Chem. Phys.*, **2**, 599 (1934).
28. N. Bjerrum, *Kgl. Danske Videnskab. Selskab, Mat.-Fys. Medd.*, **9**, 7 (1926).
29. M. Eigen, *Z. Physik. Chem.*, (N.F.) **1**, 176 (1954).

CHAPTER 13

THE FIELD JUMP

13-1. EXPERIMENTS OF WIEN

A. Results

In the earlier days of physical chemistry, electrolytic conductivity seemed to be fully explainable on the grounds of the mobility of ions and the degree of dissociation. Later it was discovered that the degree of dissociation is not always a quantitative measure for dissociating compounds; such deviations seemed to be present with compounds which were then considered fully dissociating "strong electrolytes." At high concentrations of these electrolytes, electrostatic interaction seemed to occur, and Debye developed a special theory of strong electrolytes. To obtain better knowledge of these various phenomena in electrolyte solutions, Wien and his co-workers attempted to find new methods for the investigations of electrolyte solutions. About that time the dependence of the electric conductivity upon frequency was discovered (employing very high frequencies) and Debye and Falkenhagen developed a theory based on the relaxation of the ionic cloud.

To test the idea of the relaxation of the ionic cloud, Wien developed a new method and published his first data in 1927 (*1*). He applied very high voltages to the electrolyte solutions and observed the change in conductivity as a function of the electric field strength. He found a dependence of the conductivity upon the field strength which was quite small for strong electrolytes. It was possible to attribute this small effect to the relaxation of the ionic cloud; the atmosphere of the ion could not follow its extreme speed in the high electric field. The ionic cloud became thus distorted, allowing the (central) ion to move at higher speeds than normally at that concentration. Wien obtained only about a 0.3 per cent change in conductivity at 180 kv/cm. This phenomenon was later called the *first Wien effect*.

The *second Wien effect* was discovered when Wien and his associates applied high voltages to weak electrolytes. They found that acetic acid showed an increase in conductivity of almost 6 per cent at 120 kv/cm (*1*). This effect with weak electrolytes was dependent upon concentration, and at high dilution saturation effects were obtained. The actual conductivity at these saturation levels corresponded to the conductivity of the weak electrolytes at infinite dilution. Wien therefore concluded that the molecules were dissociated into ions by the high electric field strength. But he assumed for some time (*2*) that the molecules are ionized by ions which are accelerated in the solution and, when hitting a molecule, ionize the latter, similar to such escalating phenomena in gases. Wien also thought of another possible and quite mechanistic explanation, according to which ions which are loosened up by Brown motion in the solution are pulled away in the strong electric field. These explanations now seem rather unlikely.

B. Onsager's Description

A very good quantitative over-all description of the second Wien effect was given somewhat later by Onsager (*3*). In this description the dissociation constant is changed in the electric field and becomes dependent upon the absolute amount of the field strength (*3*):

$$\frac{K(X)}{K(0)} = 1 + b + \frac{b^2}{3} \tag{13-1}$$

with

$$b = \frac{|z_1 z_2 e_0^3 (z_1 m_1 - z_2 m_2) X|}{2\varepsilon\varepsilon_0 k^2 T^2 (m_1 + m_2)} \tag{13-2}$$

where z_1 and z_2 are the (actual positive or negative) valencies of the individual ions forming an ion pair, $e_0 = 1.6 \times 10^{-19}$ amp-sec (charge of electron), m_1 and m_2 are the (mechanical) mobilities of the ions in solution, X is the electric field strength in volts per centimeter, ε is the dielectric constant of the solution, $\varepsilon_0 = 8.85 \times 10^{-14}$ amp-sec per volt-cm (permeability of free space), and $k = 1.38 \times 10^{-22}$ watt-sec per °Kelvin (Boltzmann constant). Frequently, one of the mobilities is much larger than the other one; if this is the case and the condition $|z_1| = |z_2| = z$ holds, one obtains the simplified equation of Eigen and DeMaeyer (*4*),

$$b = \frac{|z^3 e_0^3 X|}{2\varepsilon\varepsilon_0 k^2 T^2} \tag{13-3}$$

Eigen and DeMaeyer indicate the limit of applicability for (13-1), which is $b < 1$. This condition permits one to omit terms higher than the ones given in (13-1). The first omitted term is $b^3/18$, which would only lead to corrections which are smaller than 5.5 per cent (the term thereafter is smaller than $\frac{1}{10}$ of this correction).

Onsager (3) gave a solution for $b > 3$, the abbreviated form of which is given by

$$\frac{K(X)}{K(0)} = \frac{(2\pi)^{1/2}}{(8b)^{3/4}} \exp (8b)^{1/2} \left[1 - \frac{3}{8(8b)^{1/2}} \right] \qquad (13\text{-}4)$$

The second term in the brackets gives a (subtractive) correction of always less than about 13 per cent. It is negligible for $b \gg 3$. The omitted third term gives a correction for $b \to 3$ of about 0.5 per cent (less for $b > 3$).

For valency $z = 1$, absolute temperature $T = 300°K$, and dielectric constant $\varepsilon = 80$ (representing water), (13-3) simplifies to

$$b = 2.2 \times 10^{-6}|X| \qquad (13\text{-}5)$$

One immediately derives from (13-5) that $b = 1$ at about 450 kv/cm under the stated conditions. If 2-2 electrolytes are used ($z = 2$), one obtains $b = 1$ at 56 kv/cm, under otherwise identical conditions. If another solvent is used instead of water, such as benzene with $\varepsilon = 2.2$, one obtains $b = 1$ for 12 kv/cm (and for 1-1 electrolytes). From (13-2) and (13-5) one easily derives $b = 10$ for benzene and 120 kv/cm field strength. With these values, the simplified equation (13-4) leads to $K(X) = 800K(0)$. The dissociation constant of an ion pair in benzene shifts by almost three orders of magnitude when X is changed from 0 to 120 kv/cm. Such a pronounced effect could easily be associated with considerable solvent reorientations around the many ions generated; this in turn would lead to volume changes. Since these volume changes proceed quite fast, a pressure wave is built up (its size depending upon the compressibility of the liquid), which eventually may lead to destructive shock waves.

C. Two Experimental Designs

When Wien attempted to apply high voltage to the electrolyte solution, he could not use high-voltage pulses of long duration because the high current would generate a temperature rise which would obscure the first and second Wien effects. Wien therefore developed an impulse method (5), which is shown in Figure 13-1. The capacitor C in this figure is charged via resistor R. The spark gap is strongly illuminated and externally triggered (tr.). R_1 is the electrolytic resistor and R_2 an ohmic one (some-times with parallel capacitive adjustment) with $R_1 = R_2$. The discharge time is then mainly given by $\frac{1}{2}R_1C$. L is an inductor to obtain an aperiod-ically damped pulse. $L \gg L_1$, L_2 are the coupling inductors to L_3, L_4.

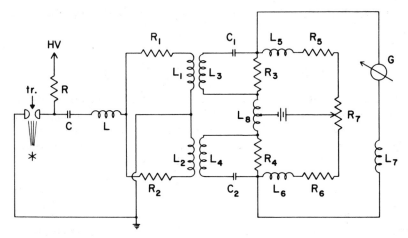

Figure 13-1. Circuit diagram of Wien for detection of the dissociation-field effect.

Each pulse current heats small filament lamps with resistances R_3 and R_4; it is $\frac{1}{2}R_1C \ll R_3C_1$, R_4C_2. As no fast oscilloscopes were available in 1927, Wien and co-workers had to store the pulse information by heating up the lamps and obtaining differences in the resistances R_3 and R_4, which they then measured differentially with the galvanometer G, $R_5 \approx R_6 \approx 20\Omega$. The inductors L_5 to L_8 are large enough to separate the pulse circuit from the measuring DC circuit. A sensitivity of below 0.1 per cent was thus obtained.

Eigen and Schoen (6) had available fast oscilloscopes which they used directly for indication in a bridge circuit. Figure 13-2 shows their circuit diagram. R_3 and R_4 are large charging resistors for capacitance C. The voltage across this capacitance is derived from the arc-over distance of the well-defined spheres at M. R_1 and R_2 are also large and provide for the charging of C_a and C_b ($\ll C$). $C_a = C_b$ and $R_a = R_b \ll R_1$, R_2. $L_a = L_b$ provide for an aperiodically damped pulse, when spark gap B for the bridge is triggered. $R_D C_D$ is a variable delay section, which may be used for repetitively triggering the discharge. Discharge and oscilloscope may also be triggered via M, giving a rather defined discharge voltage. The voltages at C are temporarily shifted with reference to the voltages at the spheres of B, leading to (second) gap triggering via $R_D C_D$ and scope triggering via C_f. The actual voltage shift is determined by the values of R_1, R_5, and R_6 relative to each other. Z_1 is the impedance of the test solution (with the weak electrolyte) and Z_2 is the impedance of the reference solution (with the strong electrolyte). Z_3 and Z_4 are matching impedances of the bridge circuit.

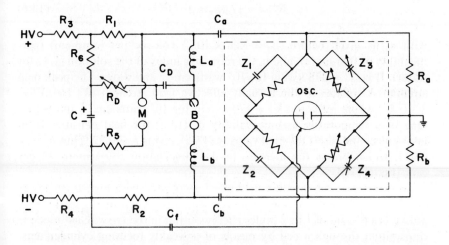

Figure 13-2. Circuit diagram of Eigen and Schoen, to detect the second Wien effect.

It is evident from these pulse techniques that the short pulses can only indicate chemical relaxation when the pulse length is such that the chemical relaxation time is neither much faster nor much slower than the pulse width. As the perturbing and detecting pulses are identical, any time lag in the chemical system can only be detected by distortion of the pulse, which would show up quite well in a properly designed bridge circuit. The field effect could certainly be investigated much more appropriately if it were possible to maintain the electric field strength constant over a wide time range. Unfortunately, aside from Joule heating, several other phenomena would show up: electrode polarization at very long times, orientational effects of large molecules, electronic and ion cloud polarization. All these side effects could be prevented if giant laser pulses could be employed and could be made wide enough (also depending upon the actual mechanism!; see below).

13–2. GIANT LASER PULSES

The output of a laser pulse is either measured in joules (energy) or in watts (power). Important for a possible field effect of a laser beam is the power density I_0 (in watts cm^{-2}). By focusing a giant laser pulse, one obtains 10^8 watts cm^{-2} easily. The power density I_0 relates to the peak electric field strength X' by the Pointing equation:

$$X' = \frac{1}{\eta_r} [I_0(\mu_0/\varepsilon_0)^{1/2}]^{1/2} \tag{13-6}$$

with ε_0 as given before, $\mu_0 = 1.26 \times 10^{-8}$ volt-sec per (amp-cm) (permeability of free space), and η_r the refractive index of the solution (1.33 for water). It is $X' = 238$ kv/cm for 10^8 watts cm^{-2} and water. The peak field strength X' relates to the actually effective field strength $|X|$ by $|X| = 2^{-1/2}X'$, which leads to $|X| = 170$ kv/cm for 10^8 watts cm^{-2} and water. One may temporarily assume validity of (13-5) for field densities from laser pulses and insert the final value in (13-5), giving $b = 0.37$. Thus $b^2/3 = 0.047$, which brings the increase in the dissociation constant to 42 per cent [Eq. (13-1)].

To investigate the possible field effect associated with high-laser-power densities, an instrument was proposed which is shown in Figure 13-3. A pulsed laser beam of 1 to 2 joules energy output in the Q-switched mode is transmitted through a cell by means of a weakly focusing cylinder lens. This lens provides for the laser beam having sufficient power density within the cell containing the aqueous system (near 200 Mw cm^{-2}, corresponding to ≈ 300 kv cm^{-1} electric field strength). A CW laser is used to observe the changes during the time of impact of the laser pulse on the aqueous system and afterward. The use of a CW laser is necessary to obtain an adequate signal-to-noise ratio for the very fast optical-detection system. A long parallel beam from the CW laser is needed for the optical decoupling of the pulse light from the transmitted detection light. For this purpose the circular diaphragms B_1, B_2, and B_3 are inserted.

The disturbance seen by the photocathode should be determined by Rayleigh scattering from the aqueous system only. To accomplish this the photocathode should not see any light coming from primary scattering of the pulsed laser beam at dielectric interphases. Secondary scattering at interphases cannot be avoided and would be visible on the photocathode. If all surfaces in contact with laser beams are polished flat to $\lambda/20$, secondary scattering should be negligible compared to Rayleigh scattering from the water. To have the apparatus Rayleigh-scattering-limited, the following relationship is specified:

$$\frac{w_2}{d_2} > \frac{w_1}{d_1} \tag{13-7}$$

The dimensions for the imagined apparatus are as follows (see Figure 13-3): $d_1 = 2$ cm, $d_2 = 15$ cm, $d_3 = 0.9$ cm, $d_4 = 1.0$ cm, $w_1 = 0.025$ cm, $w_2 = 0.15$ cm, $w_3 = 0.2$ cm. It is evident from the numbers given that condition (13-7) is fulfilled with an adequate "safety" factor.

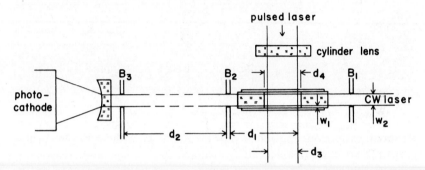

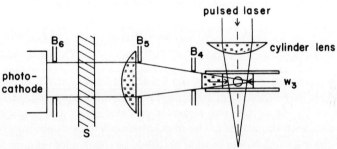

Figure 13-3. Arrangement to observe the effects of high-laser-power densities during impact (upper section) and afterward (lower section).

The key parameter in Rayleigh scattering is the turbidity τ_λ (7,8). For pure water this turbidity is close to 2×10^{-5} cm^{-1} at 0.546-μ wavelength. The turbidity at other wavelengths is given by

$$\tau_\lambda = \tau_{0.546}\left(\frac{0.546\,[\mu]}{\lambda[\mu]}\right)^4 \tag{13-8}$$

Table 13-1 shows the turbidity derived with (13-8) for the various wavelengths used for the laser instrumentation. The first wavelength is that of the helium-neon laser; the third column in the table gives the

TABLE 13-1

VARIOUS CHARACTERISTICS OF AQUEOUS SYSTEMS AT THE
VARIOUS LASER WAVELENGTHS

CONCEPT:	LASER WAVELENGTH	COMPUTED TURBIDITY	OBSERVED EXTINCTION FOR 2-mm PATH	ABSORBED RELATIVE AMOUNT	COMPUTED SCATTERING
SYMBOL:	λ	τ	E_{2mm}	$1 - I_1/I_0$	I_s/I_0
DIMENSION:	μ	cm^{-1}	none	none	none
	0.633	1.2×10^{-5}	?	?	2.4×10^{-6}
	0.694	8.0×10^{-6}	0.0009	2×10^{-3}	1.6×10^{-6}
	1.07	1.3×10^{-6}	0.012	2×10^{-2}	2.6×10^{-7}
	1.35	0.5×10^{-6}	0.3	0.5	10^{-7}

measured extinction E, which was obtained with the Cary recording spectrophotometer by differential methods. The values agree reasonably well with those of the more recent literature and are referred to 2 mm, the depth of penetration of the pulsed laser beam into the solution ($w_2 + 2w_1$ of Figure 13-3). The extinction E relates to the transmission according to

$$\frac{I_1}{I_0} = 10^{-E} \tag{13-9}$$

The values of the fourth column of Table 13-1 are derived from the observed density in the third column. They actually represent the relative amount of the light intensity scattered (or absorbed) and are therefore comparable with the values of the fifth column. This last column gives the ratio of the intensity of all the light scattered to the incident intensity. This ratio is computed according to

$$\frac{I_s}{I_0} = \tau_\lambda(w_2 + 2w_1) \tag{13-10}$$

One realizes that the agreement between these last two columns is poor, especially at high wavelengths, owing to the fact that the absorption of water is not negligible.

The intensities in equations (13-9) and (13-10) are generally measured in watts cm^{-2}. The relationship of conversion between power P and intensity I for one of the intensity parameters I_0 (valid for any I_i) is given by

$$P_0 = I_0 \, d_3 w_3 \tag{13-11}$$

Since $I_0 = 2 \times 10^8$ watts cm^{-2}, one obtains a total power of $P_0 = 3.6 + 10^7$ watts with the values d_3 and w_3.

The last column of Table 13-1 demonstrates a 24-fold change over the total wavelength range. Such a calculated increase in scattering corresponds to reality only if the refractive index does not change over this wavelength range. This requirement is very doubtful, as the observed optical density demonstrates considerable increase in absorption. One may therefore assume in zero approximation that the first (the highest) value remains more or less constant over this wavelength range. Employing equations (13-10) and (13-11) at the indicated value of I_s/I_0, one obtains $P_s = 86$ watts for the over-all scattered power in this specific case. The relationship between the scattered power P_s, transmitted beyond diaphragm B_3, and the remaining geometric parameters of the system (under the assumption that the over-all scattered power originates from one point within the center of the cell at the half-point of d_4, and the scattering from this point proceeds in a fully isotropic manner) is given by

$$P_s = \frac{(w_2)^2 P_2}{16(d_1 + d_2 - \frac{1}{2}d_4)^2} \tag{13-12}$$

With the design values indicated above, one obtains $P_s = 4.3 \times 10^{-4}$ watts. The power transmitted from the CW laser was designed to be large enough to allow measurements in the nanosecond range. If, therefore, the scattering light power is of the same magnitude as the CW light power, scattering could be observed directly without the use of the CW laser. If small changes in the properties of the solution are to be measured with a CW laser, the Rayleigh-scattered light from the pulsed laser has to be attenuated by liquid and solid filters with suitable cut-off properties. Filters with adequate cutoff properties (of several orders of magnitude) have been used before. The degree of polarization of the scattered light from the pulsed laser might be large enough so that the scattered light could be highly reduced with a very good analyzer (electric vector parallel to that of the CW laser). Finally, it is always possible to increase d_2, which has little effect on the power transmitted from the CW laser (as long as the light path is kept dust-free).

Enzyme solutions of moderate concentration (not over 1 per cent by weight) and size (molecular weight below 50,000) give considerably more Rayleigh scattering than water alone, but generally stay within three orders of magnitude above the value for water. This would require some attenuation of the beam originating from Rayleigh scattering, so that the photodetector is not overloaded. It should still be quite possible to cut down this scattered light sufficiently so that direct observation of the changes occurring during the pulse can be observed (with or without the CW laser).

Certainly, the photodetector would also pick up any fluorescence or phosphorescence originating from the aqueous system or from the walls of the system-containing chamber. While timing and wavelength of *scattered* light directly coincide with those of the laser pulse, some shift in time and wavelength will occur in fluorescence emission and even more so in phosphorescence emission. Spectral cutoff filters should be used to detect fluorescence and phosphorescence emission. In addition, one might have to incorporate electronic switches at and behind the photodetector. The optical geometry has to be devised with great care to reduce non-Rayleigh scattering to a level which does not interfere with the individual cutoff characteristics of the detection circuit.

To measure a 42 per cent change in the dissociation constant, as computed following (13-6) with the apparatus described in Figure 13-3, one would have to know the response time of the indicating system. Sulfonphthaleins may be used, as they have a rate constant for recombination with H_3O^+ of about 3×10^{10} M^{-1} sec^{-1}. This rate constant is defined according to

$$I^- + H^+ \underset{k_2}{\overset{k_1}{\rightleftharpoons}} IH \qquad (13\text{-}13)$$

The equilibrium constant of this sytem is given by a concentration ratio of the individual components

$$K_{2,1} = \frac{k_2}{k_1} = \frac{\bar{c}_I \bar{c}_H}{\bar{c}_{IH}} \qquad (13\text{-}14)$$

The response time of the indicating system would approximately be given by the chemical relaxation time

$$\tau = [k_1(\bar{c}_I + \bar{c}_H + K_{2,1})]^{-1} \qquad (13\text{-}15)$$

For quick system response one has to require $\tau \leqslant 10^{-8}$ sec, giving with (13-15) and k_1,

$$\bar{c}_I + \bar{c}_H + K_{2,1} \geqslant 3.3 \times 10^{-3} M \qquad (13\text{-}16)$$

If one sets $\bar{c}_H = 4K_{2,1}$, one must have $\bar{c}_{IH} = 4\bar{c}_I$ to fulfill (13-14). Sulfonphthaliens are generally used with $\bar{c}_I < 10^{-5}$ M, so that $\bar{c}_I$ may be neglected in (13-16). Then one obtains, from (13-14) with (13-16), $K_{2,1} = 6.6 \times 10^{-4}$ M as the lower limit for these conditions. One should observe the condition $\bar{c}_I \ll \bar{c}_{IH}$, $\bar{c}_H$ for the best indicative response.

To obtain about 50 per cent absorption of the HeNe-laser illumination, one must establish

$$\bar{c}_I = \frac{0.3}{\varepsilon_I d_4} \tag{13-17}$$

where ε_I is the molar extinction coefficient of this component at 633 mμ (ε_{IH} negligible) and d_4 is the length of the detecting light path in the solution (1.0 cm, see Figure 13-3). Since one may assume that the monomolecular interconversion between the ion pair and the covalent component is sufficiently fast, an experiment for the detection of the dissociation field effect generated by giant laser pulses has been sketched. Eigen and DeMaeyer [see the paper with K. Bergmann (9)] are aware of the fact that the dissociation field effect with single high-voltage pulses does not lead to true equilibrium shifts, because the dissociation products are charged and removable from the reaction mixture by the high electric field. They employed special techniques to circumvent the problem [Eigen and Schoen (6)]. The employment of high-power laser pulses represents another and elegant way of producing true equilibrium shifts, if field dissociation goes with $|X|$ even for visible light (see below).

Eigen and DeMaeyer (4) described a chemical contribution to the dielectric constant D_{ch} at high electric field strength. Their equation may be condensed to

$$D_{ch} = \chi \varepsilon_0 |X|2/RT \tag{13-18}$$

with R the gas constant and χ a system-specific constant. χ is different from zero only for dipolar reactions, such as the association of two dipolar molecules to form a complex with dipole compensation. The effect is very weak, however, estimated to be 10^{-6} for benzoic acid in benzene at 10^5 volts cm^{-1}. Appropriate for optical detection would be a system such as

$$A + I \longleftrightarrow AI \tag{13-19}$$

with I the strongly dipolar indicating component, A the strongly dipolar but "colorless" reactant, and AI the dipole-compensated complex with strongly shifted absorption bands. If X is increased to the dangerous range 10^6 volts cm^{-1}, χ would still have to be increased 100 times to allow its rapid detection during the time of the laser flash [and following its time course! (assuming response at 10^{15} cps)].

Bergmann, Eigen, and DeMaeyer (9) recently measured the dielectric absorption attributable to chemical relaxation. They used a high-voltage DC field and measured the absorption of a superimposed high-frequency field of low amplitude in a special bridge circuit. They recognized the difficulties of this method, since they had to diminish a number of side effects sufficiently. These effects are heating (by ohmic conduction), electrostriction (changes in the structure of a liquid by dipolar orientation), dissociation field effect (only with "dissociable" compounds, which should either be avoided, or their concentration dependence controlled), and electrostatic interactions of dipolar molecules at high concentrations (similar to the formerly discussed electrostatic interactions of electrolyte molecules at high concentrations). The previous discussions show clearly that only the dissociation field effect could not be avoided by using giant laser pulses. This reduces the number of possible effects to two, which may easily be separated by various means. Such laser pulses would therefore be ideal for investigating the chemical relaxation of dissociating ion pairs and dipole pairs, *if* the actual mechanism allows the use of fields which are oscillating at about 10^{15} cps.

13–3. ON THE MECHANISM OF THE FIELD EFFECT

Onsager's equation contains the absolute amount of the electric field strength. In the derivation he had to consider its vectorial character, but the direction canceled out in conjunction with the direction of the moving ions (3). But this cancellation holds only as long as the field vector maintains one direction for a "sufficiently long" time. The critical time constant is that for the relaxation of the ion cloud, which is about 10^{-10} sec. If the electric field vector of a light beam would act upon an ion pair according to Onsager's model, field dissociation should be vanishingly small.

Aside from ("slow") ionic polarizability, one may also consider ("fast") electronic polarizability. Assuming the monomolecular interconversion (eventually in a reaction sequence)

$$A \xrightleftharpoons[k_2]{k_1} B \qquad\qquad (13\text{-}20)$$

with the polarizability of B *much* larger than the polarizability of A, one may be able to affect this equilibrium in *strong* alternating fields: The responding electrons in B may alter the transition probability from B to A (and thus k_2). No calculations are available yet concerning the field densities, at which such effects could become detectable. It is only known that exceedingly high field densities actually release electrons from particles. Induced dipolar dimerization could also be imagined in high light-power densities. These latter two (electronic) phenomena would actually represent new effects; their actual occurrence will probably be tested within the next few years.

PROBLEMS

1. How could Wien's circuit of Figure 13-1 be modified with presently available instrumentation (such as a fast oscilloscope)?
2. What would be the changes in the design parameters if the CW laser beam should have twice the diameter of the beam in Figure 13-3? Compute also the various revised power levels.

REFERENCES

1. M. Wien, *Ann. Physik*, (IV)**83**, 327 (1927).
2. M. Wien, *Physik. Z.*, **32**, 545 (1931).
3. L. Onsager, *J. Chem. Phys.*, **2**, 599 (1934).
4. M. Eigen and L. DeMaeyer, *in* A. Weissberger (ed.), *Technique of Organic Chemistry*, Vol. VIII, Pt. 2, p. 940, Wiley (Interscience), New York, 1963.
5. J. Malsch and M. Wien, *Ann. Physik*, (IV)**83**, 305 (1927).
6. M. Eigen and J. Schoen, *Z. Elektrochem.*, **59**, 483 (1955).
7. P. Debye, *J. Appl. Phys.*, **15**, 338 (1944).
8. K. A. Stacey, *Light Scattering in Physical Chemistry*, Academic Press, New York, 1956.
9. K. Bergmann, M. Eigen and L. DeMaeyer, *Ber. Bunsengesellschaft*, **67**, 819 (1963).

CHAPTER 14

THE PRESSURE JUMP

The pressure jump and the consecutive relaxation processes may either be observed at constant temperature (isothermal) or at constant entropy (adiabatic). As the thermal conduction in the medium proceeds generally quite slowly compared to the relaxation phenomena under observation, one may consider only the adiabatic condition. The change of an equilibrium constant upon pressure is then given by

$$\left(\frac{\partial \ln K^0}{\partial p}\right)_S = \left(\frac{\partial \ln K^0}{\partial p}\right)_T + \left(\frac{\partial \ln K^0}{\partial T}\right)_p \left(\frac{\partial T}{\partial p}\right)_S \tag{14-1}$$

In this equation (and the following ones) the superscript zero refers to zero ionic strength (infinite dilution). K is an equilibrium constant, S the entropy. The individual terms on the right side of (14-1) are given by

$$\left(\frac{\partial \ln K^0}{\partial p}\right)_T = -\frac{\Delta V^0}{RT} \tag{14-2}$$

$$\left(\frac{\partial \ln K^0}{\partial T}\right)_p = \frac{\Delta H^0}{RT^2} \tag{14-3}$$

$$\left(\frac{\partial T}{\partial p}\right)_S = \left(\frac{\partial V}{\partial T}\right)_p \frac{T}{C_p} \tag{14-4}$$

ΔV^0 is the (standard) volume change of the reaction given with the equilibrium constant K^0, ΔH^0 is the enthalpy change of this reaction, and C_p represents the specific heat. Equation (14-4) gives the adiabatic temperature rise upon compression; it vanishes for dilute aqueous solutions at 4°C and reaches 0.07°C per 100 atm at 20°C (1). If aqueous solutions are used and ΔV^0 has a reasonably large value, the second term in (14-1) may be neglected.

Pressure-jump instruments have so far only used conductometric detection within a bridge circuit. Although the temperature rise may have a negligible effect upon the chemical contribution to the pressure relaxations, the mobility of the ions may be affected sufficiently to result in a conductometric change in a bridge circuit. The mobility of conducting ions may also be affected by the nonvanishing compressibility of the solution, leading to a small increase in the effective concentration of the conducting ions. In conductometric detection one would therefore find a background change concurrent with the pressure change. If the ionic strength is not zero, one would have to incorporate the activity coefficients in the equation. Instead, one may also employ the thermodynamic parameters of the above four equations in approximation at constant ionic strength.

Although it is quite easy to trace the origin of the temperature-jump method, this is rather different for the pressure-jump technique. This latter method seems to be a natural outgrowth of the sound-absorption technique, and the application of sound absorption to chemical systems seems to go back to investigations in the laboratory of Nernst on N_2O_4 (2). Albert Einstein investigated this further (3). Einstein developed the theory and considered the dissociation of iodine molecules into atoms to be the simplest type. These reactions in the gas phase, and later on pressure jumps of very large magnitude, were generated by shock-wave techniques and applied to gas reactions (4).

The application of the pressure-jump method to reactions in solution seems to go back to almost simultaneous work in two laboratories. Ljunggren and Lamm (1) published in 1958 a comparatively slow pressure-jump apparatus which they claim to have reached a time resolution of 50 msec. Figure 14-1 depicts the pressure vessel together with the conductivity cell. The pressure from a tank of 150 atm is quickly released into the pressure vessel, generating a correspondingly quick pressure rise. The simplified detection system of Ljunggren and Lamm is shown in Figure 14-2. They followed a slow step in the combination of CO_2 and H_2O, measuring a relaxation time of about 1 sec.

Shortly afterward, Strehlow and Becker (5) published a pressure-jump apparatus with a time resolution which was much larger than that of Ljunggren and Lamm. Strehlow and Becker produced a pressure jump in the opposite direction (compared to the authors just mentioned) by going from 55 atm to room atmospheric pressure with a time constant of about 50 μsec. They were thus able to extend the time range by three orders of magnitude beyond the range indicated by Ljunggren and Lamm. Figure 14-3 shows a cross-sectional view of the pressure-jump vessel of Strehlow and Becker (5). They had two cups with electrodes to subtract the non-chemical effects and used an external liquid for pressure transfer. The pressurized air is kept between the two membranes. Figure 14-4 indicates schematically the measuring circuit of Strehlow and Becker. To observe down to 50μsec, they employed a 100-kc oscillator. Their resistances R_3 and R_4 are quite small, 10 ohms.

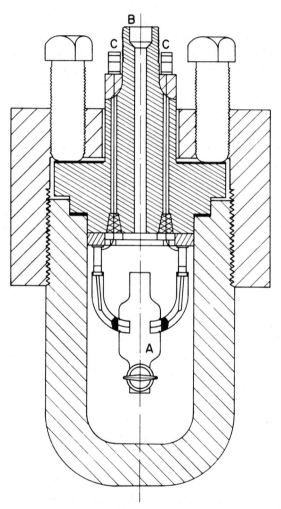

Figure 14-1. Pressure vessel of Ljunggren and Lamm. A = container of the chemical system, B = connection to pressure tank, and C = connection to bridge circuit.

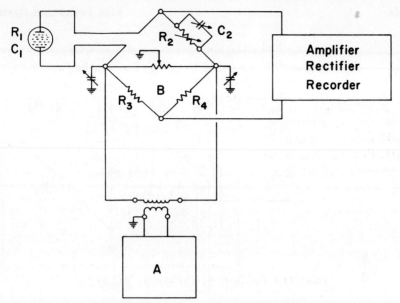

Figure 14-2. Circuit diagram of Ljunggren and Lamm to follow the change in conductivity upon increase in pressure. R_1 and C_1 in the cell are compensated by R_2 and C_2 in one bridge arm; A = oscillator, B = bridge.

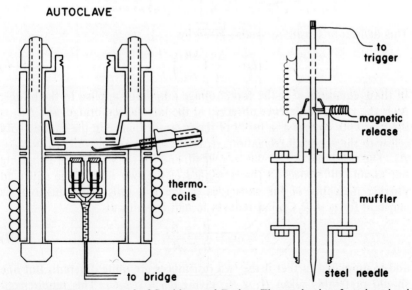

Figure 14-3. Pressure vessel of Strehlow and Becker. The mechanism for triggering is indicated on the right side, which in operation is screwed onto the pressure vessel. The inlet of pressurized air is directly above the thermostating coils.

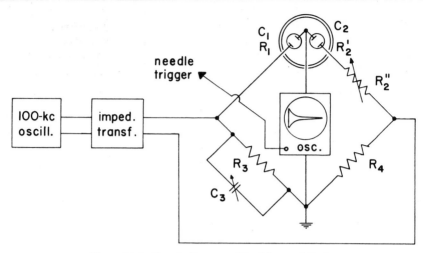

Figure 14-4. Circuit diagram of Strehlow and Becker.

In the experiment, one maintains $C_1 = C_2$ and $R_1 = R_2$ (compare Figure 14-4) and thus also $R_3 = R_4$ (C_3 is compensating). The frequency dependence of the sensitivity for an ohmic range is then given by

$$S(\omega) = R_1 R_3 [(R_1 + R_3)^2 + \omega^2 R_3^2 R_1^2 C_1^2]^{-1} \qquad (14\text{-}5)$$

This deflection sensitivity is also given by

$$S(\omega) = \frac{\Delta u}{u} \left(\frac{\Delta R_1}{R_1} \right)^{-1} \qquad (14\text{-}6)$$

In these equations u is the total voltage amplitude applied to the bridge, Δu is the voltage difference observed at the unbalanced bridge, and ΔR_1 is the resistance change as a result of the pressure change in the conductivity cell with the chemical relaxation. R_1 refers to the sample cell: $R_1 = R_2' + R_2''$. The resistance R_2'' is relatively small, and for the purpose of balancing out minute differences in the resistance of the two cells. C_3 is added to provide matching of the capacities of the two cells. The sensitivity is constant for $\omega \ll R_1 C_1$, but reduces to half its value at

$$\omega_0 = \frac{R_1 + R_3}{R_1 C_1 R_3} \qquad (14\text{-}7)$$

and is simplified further if the two resistances are quite different. But one should preferably select $R_3 \ll R_1$, giving $\omega_0 = 1/R_3 C_1$. This requirement of linearity then leads to the small resistances in the above-mentioned bridge circuit. The difference signal Δu taken from the bridge will then be quite small, and one would have to employ a rather sensitive wide-band differential amplifier. As the signal carrier produces a symmetric relaxation curve, AC coupling can fortunately be employed.

The bridge is first balanced before the pressure is applied to the space between the two membranes in Figure 14-3. Application of the pressure then results in an unbalance, visible on the oscilloscope screen. Upon triggering, the scope deflection starts, and after puncture of the copper beryllium membrane, any chemical relaxation process could become visible, depending upon the time deflection of the oscilloscope.

The hydration of α-ketocarbonic acid was investigated with this method (7). Also, the association behavior of various metal sulfates was observed, with the time-limiting step being the ejection of the last water molecule between the two oppositely charged ions (8,9,10).

The lower limit of the pressure-jump apparatus is given by the propagation velocity of sound in the liquid. One can therefore not expect to push the time resolution much further down than was obtained by Strehlow and Becker. Only conductometric detection has so far been applied to the pressure-jump method. An apparatus employing optical detection is in the developmental stage. As with the temperature-jump apparatus, optical detection of chemical relaxation as a result of pressure changes would considerably broaden the range of applicability of the pressure-jump method. Although the enthalpies ΔH^0 are widely known for chemical reactions, the ΔV^0 of such reactions are rarely known. Such ΔV^0 values, on the other hand, could easily be obtained as by-products of relaxation measurements with the pressure-jump method, employing optical detection; in that respect, then, this method could become comparable with the temperature-jump method.

A shock wave-pressure jump apparatus with optical detection is actually in development in the laboratories of Manfred Eigen, Göttingen. A. Jost developed this apparatus together with L. DeMaeyer. A field jump method (cable discharge) with optical detection is also in development there (G. Ilgenfritz and L. DeMaeyer), as well as two instruments for perturbation by ultrasound (F. Eggers, G. Vidulich, and H. Busse, together with L. DeMaeyer).

PROBLEM

What are the requirements for designing a pressure-jump apparatus with a detection carrier frequency of 1 Mc?

REFERENCES

1. S. Ljunggren and O. Lamm, *Acta. Chem. Scand.*, **12**, 1834 (1958).
2. S. Keutel, Dissertation, Berlin, 1910.
3. A. Einstein, *in Sitzber. Preuss. Akad. Wiss. Physik. Math. Kl.*, Pt. 1–2, **18**, 380 (1920).
4. E. F. Greene and J. F. Tönnies, *Chemische Reaktionen in Stosswellen*, Steinkopf, Darmstadt, 1959.
5. H. Strehlow and M. Becker, *Z. Elektrochem.*, **53**, 457 (1959).
6. M. Eigen and L. DeMaeyer, *in* A. Weissberger (ed.), *Technique of Organic Chemistry*, Vol. VIII, Pt. II, p. 895, Wiley (Interscience), New York, 1963.
7. H. Strehlow, *Z. Elektrochem.*, **66**, 392 (1962).
8. H. Strehlow and H. Wendt, *Inorg. Chem.*, **2**, 6 (1963).
9. B. Behr and H. Wendt, *Z. Elektrochem.*, **66**, 223 (1962).
10. H. Wendt and H. Strehlow, *Z. Elektrochem.*, **66**, 228 (1962).

CHAPTER 15

THE CONCENTRATION JUMP

Whenever an external parameter such as temperature, pressure, or electric field strength is changed, the rate constants of the system are instantaneously changed, and, consecutively, the individual concentrations follow according to the actual magnitude of the rate constants and of the concentration of the individual species. If a chemical reaction is not dependent upon these external parameters, this reaction may be coupled to another reaction which is highly dependent upon one of these external parameters and the kinetics of which is much faster than that of the initially nonresponding system. One may then say that the chemical relaxation of the original nonresponding system is initiated by a concentration jump from the chemical reaction responding to the change in the external parameters.

There are also other ways in which internal parameters can be changed by a small amount to initiate chemical relaxation. One such method was already suggested by Ljunggren and Lamm (1). They suggested "a rapid dilution of the sample solution followed by conductivity registration." Although this method was later also suggested by Czerlinski (2) in a more general way, he did not derive the equations necessary for this case. This method of perturbation was also mentioned in Section 2-1C. Certainly, for chemical relaxation to be applicable, one has to observe the relationship

$$c_i^0 \gg \Delta c_i^0 \qquad (15\text{-}1)$$

But the concentration should only be that of one (the ith) component in the over-all chemical reaction system. The various methods of producing a small change in an internal parameter of the system will now be considered.

Figure 15-1 shows an apparatus which could be employed for the dilution experiment suggested by Ljunggren and Lamm. S_1 and S_2 are the driving

269

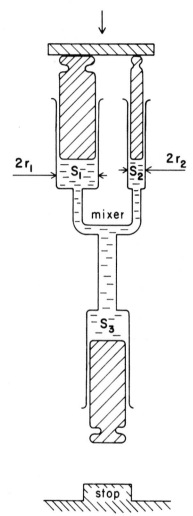

Figure 15-1. Schematic of a stopped-flow apparatus for producing concentration jumps.

syringes, while S_3 corresponds to the stopping syringe. S_1 contains the system under investigation; S_2 contains the diluting solvent. To fulfill (15-1) the following condition has to be fulfilled for the radii r_1 and r_2:

$$r_1^2 \gg r_2^2 \qquad\qquad (15\text{-}2)$$

Chemical relaxation is followed after the stopping syringe hits the solid stop. Figure 15-1 actually represents a highly abbreviated scheme of the stopped-flow apparatus, a type of kinetic instrument, which will be treated more extensively in Chapter 16. To demonstrate the employment of the various means for generating Δc_i^0 (positive or negative) more clearly, a specific case will be considered, which is related to some aminotransferase system (3). This reaction system may be represented by

$$E + A \xrightleftharpoons[k_2]{k_1} EA \xrightleftharpoons[k_4]{k_3} X \xrightleftharpoons[k_6]{k_5} Y \xrightleftharpoons[k_8]{k_7} E' + A' \qquad (15\text{-}3)$$

Among some of the velocity constants, the following relations hold:

$$k_3 + k_4 \gg 2k_2 \gg k_5 + k_6 \qquad (15\text{-}4)$$

If now this system is in equilibrium in syringe S_1 and only solvent (water) in syringe S_2, the following reactions would occur under the assumption that all the detectable chemical processes are slower than the time between mixing and observation. All the concentrations will be diluted by an amount which is given by r_2^2/r_1^2. The monomolecular components will not be affected, as their equilibrium concentration-ratio is still fulfilling the equilibrium condition. For the bimolecular components, the diluted concentrations no longer fulfill the equilibrium conditions and have to be readjusted. As these concentrations adjust, the concentrations of the monomolecular interconversions become disturbed and their concentrations are therefore following. It becomes immediately evident that monomolecular steps which are *faster* than the bimolecualr ones are not resolvable by this method. The first relaxation process would encompass the bimolecular step plus all faster monomolecular steps directly connected to the bimolecular one. This would mean according to (15-4) that $k_3 + k_4$ could not be elucidated by this method. One realizes that changes of concentrations initiated by external parameters are more advantageous. The mentioned method of perturbation also has a higher time resolution than can be obtained by stopped-flow methods. Stopping times are of the order of 10 msec for the simpler designs.

Instead of using a negative concentration step, one could also use a positive one. Syringe S_2 may then be filled with some high concentration of component A. To obtain clear-cut experiments, one should now be able to neglect the dilution effects. This is accomplished by

$$r_1^2 \geqslant 100r_2^2 \qquad (15\text{-}5)$$

To produce an initial concentration change of 10 per cent one has to set the initial concentrations according to

$$\frac{c_{A,2}^0}{c_{A,1}^0} = \frac{1}{10}\frac{r_1^2}{r_2^2} \qquad (15\text{-}6)$$

The second index in the concentration refers to the syringe number. The concentration increase after mixing produces a "pumping" of reaction (15-3) from the left side. Again, any monomolecular steps faster than any bimolecular one cannot be measured. But this method has the advantage of informing on the sequence of reactions steps, a general feature of rapid-flow methods. This method has the same restriction in time resolution as the dilution method.

The concentration of an individual species can be changed by photolytic means. This method allows theoretically a very high selectivity, as any species may be "knocked out." If X is a component of a chemical system and Z a "dead-end" component, inert to this chemical system, one could develop the following two perturbations:

$$X \xrightarrow{hv} Z, \text{ annihilation} \qquad (15\text{-}7)$$

$$Z \xrightarrow{hv} X, \text{ generation} \qquad (15\text{-}8)$$

These are idealized cases of reactions. On the right side of each reaction there may appear intermediates of much higher reactivity than the end products, which may give rise to difficulties in the interpretation of data.

Recently a rather important biological reaction was investigated in such a way that one of the reacting components was *generated* by flash photolysis (*4*). The abbreviated reaction scheme is

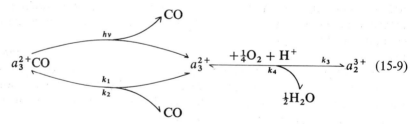

a_3^{2+} is the terminal group in the cytochrome chain of electron-transport particles, available in all cells and providing the energy-generating pump for the cell processes. This compound a_3^{2+} reacts with oxygen in a way presented in a simplified manner on the right side of the equation. For a detailed treatment of this reaction system one is referred to the original (*4*). The right half of the scheme is actually based on a suggestion of Chance (*5*). Experimentally the following velocity constants were found: $k_2 = 8 \times 10^4 \ M^{-1} \ sec^{-1}$ and $k_1 = 0.023 \ sec^{-1}$ (together they give $K_{2,1} = 3 \times 10^{-7} \ M$); $k_3 = 6 \times 10^7 \ M^{-1} sec^{-1}$, $k_4 < 0.2 \ sec^{-1}$. The carbon monoxide compound of cytochrome a_3 initially protects the cytochrome from its reaction with oxygen. A light flash of the proper wavelength region photodissociates the a_3^{2+} CO into its components, and the free cytochrome a_3 reacts immediately with oxygen. In the natural system the reaction with oxygen is irreversible, so that chemical relaxation experiments with the right reaction can never be conducted.

In the absence of oxygen the left reaction could be investigated by photodissociating the a_3^{2+}CO compound. The ordinary dissociation constant of this compound is 3×10^{-7} M, as computed above. This dissociation constant is quite small and makes experiments in chemical relaxation rather difficult with present detection methods. Photodissociation would only have to disturb the system by 10 per cent, and the relaxation into the previous equilibrium state would have to be observed with resulting observable relaxation time constants in the range of about 20 sec, quite slow for most chemical relaxation experiments and also slow enough to perform relaxation experiments just by quick addition of either a small amount of CO or of a_3^{2+}.

The triggering of a reaction by photolytic generation of one of the components seems to have been suggested originally by Gibson (6) using sperm-whale myoglobin. Equation (15-10) describes the over-all reaction mechanism. The monomolecular rate constants are again so very small that ordinary chemical relaxation experiments are not worthwhile. Gibson actually primarily investigated the left reaction system but also obtained some information on the right reaction.

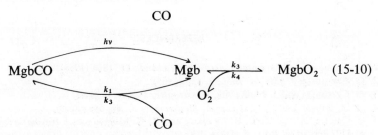

$$\text{MgbCO} \quad \underset{k_3}{\overset{k_1}{\rightleftharpoons}} \quad \text{Mgb} \quad \underset{k_4}{\overset{k_3}{\rightleftharpoons}} \quad \text{MgbO}_2 \quad (15\text{-}10)$$

Gibson obtained the following velocity constants: $k_1 = 0.04$ sec^{-1}; $k_2 = 7 \times 10^5$ M^{-1} sec^{-1}; $k_3 = 1.25 \times 10^7$ M^{-1} sec^{-1}; $k_4 = 18$ sec^{-1}.

The disturbance of an equilibrium by photolytic means was originally demonstrated by Hartridge and Roughton (7). They investigated by this method at that time the binding of carbon monoxide to hemoglobin, a much more complicated reaction than the binding of CO to myoglobin, owing to the fact that hemoglobin binds four molecules and with different binding constants.

Photodissociation can certainly be extensively used for initiating chemical relaxation processes, but photodissociation should disturb the equilibrium by not more than 10 per cent to allow linearization of the differential equations. Also, the experimenter has to make sure that intermediates in the photodissociation sequence do not enter into side reactions with other components of the system. This danger is rather unlikely in the above-mentioned reactions, as the site where carbon monoxide is located is somewhat inside the large macromolecule. Reactions with the surrounding medium seem therefore rather unlikely and have never been observed yet. The nonappearance of side reactions was the major reason for selecting macromolecules as examples of two reaction types, although they are not at all ideal representatives of demonstrating chemical relaxation by photolytic initiation.

PROBLEMS

1. Assume a stopped-flow apparatus, which is different from the design of Figure 15-1 by the fact that $r_1 = r_2$. Assume only the left step of (15-3). In the left syringe there are c_E^0 and c_A^0, in the right syringe $c_E^0 + 2\Delta c_E^0$ and $c_A^0 + 2\Delta c_A^0$ with $\Delta c_E^0 = \Delta c_A^0$. Compute the size of the relaxation process for $\Delta c_A^0 = 0.1 c_A^0$ and $c_E^0 \approx c_A^0$ (no equality).
2. Repeat the calculation of Problem 1 for $\Delta c_A^0 = 0.1 c_A^0$ and $c_E^0 \equiv 0$.

REFERENCES

1. S. Ljunggren and O. Lamm, *Acta Chem. Scand.*, **12**, 1834 (1958).
2. G. Czerlinski, *J. Theoret. Biol.*, **7**, 435 (1964).
3. G. Czerlinski and J. Malkewitz, *Biochemistry* (1965), in press.
4. Q. H. Gibson and C. Greenwood, *Biochemistry J.*, **86**, 541 (1963).
5. B. Chance, *in* J. E. Falk, R. Lemberg and R. K. Morton (eds.), *Haematin Enzymes*, p. 313, Pergamon Press, London, 1961.
6. Q. H. Gibson, *J. Physiol.* (*London*), **134**, 112 (1956).
7. H. Hartridge and F. J. W. Roughton, *Proc. Roy. Soc.* (*London*), **B94**, 336 (1923).

CHAPTER *16*

STOPPED-FLOW METHOD

The principles of the stopped-flow method seem to have been introduced in 1923 by Stewart and Edlund (*1*). They followed (manometrically) the course of the reaction

$$C_2H_4 + Br_2 \rightarrow C_2H_4Br_2 \qquad (16\text{-}1)$$

The first comprehensive treatment of the stopped-flow method for reactions in solution was published in 1940 by Chance (*2*). Since then Chance has developed a number of stopped-flow instruments (*3*). Gibson developed a somewhat different stopped-flow apparatus (*4*). Presently there are a number of such instruments available all over the world and a quite extensive treatment would be necessary to discuss the various stopped-flow (and other flow) instruments adequately. As this treatment deals primarily with relaxation techniques, flow methods will only be dealt with as far as they are supplementary to relaxation methods. It also seems to be advisable to develop special criteria for the performance of rapid-flow instruments in general and stopped-flow apparatus in particular. A table on rapid-flow designs will be given in Chapter 17.

Here, and also later with reference to the constant-flow method, eight criteria will now be considered. The first six criteria will be considered more extensively, while the last two will only be discussed briefly, as they are largely dependent upon the mixing device and will be treated more extensively in the next chapter.

16–1. MECHANICAL DISTURBANCES

Closest to the start of measurement is the moment of mechanically stopping the flow. This stopping can be done in one of two ways:

A. From Front

The stopping is performed at the *front* of the flow by, for instance, a stopping syringe, as shown in Figure 15-1. The stopping should be quite "damped," so that no reflection is transmitted back through the solution, causing mechanical disturbances. This stopping at the front can certainly also be performed by a stopcock in the flow after the observation section, which is quickly turned. Although the stopping process with the stopcock may take about a tenth of a second, stopping with a stopping syringe could be accomplished within one hundredth of a second. More recent designs even allow the flow to be stopped within a very few milliseconds. Recently Berger (5) reported on a zero-displacement stopping valve with which he obtained 0.2 msec stopping time. He also demonstrated that at such short stopping times exceedingly high pressures can be generated in the observation tube.

B. From Rear

The flow may also be stopped "from the rear." The principle may be visualized from Figure 15-1. If the stopping syringe is eliminated, the bar connecting the two syringes then would hit a mechanical stop at a certain point of its travel, thereby also triggering the electronic recording system. If the speed of the liquid is very high, a sudden stop of the driving syringe could generate a vacuum between the end of the syringe and the liquid. Such an effect would cause considerable disturbance in the detection of stopped-flow processes. The occurrence of this disturbance could be reduced by an "S-shaped" stopping function of the driving piston, and by the addition of back pressure applied to the front of the liquid.

16–2. COMPLETENESS OF EXPELLING THE OLD SOLUTION

If V_1 is the volume for cleaning out the observation tube per individual flow experiment, one may consider as an adequate volume

$$V_1 = 2\pi r_0^2 L_2 \tag{16-2}$$

The parameters in (16-2) are defined in Figure 16-1. Figure 16-1 shows an operational schematic of a flow apparatus with driving syringes I and II. The solutions are mixed at the point $t = 0$. At this point the concentration c^0 may show up in a step function for an idealized flow. As the solution proceeds along the flow tube with the average linear flow velocity u_0, a dispersion of the concentration front appears. The dispersion length L_d

is given by the distance between 10 and 90 per cent of c^0. The distance $L_2 - L_1$ is the length of the light beam through the observation tube for detecting the changes. p_0 is the initial, p_z the final pressure in the flow system. Details of the mixer are not considered here, as its detailed discussion will follow in Chapter 17.

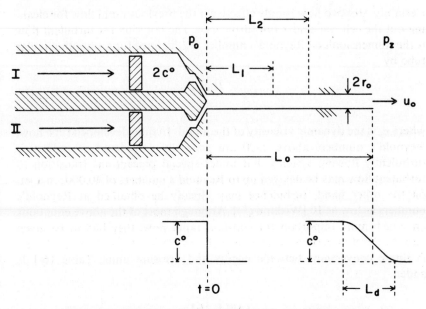

Figure 16-1. Definition of parameters around a rapid-flow system.

Equation (16-2) only gives a " safe value" for the volume necessary to expel the old solution completely. If one knows the dispersion length L_d, the minimal volume is given by (assuming fast sequencing)

$$V_1' = \pi r_0^2 (L_2 + 2L_d) \tag{16-3}$$

Taylor (6) determined an expression for the dispersion length L_d, given by

$$L_d = 6.83[u_0 r_0 t_2 (f_0)^{1/2}]^{1/2} \tag{16-4}$$

The (dimensionless) friction factor f_0 is defined by

$$p_0 - p_z = f_0 \frac{L_0}{2r_0} \tfrac{1}{2} \rho u_0^2 \tag{16-5}$$

with ρ the density of the liquid and $L_0/2r_0 \gg 40$ in a flow system with mixer to allow the experimental determination of f_0 [see also below and Chance (2)]. Equation (16-4) may be further simplified by the definition for the maximum measuring time t_2 (for constant flow):

$$L_2 = u_0 t_2 \qquad (16\text{-}6)$$

Certainly, stopped flow is only effective if the previous rapid flow for cleaning out the cell was under full turbulence. The criterion for turbulent flow is the (dimensionless) Reynold's number N_R, defined for a smooth circular tube by

$$N_R = \frac{2 r_0 u_0 \rho}{\eta_v} \qquad (16\text{-}7)$$

where η_v is the dynamic viscosity of the liquid. In fully developed tube flow, Reynold's numbers above 2500 are generally considered as indicating turbulently flowing systems, but under special precautions transition to turbulent flow may be delayed up to Reynold's numbers of 40,000; in a jet, on the other hand, turbulence may already be obtained at Reynold's numbers as low as 10 [Wiskind (7)]. Although most of the above equations are much more important for constant rapid flow, they had to be given here to develop certain criteria, namely, those involving V_1 and V_1'. To facilitate conversions between energy and pressure units, Table 16-1 is added.

TABLE 16-1

DIMENSIONAL RELATIONSHIPS

REFERENCE UNIT	DERIVED UNITS[a]
1 watt-sec = 1 newton-meter = 1 joule	$= 10^7$ g-cm^2 sec^{-2} $= 10^7$ dyne-cm $= 6.24 \times 10^{18}$ e-volt $= 0.239$ cal $= 1.02 \times 10^{-2}$ liter-atm $= 2.5 \times 10^{-6}$ Einstein (for 300-mμ light[b]).
1 atm	$= 736$ mm Hg $= 10^4$ mm water $= 14.6$ lb in.$^{-2}$ $= 9.8 \times 10^4$ newton m^{-2} $= 0.98$ bar $= 0.098$ watt-sec cm^{-3} $= 0.98 \times 10^6$ g cm^{-1} sec^{-2}

[a] Conversion constants among the derived units can be obtained by dividing them through each other.

[b] The value for any other wavelength λ (in mμ) is obtained by multiplying the given one with $300/\lambda$.

16–3. VOLUME PER FLOW EXPERIMENT

If completeness of expelling the old solution is defined by (16-2) and (16-3), this certainly is also the minimum volume per-flow-experiment. Equation (16-3) remains still highly simplified, as it neglects any diffusion of the two solutions against each other prior to the initiation of the flow and after its stopping. For (16-3) to be valid, it is also assumed that constant rapid flow is reached "instantaneously." Certainly, V_1' should be the volume for fully developed turbulent flow. One therefore may have to add some more volume for the acceleration and deceleration range. Equation (16-2) may then be accepted as a more conservative relation. On the other hand, even (16-2) still assumes relatively small values of L_d and rather fast acceleration and deceleration. The detailed time-range still will be discussed in Chapter 17. As only short pulses of volume flow are required for the stopped-flow method, one may term a technique employing such short flow pulses the "pulsed" flow method [Chance (8)].

16–4. INFORMATION CONTENT PER FLOW EXPERIMENT

The stopped-flow method has the advantage that with a single experiment one may cover a wide time range, limited at the lower end by the dead time (Section 16-5), at the upper end by the stability of the instrumentation. The information content of the stopped-flow method is much larger than that of the constant-flow method, which represents one of the advantages of the stopped-flow method over the constant-flow method. The constant-flow method, on the other hand, has a higher time resolution and a better signal-to-noise ratio (see below).

16–5. DEAD TIME (TIME RESOLUTION)

The time resolution of the stopped-flow method is largely due to the dead time of the system, in turn given by the time required for stopping the flow *and* the distance between mixing chamber and observation area. The dead time t_0 of a well-performing flow apparatus should be such that the reaction has not proceeded beyond the 10 per cent, where the course of the reaction is still reasonably linear. This dead time t_0 would then also define the most distant point for observation by

$$L_2' = t_0 u_0 \qquad (16\text{-}8)$$

This equation then relates the dead time t_0 to the largest experimentally permissible length for observation, L_2', for the case of "instantaneous" stopping.

16–6. SIGNAL-TO-NOISE RATIO IN DETECTION

In the stopped-flow method the length of observation, $L_2 - L_1$, should be as large as possible. If L_1 is the distance from the mixing chamber where just complete mixing is obtained even with the poor mixing during the stopping time, the optimum length for the detection is given by $L'_2 - L'_1$. The light source then should have the appropriate shape, so that the image is appearing within the flow tube along this maximum length of observation at a *width* r_0 and in the axis of the flow tube. The geometric flux of the detection system should otherwise be kept as large as possible in accordance with the discussion on limitations in detection (Chapter 9). Only half the diameter of the flow tube ($2r_0$) was chosen as the optimum width of the image of the light source, which is in contrast to the suggestion of Chance (2) for the following reasons: A considerable amount of refractive scattering is obtainable where the light beams hit the interfaces tangentially, as recommended by Chance (2). *Beer's law* is much better fulfilled if the light beam passes only through the middle portion of the flow tube, thus actually improving that signal-to-noise ratio which refers to the changing absorption. Important for the evaluation of the flow equipment is information on the electronic rise time in reference to t_0, giving the over-all bandwidth of the detection system, the "rms noise-equivalent extinction" at specified wavelengths (optical bandwidths) and background optical densities. Only all these factors together allow judgement of the performance of a stopped-flow apparatus.

16–7. COMPLETENESS OF MIXING NEW SOLUTION

The completeness of mixing of a new solution is rather important and was mentioned earlier in conjunction with L'_1. This aspect seems to be of particular importance with reference to the pulsed-flow method, where only very small volumes are exchanged within a very short time. The aspect of complete mixing will be discussed more extensively in Chapter 17.

16–8. "RESIDUAL" CAVITATIONS

Residual cavitations can remain in the system after stopping the flow, if the relaxation of the cavitation is rather slow for some reason, primarily because of the containment of formerly dissolved gases in the cavitation bubbles. If this problem should occur, one would have to de-gas the solution. On the other hand, one actually should avoid cavitation from the onset, as will be discussed in more detail in Chapter 17.

PROBLEMS

1. Compute the minimum and the practical volume necessary for replacing the reaction mixture in a stopped-flow apparatus with $f_0 = 3 \times 10^{-3}$; $2r_0 = 5$ mm; $L_2 = 1.5$ cm.

2. The viscosity at 20°C is $\eta_v = 10^{-3}$ newton-sec^4 cm^{-2} ($= 10^{-2}$ poise) for water and $\eta_v = 0.85$ newton-sec cm^{-2} for glycerol. Compute N_R for $2r_0 = 5$ mm and $2r_0 = 1$ mm with $u_0 = 1.0$, 10, and 100 m sec^{-1} (density of glycerol is 1.26 g ml^{-1}).

REFERENCES

1. T. E. Stewart and K. R. Edlund, *J. Am. Chem. Soc.*, **48**, 1014 (1963).
2. B. Chance, *J. Franklin Inst.*, **229**, 455 (1940).
3. B. Chance, *in* A. Weissberger (ed.), *Technique of Organic Chemistry*, Vol. VIII, Pt. II, p. 728, Wiley (Interscience), New York, 1963.
4. Q. Gibson, *J. Physiol. (London)*, **117**, 49 (1952); *Discussions Faraday Soc.*, **17**, 137 (1954).
5. R. L. Berger, *in* B. Chance, R. Eisenhardt, Q. Gibson and K. Lonberg-Holm (eds.), *Rapid Mixing and Sampling Techniques in Biochemistry*, p. 105, Academic Press, New York, 1964.
6. G. I. Taylor, *Proc. Roy. Soc. (London)*, A219, 186 (1953); A223, 446 (1954).
7. H. K. Wiskind, p. 355 of Ref. 5.
8. B. Chance, p. 125 of Ref. 5.

CHAPTER 17

CONSTANT-FLOW METHOD

The rapid-flow method for liquid systems was originally introduced in 1923 by Hartridge and Roughton (*1*). One of their original designs is shown in Figure 17-1 (*2*). In 1923 they also proposed a closed system, the type of part (a) in Figure 17-1, which apparently has never been constructed by anyone in spite of its advantages in reference to signal-to-noise and the small amount of volume actually needed for a practically unlimited time

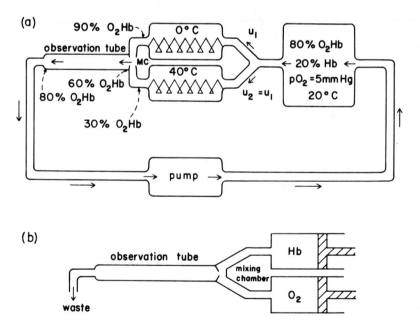

Figure 17-1. Original designs of Hartridge and Roughton.

of experimentation! For equal cross-sectional area in the two inlet tubes to the heat exchangers one has to keep $u_1 = u_2$. This equality of velocities can only be maintained with one pump (as shown) if the over-all resistances in both heat-exchanger arms are identical. If they are not identical, then $u_1 = u_2$ has to be controlled by flow meters and a correction valve, or two (coupled) pumps have to be inserted into both arms of the heat exchanger.

Several types of mixers had already been investigated around 1923, the tangential multijet mixer becoming the most effective one. The flow method was further developed later by Roughton and Millikan (3). More quantitative investigations followed in 1940 by Chance (4). Many new developments have appeared since, and it is not the purpose of this chapter to give a complete account of the recent literature. For this purpose one is referred to Roughton and Chance (5) and to a recent book by Chance and co-editors (6). Here the criteria developed in Chapter 16 will be discussed again.

17–1

Mechanical disturbances in the rapid-flow method can be rather severe, originating primarily from the acceleration process, although the high pressure at constant speed may also produce some disturbances. These disturbances can be reduced below noise level by rigid mechanical construction, a sinusoidal acceleration curve of not too great a steepness, and especially without any sharp edges in the acceleration curve.

17–2

There is generally no problem in expelling the old solution completely when using the rapid and constant-flow techniques where much larger volumes are expended. These necessarily large volumes are the primary drawback in the application of the constant-flow method to biological systems.

17–3

Chance developed a relationship for the total volume expended in a constant flow experiment (4), given by

$$V_0 = \frac{1}{2B}\frac{dV}{dt} \tag{17-1}$$

B is the bandwidth of the electronic detection system, as elaborated upon in Chapter 9. The *volume* flow rate is defined by

$$\frac{dV}{dt} = r_0^2 u_0 \tag{17-2}$$

The definition of the total flow volume contains the electronic bandwidth, which should be as small as possible for high signal-to-noise ratios, requiring in turn large volumes V_0. Equation (17-1) with small B also indicates relatively poor linearity in the response, requiring a number of calibration runs. Modern detection methods should permit a less stringent condition than given by (17-1).

In Chapter 16 it was mentioned that (16-5) is only valid for ratios $L_0/2r_0 \gg 40$, as determined experimentally by Chance (4). In the more general case, the Prandtl-Karman equation for a pressure drop is valid for a tube with sharp entrances:

$$p_0 - p_z = \left[f_0 \frac{L_0}{2r_0} + (1 + \gamma_t) \right] \tfrac{1}{2}\rho u_0^2 \tag{17-3}$$

$1 + \gamma_t$ is an energy-distribution factor. f_0 is defined by (16-5) and ρ is the density of the solution. For the definition of terms, see Figure 16-1. The first term in the brackets of (17-3) becomes negligible for $L_0/2r_0 < 40$. In ordinary rapid-flow systems this condition is generally fulfilled. One might be interested to look somewhat closer at the factor $1 + \gamma_t$, for which Chance obtained the value 1.40 (4). This value indicates that an additional 40 per cent of the energy expended in transporting the liquid system is used for turbulent mixing. Recently this factor was reinvestigated with a somewhat different flow apparatus, resulting in a value of 2.16 (7). This value remains reasonably constant up to the highest average linear flow velocities used (near 70 m/sec).

This factor $(1 + \gamma_t)$ is certainly an over-all factor which does not say anything about turbulence distribution in the mixer and along the flow tube. Different designs of mixers may therefore be expected to have different factors. The energy not used up in the transport is finally bound to appear as heat. This heat dissipation will partly occur in the mixer and there primarily rather close to the surface, where the heat can quickly be conducted away. Another part of the energy is converted temporarily into transverse kinetic energy within the mixer and then transported away; the transverse kinetic energy is then converted into heat, as the turbulence dies out. One should therefore not expect to detect much temperature rise within the observation region, even at high flow velocities, as actually found experimentally.

17-4

The information content in constant rapid flow is rather poor, as one would only obtain one single point in time, given by

$$\bar{t} = \frac{L_1 + L_2}{2u_0} \qquad (17\text{-}4)$$

This point, on the other hand, can be obtained with reasonably high precision, which is primarily due to the bandwidth relation according to (17-1).

17-5

The "dead time" is given as the time between "half-mixing" and the point of observation. This latter point is here much more an area of small dimensions than in the stopped-flow method. Equation (17-4) is also the

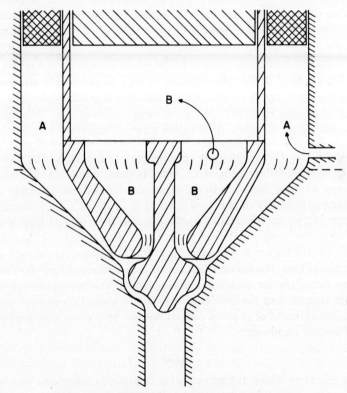

Figure 17-2. Original design of an infinite jet mixer.

equation for the time resolution, indicating that L_1 and L_2 should be as small as possible, while u_0 should be quite large. Chance already seems to have obtained the best arrangement of a multijet mixer with the jets neither entering tangentially nor directly opposed but somewhere intermediate (4). This arrangement also reduced cavitation the most, leading in special designs to flow velocities of 25 m/sec without any cavitation.

Multijet mixers have been used extensively since, most recently by Berger (8). The tangential two-jet mixer was originally introduced by Hartridge and Roughton (1). In the aim of obtaining high speed and complete mixing, an "infinite jet mixer" was recently devised by Czerlinski (9). A cross-sectional *axial* view of this mixer is shown in Figure 17-2. Section B is connected to the inner part of the co-axial syringe system; section A is connected to the outer part. The outer body below the dashed line in Figure 17-2 consists of plexiglass. The remaining parts are of stainless steel. It is interesting in this connection that Hunsaker mentioned in 1935 the advantage of having the mouth of the observation tube bell-shaped for reduced cavitation. This is exactly the shape of the mixing arrangement in Figure 17-2.

17–6

If a time spread in the measurement of only 10 per cent is allowed, this time spread in terms of measurable parameters is given by

$$\Delta \bar{t} \equiv \frac{1}{10} \bar{t} \doteq \frac{1}{10} \frac{L_2}{u_0} \tag{17-5}$$

This means that the length of the observation region along the flow tube, $L_2 - L_1$, is only 10 per cent of L_2. This is quite small but unfortunately necessary, as some precision in the experiment is desired. The light source is imaged in the axis of the flow tube at a width of r_0, as described in Chapter 16, while considering detection for the stopped-flow method. Otherwise, the same conditions have to be maintained for detection as mentioned in Chapter 9. For any rapid-flow apparatus one should obtain the minimal time resolution. One could measure according to (17-4) the volume necessary for making one experiment, the bandwidth of the recording system, and the rms noise-equivalent extinction change which is or the background of a given optical density at a given wavelength with stated optical bandwidths.

17–7

The extent to which the mixing of a solution is completed can best be followed by optical means, although the ordinary methods are generally integrating. For such experiments it is most suitable to use a pH indicator in a weakly buffered solution with pK_H of indicator and buffer near 7, pH < 1. The other solution contains only base with pH > 13, but such that the two solutions exactly neutralize upon mixing. If the two solutions are *isothermally* mixed and have fully reacted, they should reach a pH $\approx pK_H$ of the indicator. In a rapid-flow apparatus, mixing and reacting proceed so fast that the processes may be considered adiabatic in the beginning. As the heat of neutralization of water is large, a large pH shift would result, if enthalpy of indicator and buffer are rather different. The pH indicator will only reach the equilibrium color of the neutralization-heated solution after the mixing is really complete, assuming that the reaction is diffusion-limited under all experimental conditions. In the region of incomplete mixing an *average* color may appear, which is intermediate between the isothermal and the adiabatic color. Any variation from the equilibrium color then can be used for the computation of the extent of mixing under the assumption that all other effects are negligible (such as mechanical distortion). Adiabatic heating can be rechecked by employing two buffers of different enthalpies. Mechanical distortion can be detected by using an equilibrium indicator mixture for the flow apparatus (premixed long before). As pH adjustments and calibrations are rather difficult for the indicated test, one might better collect a set of suitably different irreversible reactions. If one could employ chemiluminescence with very rapid response, its light emission would be a direct indication of the amount mixed. No light would be emitted upon complete mixing, resulting in a "differentiated curve."

Very little is known about how mixing can be made more complete. Most ideal would be a mixing arrangement which accomplishes complete mixing just shortly before the point of observation and employs in the mixing process as little energy as possible, thus expending most of the energy supplied in driving the liquid system.

17–8

Cavitations have long prevented the extensive development of the flow method, limiting the time resolution of such methods to about 1msec. Chance has already extensively worked on the avoidance of cavitations in his experiment (4). Hunsaker found from much larger tubes that cavitations are affected by the shortest radius of the flow-tube entrance, around which the liquid flows, the over-all flow velocity, the vapor pressure of the liquid, the amount of incorporated gas, and the back pressure applied to the system (10). Chance had originally little success with avoiding cavitations by back pressure using comparatively small pressure (4). When he later employed higher pressures, he was quite successful in diminishing cavitation effects (6). Certainly nothing can be done concerning cavitation with reference to the over-all flow velocity or to the vapor pressure of the fluid. But any gas dissolved in the solution can be extracted by treatment in a vacuum or handling with ultrasound. It is also interesting that Hunsaker had already discovered that any small radius is highly effective in generating cavitation (10). Such small radii have been highly reduced in the mixer described by Figure 17-2, where the smallest radius of curvature is 2 mm.

The vapor pressure of the liquid is certainly quite important in the generation of cavitation if all other effects have been taken care of. This is easily visible from (17-3). In the mixer the pressure p_z may easily become so small locally that the vapor pressure of the liquid is reached, thus generating evaporation. It is immediately apparent that this vapor pressure is less likely reached if the residual pressure at the exit of the flow tube is comparatively large, so that the pressure drop has to be quite considerable to reach the vapor pressure of the liquid.

17–9. SPECIFIC DESIGNS

The complete apparatus of the author is shown in Figure 17-3 in its functional arrangement, also introducing the various parameters. First, the functioning of the whole apparatus is described in reference to Figure 17-3. The piston B has traveled previously the distance L_s and is resting in its lower position. The valve f is closed and the stopcock on the left side is opened into the syringe volume; fresh solution is inserted with pressure, driving the piston B up to its proper position, where it is closing a channel. Positioning of the pressure seals is indicated by the full triangles. There is no pressure in the accumulator of V_a. When the piston B is locked into position, the stopcock for the fresh solution is closed and nitrogen is inserted into the accumulator up to a pressure p_0. The nitrogen supply is then shut off and valve f opened. The trigger pulse of height E_R is supplied to the electromagnetic relay R. The leading edge of this triggering step function is time-reference zero. The relay opens a channel between the accumulator and the top of the piston B, releasing the piston from its seating; from there on the piston is pressed down with full pressure p_0. The piston B very quickly approaches its velocity u_s, which it maintains all the way until it has moved the total length L_s at which time the pressure is released from the accumulator (automatically). During the constant move of the piston B the solution moves out of the flow tube with velocity u_0.

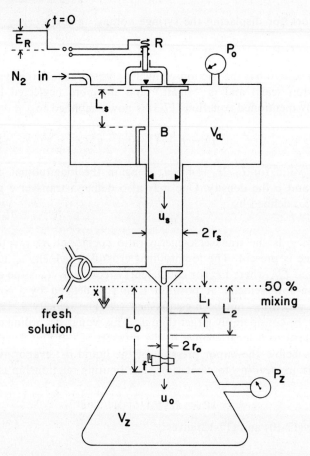

Figure 17-3. Schematic of the pressure-driven flow apparatus of the author (manufactured by Science Products, Dover, N.J.) with the definition of various parameters (see the text).

The velocity ratio between syringe flow and tube flow is given by

$$\frac{u_s}{u_0} = \frac{r_0^2}{r_s^2} \tag{17-6}$$

To maintain constant longitudinal flow velocities, one has to fulfill

$$V_a, V_z > 10V_s \tag{17-7}$$

with V_a the accumulator volume, V_z the receiver volume, and V_s the displacable syringe volume. The latter volume is given by

$$V_s = \pi r_s^2 L_s \tag{17-8}$$

The work for displacing the syringe volume in the receiver volume is given by

$$W_s = (p_0 - p_z - p_f)V_s \qquad (17\text{-}9)$$

p_f in this equation is the friction-equivalent pressure drop (the dynamic one from piston seals) and is "small," and therefore neglected later. The previously mentioned equation (17-3) is now simplified to

$$p_0 - p_z = (1 + \gamma_t)\frac{\rho}{2}u_0^2 \qquad (17\text{-}10)$$

which is valid for $L_0/2r_0 < 40$; u_0 is again the longitudinal gross flow velocity and ρ the density. One may also define a transverse gross flow velocity u_t, defined by

$$u_t^2 = \gamma_t u_0^2 \qquad (17\text{-}11)$$

The term γ_t is the transverse-energy-ratio coefficient. If $\gamma_t = 0$, laminar flow alone is present. The longitudinal gross flow velocity u_0 is constant throughout L_0, where πr_0^2 (or equivalent) is constant. u_L is the equivalent transverse-flow velocity at position L and is defined by a complicated function which has not been established yet. The velocity u_L can locally, certainly, be considerably larger than u_t. This would, according to (17-10), have to lead to a local change in the pressure p_z. If this local pressure decreases below the vapor pressure of the liquid p_v, evaporation of the liquid occurs, leading to cavitation. The limiting relationship is given by

$$(p_0 - p_v) = (1 + \gamma_v)\frac{\rho}{2}u_0^2 \qquad (17\text{-}12)$$

Dividing (17-10) and (17-12) gives

$$\frac{1 + \gamma_v}{1 + \gamma_t} = \frac{p_0 - p_v}{p_0 - p_z} \qquad (17\text{-}13)$$

This latter equation may then be solved for γ_v, resulting in

$$\gamma_v = \gamma_t + \frac{p_z - p_v}{p_0 - p_z} \qquad (17\text{-}14)$$

As one would expect, γ_v is always larger than γ_t, but the second term may contribute as little as 2 per cent, which is quite a small amount, to accomplish generation of cavitations. The time for emptying the syringe with the definitions of Figure 17-3 is given by

$$t_s = \frac{V_s}{\pi r_0^2 u_0} \qquad (17\text{-}15)$$

In a special flow apparatus t_s was found to be 74 msec at 50 atm for 100 cm³ displacable solution volume, V_s. Figure 1 of Ref. 7 resulted in a slope of 0.27 sec² from a plot of p_0 (atm) against t^{-2} (sec^{-2}). Employing the already mentioned values for V_s, p_0, t_s, and $p_z = 1$ atm, $\rho = 1$ g cm^{-3} (for water), $\pi r_0^2 = 0.2$ cm², and a conversion factor of 1.02×10^{-6} g cm^{-1} sec^{-2} atm^{-1} (Table 16-1), one obtains for $(1 + \gamma_t) = 2.1$, close to the value mentioned above. $p_z = 12$ mm Hg for water at room temperature, which is negligible to 736 mm Hg for 1 atm. It is therefore apparent that $1 + \gamma_v$ is only 2 per cent larger than $1 + \gamma_t$. These brief calculations therefore show quite clearly that in processes where high pressures are used for accelerating the flow, p_z should not be ordinary atmospheric pressure, but should perhaps even reach 10 per cent of p_0, to reduce the appearance of cavitation in the flow system, particularly at the narrow jets. γ_t seems to be an important instrumental parameter for flow systems, as its size would indicate the relative amount of energy expended in turbulence, and would also give an indication of the ease with which cavitation can show up.

In conjunction with this chapter, a copy of Figure 17-4 was sent to several designers of rapid-flow instruments. Table 17-1 summarizes some of the data of these designers. The indicated rate constants are maximal ones, which have been obtained experimentally. Sturtevant (11) used a stopped-flow apparatus with fluorescence detection. Dulz and Sutin (12)

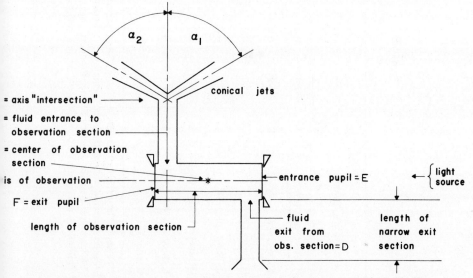

Figure 17-4. Schematic flow apparatus for defining individual terms used in Table 17-1.

TABLE 17-1

RAPID-FLOW INSTRUMENTS[a]

DESIGNER (YEAR)	NO. OF JETS	$\alpha_1 = \alpha_2$	AREA AT B, cm^2	AREA AT D, cm^2	DISTANCE $A \cdots B$, cm	DISTANCE $E \cdots F$, cm	AREA AT E, cm^2	AREA AT F, cm^2	RATE CONSTANTS BIMOLEC., $M^{-1} sec^{-1}$	MONOMOL., sec^{-1}
J. M. Sturtevant (1961)	4	90°	0.04	0.04	0.3	0.2	0.2	0.2	$\leqslant 10^8$	$\leqslant 500$
N. Sutin (1962)	8	90°	0.03	0.03	1.0	0.2	0.02	0.02	$\leqslant 2 \times 10^7$	$\leqslant 340$
L. H. Piette (1962)	2, 4	90°	0.03	0.03	0.2	—	—	—	$\lesssim 10^9$	10^4
D. C. Borg (1962)	2		0.02	0.03	0.15	—	—	—	$\lesssim 10^9$	
L. DeMaeyer (1964–1965)	8	45°	0.01	0.01	0.3	0.1	0.01	0.01	b	
R. L. Berger (1964–1965)	8	80°, 90°	0.07	0.07	0.3	0.3	0.07	0.07	2×10^7	
G. Czerlinski (1964)	∞	~60°	0.2	0.2	1.0	0.5	0.1	0.1	c	d

[a] The capital letters refer to labels in Figure 17-4; observation is always perpendicular to flow.
[b] A special annular mixing chamber is employed, containing high-voltage electrodes.
[c] Various types manufactured by Science Products Corp., Route 46, Dover, N.J.
[d] Preliminary testing gave 0.05 to 50 sec^{-1} on one system, employed in the stopped-flow mode.

also determined the noise-equivalent optical density at the 1-kc electronic bandwidth with no absorbing background and obtained 0.0013 at 560 and 366 mμ. Piette, as well as Borg, used electron spin resonance for detection (compare Ref. 6) and constant-flow designs. The design of Czerlinski (7) has not yet been applied extensively.

PROBLEMS

1. Recompute the value $1 + \gamma_t = 2.1$ with the values given following (17-15).
2. Assuming this value for $1 + \gamma_t$, what would be the extrapolated pressure drop for $u_0 = 100$ m sec^{-1}? And what percentage is $1 + \gamma_v$ larger than $1 + \gamma_t$ under these conditions and $p_z = 1$ atm?

REFERENCES

1. H. Hartridge and F. J. W. Roughton, *Proc. Roy. Soc.* (*London*), **A104**, 376 (1923).
2. H. Hartridge and F. J. W. Roughton, *Proc. Roy. Soc.* (*London*), **B94**, 336 (1923).
3. G. A. Millikan, *Proc. Roy. Soc.* (*London*), **A155**, 277 (1936); F. J. W. Roughton and G. A. Millikan, *Proc. Roy. Soc.* (*London*), **A155**, 258 (1936).
4. B. Chance, *J. Franklin Inst.*, **229**, 455, 613, 737 (1940).
5. B. Chance and F. J. W. Roughton, *in* A. Weissberger (ed.), *Technique of Organic Chemistry*, Vol. VIII, Pt. II, p. 703, Wiley (Interscience), New York, 1963.
6. B. Chance (ed.), *Rapid Mixing and Sampling Techniques in Biochemistry*, Academic Press, New York, 1964.
7. G. Czerlinski, p. 367 of Ref. 6 (error in decimal place).
8. R. L. Berger, p. 33 of Ref. 6.
9. G. Czerlinski, p. 21 of Ref. 6.
10. J. C. Hunsaker, *Mech. Eng.*, **57**, 211 (1935).
11. J. M. Sturtevant, p. 89 of Ref. 6.
12. G. Dulz and N. Sutin, *Inorg. Chem.*, **2**, 917 (1963).

CHAPTER 18

RAPID FLOW PLUS *T*-JUMP

18–1. GENERAL CONSIDERATIONS

Combinations of the flow method and the temperature-jump method were described in some detail by Eigen and DeMaeyer (*1*) and by Czerlinski (*2*). These two designs can barely be more different from each other than they actually are. The apparatus of Eigen and DeMaeyer employs a flow apparatus with a very small bore for the flow and heating by electric discharges with the field lines going parallel to the direction of the flow. (B. Havsteen is presently working on this apparatus together with L. DeMaeyer.) Czerlinski described an apparatus employing a pulsed laser for the heating and a continuous wave laser for the detection process.

There are two aspects under which one could consider the combination of flow and temperature-jump techniques. One can start from the flow technique and ask if it is possible to extend the time range of this method. Turnover numbers of enzyme systems rarely exceed 10^3 or 10^4 sec^{-1} and one may obtain a steady state in the flow tube which can then be perturbed by a sudden change in temperature, leading to a relaxation process which involves all the steps prior to the rate-limiting one. These steps are important for the understanding of the over-all mechanism of an enzyme reaction. The rate constants of these steps may be obtained from the spectrum of relaxation time constants. Since the time resolution of present temperature-jump methods includes the microsecond range, such a combination would extend the range of application of the flow method down to the microsecond range.

On the other hand, one may start with the temperature-jump method and ask if its range of application can be extended further. The relaxation methods are restricted by the fact that they are usually applicable only to systems at equilibrium. The combination of the two methods allows an extension of the temperature-jump method to nonequilibrium systems. Since many enzyme processes involve equilibria which are far on one side, such an extension could become of very practical importance.

It actually is of high interest to extend the time resolution of the rapid-flow method to 100 μsec and that of the temperature-jump method to the submicrosecond range. These requirements necessitate the introduction of new techniques for mixing, heating, and detecting. The "infinite jet system" seems to be quite suitable. Very rapid heating is obtainable with giant laser pulses, employing vibrational excitation of water molecules, as described in Chapter 12. High light levels are necessary to obtain a sufficiently high signal-to-noise ratio at wide electronic bandwidths, making the use of continuous wave lasers very desirable for detection purposes.

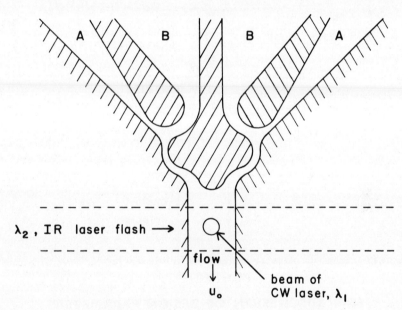

Figure 18-1. Cross-sectional view of the infinite jet mixer in the axis of flow with indication of the two laser beams.

Figure 18-1 shows an axial view of the infinite jet mixer with the laser beams perpendicular to each other and to the direction of the flow. Figure 18-2 shows the over-all arrangement in the plane of the optical beams. The flow direction is thus perpendicular to the plane of writing.

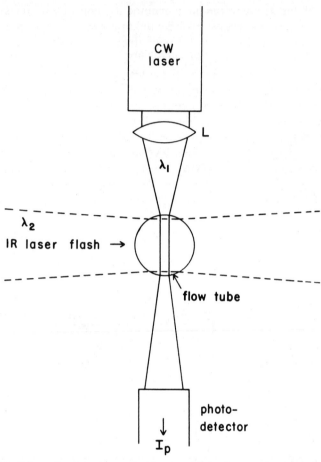

Figure 18-2. Schematic of the two optical beams with the flow perpendicular to the plane of drawing.

18-2. DISCUSSION OF DESIGN PARAMETERS

The fundamental engineering equation for the combination of a flow apparatus with a temperature-jump apparatus with generation of heat surges by giant laser pulses will now be given. One is first referred to Figure 18-3, which introduces a number of symbols for the derivation of the equations. Some of the symbols have been introduced formerly, such as $2r_0$, the diameter of the flow tube, u_0, the average longitudinal flow velocity, and the distances of the borders of the observation beam, L_1 and L_2. The observation beam operates at wavelengths λ_1 and in the plane of drawing. The pulsed laser operates at wavelengths λ_2 and normal to the plane of drawing, indicated by dashed bordering lines of the beam. The distances of the borders from the plane of mixing are given by L_3 and L_4. Another dashed line, a circle, is labeled H, indicating a magnetic field normal to the plane of writing and used for the electromagnetic flow meter (3,4). E_1 and E_2 are the output leads of this flow meter, which are fed directly into a Tektronix oscilloscope with a high-gain preamplifier. r_s is the radius of the syringe containing the liquid, represented as one single cylinder, while normally it is a coaxial set of two cylinders. Reference zero is given by the dotted line in Figure 18-3, corresponding to 50 per cent mixing under the assumption of a sigmoid curve for the extent of mixing in the jet as a function of longitudinal distance. One may then consider some other percentage extent of mixing as "complete" and define this time as the mixing time τ_M.

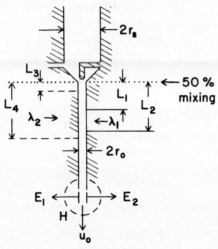

Figure 18-3. Schematic of Figure 18-1 with the introduction of various symbols used in the theoretical treatment. One should remember that the measuring light (λ_1 with solid bordering) is perpendicular to the flashed light (λ_2 with dashed bordering).

If L_M is the distance from reference zero where mixing is considered complete, the mixing time τ_M is defined by

$$\tau_M = \frac{L_M}{u_0} \qquad (18\text{-}1)$$

τ_{min} is defined as the minimal chemical relaxation time anticipated to be measured by the T-jump generated in the flow tube. The length L_3 is then defined by

$$u_0(\tau_M + 10\tau_{\min}) \leqslant L_3 \tag{18-2}$$

$\tau_{\min}$ in this equation is multiplied by at least 10 to assure practically complete equilibration of the mixed solutions at the point where the laser beam heats the system. Another important chemical parameter is k_{slow}, the velocity constant for slow monomolecular interconversion. This slow reaction is cut off by the flow apparatus and therefore its changes should not affect the chemical system. To assure this, L_4 is defined by

$$\frac{u_0}{10k_{\text{slow}}} \geqslant L_4 \tag{18-3}$$

t_1 is defined as total length of observation time in the flow tube by the light of wavelength λ_1. Its relation with reference to $\tau_{\min}$ is given by

$$t_1 \geqslant 10\tau_{\min} \tag{18-4}$$

t_1 is related to the various lengths in the flow tube by

$$u_0 t_1 = L_4 - L_3 - 2L_d - L_2 + L_1 \tag{18-5}$$

in which L_d is defined according to (16-4). $u_0 t_1$ is then the (geometric) length equivalent to the total observation time. The time of observation after 50 per cent mixing, $\bar{t}$, was introduced formerly, and is here just repeated for reference:

$$2u_0\bar{t} = L_1 + L_2 \tag{18-6}$$

One may also define the duration of observation after mixing, $\Delta\bar{t}$, according to

$$\Delta\bar{t}u_0 = L_2 - L_1 \tag{18-7}$$

To cover as wide a range as possible, L_2 should be as large as permissible, and its upper limit is given by

$$L_2 + L_d = L_4 \tag{18-8}$$

The output power level required from a giant pulse laser P_L^0 is then given by

$$L_4 - L_3 = (P_L^0 - P_L')\tau_0 \frac{\alpha}{\pi r_0^2 \kappa_w \Delta T} \tag{18-9}$$

in which P_L' is the power not absorbed in the flow tube, τ_0 is the effective heating time of the system, α is the energy conversion factor, 0.24 cal watt-sec^{-1}, κ_w is the specific heat of water, 1 cal deg^{-1} cm^{-3}, and ΔT is the temperature rise, here set at 5°C. In a design described earlier (5), $\pi r_0^2 = 0.2$ cm^2. Unfortunately, presently available lasers do not give a power output just as desired; and therefore experimentally one generally has to start with (18-9). For purposes of actual computation, it may be assumed that the energy absorbed is given by $(P_L^0 - P_L') \tau_0 = 4$ joules. With the various values given above, a temperature rise of 5°C leads to $L_4 - L_3 = 1$ cm. If $L_M = 0.25$ cm and $u_0 = 5 \times 10^3$ cm sec^{-1}, one obtains $\tau_M = 50$ μsec. If we further assume that $\tau_{min} = 10$ μsec, one obtains from (18-4) a value of $t_1 = 10^{-4}$ sec. L_3 becomes 0.75 cm, and $L_4 = 1.75$ cm. From (18-3) one obtains $k_{slow} = 290$ sec^{-1}. $L_2 - L_1$ is obtained from (18-5) and should be smaller than 0.5 cm, resulting in $L_1 < 1.25$ cm. This sample calculation shows the general usefulness of the method combining the temperature-jump method with the constant- and rapid-flow techniques.

18-3.　CHEMICAL RESTRICTIONS

To demonstrate more clearly the meaning of the chemical parameters τ_{min} and k_{slow}, a more chemical analysis is advisable. As an example one may start with a two-step reaction involving an enzyme (6) as given by

$$E + S \xrightarrow[k_2]{k_1} ES \xrightarrow[k_4]{k_3} E + P \qquad (18\text{-}10)$$

The k_i are the rate constants in the direction of the arrow. Although ES may actually consist of several components, they are not considered for this introductory investigation.

To determine easily two relaxation processes for reaction (18-10), the fundamental condition for kinetic resolution is

$$k_1(\bar{c}_E + \bar{c}_S) + k_2 \gg k_3 + k_4(\bar{c}_E + \bar{c}_P) \qquad (18\text{-}11)$$

A closer look at actual enzyme systems (see below) indicates that condition (18-11) cannot always be easily obtained, especially if one considers the additional requirements for determining *both* velocity constants. They are

$$\tfrac{1}{10}(K_{2,1} + K_{3,4}) \lesssim c_S^0 \lesssim 10(K_{2,1} + K_{3,4}) \qquad (18\text{-}12)$$

with

$$K_{2,1} = \frac{k_2}{k_1} = \frac{\bar{c}_E \bar{c}_S}{\bar{c}_{ES}} \qquad (18\text{-}13)$$

$$K_{3,4} = \frac{k_3}{k_4} = \frac{\bar{c}_E \bar{c}_P}{\bar{c}_{ES}} \qquad (18\text{-}14)$$

$$c_S^0 = \bar{c}_S + \bar{c}_{ES} \qquad (18\text{-}15)$$

$$c_E^0 = \bar{c}_E + \bar{c}_{ES} \qquad (18\text{-}16)$$

$$c_S^0 \gg c_E^0 \qquad (18\text{-}17)$$

Relation (18-17) is generally established for enzyme reactions.

One may then distinguish the following conditions:

A. Relation (18-11) is fulfilled, and

   1. Relation (18-12) is also fulfilled.

   2. Relation (18-12) cannot be fulfilled:

$$K_{3,4} \gg \text{any experimental } c_S^0$$

B. Relation (18-11) cannot be established; the two steps are about equally fast, and

   1. Relation (18-12) can be established.

   2. Relation (18-12) cannot be established.

C. Relation (18-11) is reversed; the terms on the left are smaller than those on the right. Although this case is symmetric to case A, this symmetry can only be used for the condition of relation (18-12).

   1. Relation (18-12) is fulfilled; use A1.

   2. Relation (18-12) cannot be established.

A1. This represents the "classical" fully reversible case for chemical relaxation of enzyme systems (7). The equilibrium concentrations of the four components can easily be established from equations (18-13) to (18-16) together with a relation which is slightly less general than that of (18-17) ($\bar{c}_P$ may be small under special circumstances):

$$\bar{c}_S, \bar{c}_P \gg \bar{c}_E, \bar{c}_{ES} \tag{18-18}$$

Equation (18-11) then permits the derivation of the experimentally accessible parameters of the two relaxation processes in an elementary manner. One obtains

$$\tau_1^{-1} = k_2 \frac{c_S^0 + K_{2,1} + K_{3,4}}{K_{2,1} + K_{3,4}} \tag{18-19}$$

$$\tau_2^{-1} = k_3 \frac{c_E^0}{K_{2,1}} \frac{K_{2,1} + K_{3,4}}{c_S^0 + K_{2,1} + K_{3,4}} \tag{18-20}$$

Equation (18-12) establishes the range of analytical concentrations to determine k_2 and $K_{2,1} + K_{3,4}$ from (18-19), and k_3 and $K_{2,1} + K_{3,4}$ from (18-20). One obtains for the two relative concentration changes,

$$\frac{(\Delta \bar{c}_E)_1}{c_E^0} = \frac{\Delta K_{2,1}}{K_{2,1}} \frac{c_S^0}{(c_S^0 + K_{2,1} + K_{3,4})^2} (K_{2,1} + K_{3,4})$$

$$= -\frac{(\Delta \bar{c}_{ES})_1}{c_E^0} \tag{18-21}$$

$$\frac{(\Delta \bar{c}_E)_2 - (\Delta \bar{c}_E)_1}{c_E^0} = - \frac{(\Delta \bar{c}_{ES})_2 - (\Delta \bar{c}_{ES})_1}{c_E^0}$$

$$= \frac{\Delta K_{3,4}}{K_{3,4}} - \frac{\Delta K_{2,1}}{K_{2,1}} \cdot \frac{c_S^0 K_{3,4}}{(c_S^0 + K_{2,1} + K_{3,4})^2} \qquad (18\text{-}22)$$

Liver alcohol dehydrogenase (8) seems to approximate condition A1 at high concentrations of alcohol and aldehyde, if one assumes very fast equilibration between the alcohol and the aldehyde complex of the enzyme [so that a single E is justified in reaction (18-10)]. In this case, the substrate is DPN ($k_2 = 74 \text{ sec}^{-1}$) and the product DPNH ($k_3 = 3.1 \text{ sec}^{-1}$). The monomolecular velocity constants are just sufficiently separated to fulfill condition A1. Similar conditions can probably also be established with other dehydrogenases.

A2. Various enzyme systems may not allow the establishment of relation (18-12) by the mere fact that $K_{3,4}$ is too large to be reached by any experimental c_S^0. This might mean that k_4 becomes rather small, or even approaches zero (irreversible step). One may then again introduce a time constant τ_M such that τ_M is an instrumental constant,

$$k_2 \gg \tau_M^{-1} \gg k_3 \qquad (18\text{-}23)$$

associated with a rapid-flow apparatus and defined as the time between start of mixing and the instant of observation. If E and S are mixed, one may consider $c_P = 0$ for the time measurement, and for relation (18-12) one must substitute:

$$\tfrac{1}{10} K_{2,1} \lesssim c_S^0 \lesssim 0 K_{2,1} \qquad (18\text{-}24)$$

and the "maximum response" is given by

$$c_S^0 = K_{2,1} \qquad (18\text{-}25)$$

Complete derivation leads to

$$\tau_1^{-1} = k_2 \frac{c_S^0 + K_{2,1}}{K_{2,1}} \qquad (18\text{-}26)$$

and

$$\frac{(\Delta \bar{c}_{ES})_1}{c_E^0} = \frac{\Delta K_{2,1}}{K_{2,1}} \frac{c_S^0 K_{2,1}}{(c_S^0 + K_{2,1})^2} \qquad (18\text{-}27)$$

Equations (18-26) and (18-27) may also be obtained from (18-19) and (18-21) by simply setting $K'_{3,4} \equiv 0$. A "prime" is added to this dissociation a constant to indicate that it is not a true dissociation constant, but has this value *for the time of measurement* only.

Although condition (18-23) allows an easy determination of k_1, $K_{2,1}$, and the enthalpy (related to $\Delta K_{2,1}/K_{2,1}$), it does not need to be that stringent. One may also use

$$k_2 \gg \tau_M^{-1} \gtrsim k_3 \qquad (18\text{-}28)$$

It is a condition of (18-28) that $\tilde{c}_Z$, concentration of Z when measuring τ_1, remains practically constant during this measuring interval. But then one has to introduce the constant

$$K'_{3,4} = \frac{\tilde{c}_E \tilde{c}_P}{\tilde{c}_{ES}} \qquad (18\text{-}29)$$

$K'_{3,4}$ may have any size in relation to $K_{2,1}$, as long as relation (18-12) can be fulfilled when $K'_{3,4}$ is substituted for $K_{3,4}$. The relaxation process is again defined by (18-19) and (18-21) with $K'_{3,4}$ substituted for $K_{3,4}$.

Equation (18-12) and its modifications are *not* a condition for steady state. The condition for a reaction sequence of type (18-10) in an ideal steady state is

$$\tilde{c}_{ES} = c_E^0 \qquad (18\text{-}30)$$

This equality can only be approximated to a reasonable extent with a relatively small k_3 and $c_S^0 \gg 10 K_{2,1}$. This condition, however, does not satisfy relation (18-24). In a steady state, we are thus *outside* the range of determining chemical relaxation for reactions of the simple type given in (18-10), as is also evident from a brief consideration of (18-13). If $\tilde{c}_S \gg \tilde{c}_{ES} \gg \tilde{c}_E$, any change in $K_{2,1}$ must appear in $\tilde{c}_E$, which generally is below the detection limit in steady-state experiments.

We conclude that, under normal conditions, enzyme-substrate recombinations cannot be investigated in the steady state. But interconversions of enzyme-substrate complexes *can* be investigated in the steady state, using a combination of the flow method and the temperature-jump technique and employing a more complicated system, such as

$$
\begin{array}{c}
\text{fastest} \left(
\begin{array}{c}
\xrightarrow{} \text{E} + \text{S} \xrightleftharpoons[k_6]{k_5} \text{ES} \searrow \nearrow \text{BH} \\
\qquad\qquad\qquad\qquad k_8 \big| k_7 \\
\text{F} + \text{(P)} \xleftarrow[\text{slowest}]{k_9} \text{HES} \nearrow \searrow \text{B}
\end{array}
\right)
\end{array}
\qquad (18\text{-}31)
$$

The fastest and slowest steps are considered as practically irreversible, providing always $c_F = 0$. The condition for the flow apparatus is given by

$$k_7 \bar{c}_{BH}, \; k_8 \bar{c}_B, \; k_6 \gg \tau_M^{-1} \gg k_9 \qquad (18\text{-}32)$$

If, in (18-32), k_6 is also much slower than the $k_7 \bar{c}_{BH}$ and $k_8 \bar{c}_B$, one obtains the chemical relaxation of a simplified system such as the binding of DPNH to malate dehydrogenase (*9*). k_7 and k_8 can easily be as high as $10_9 \, M^{-1} \sec^{-1}$ and the chemical relaxation time associated with this proton transfer and $10^{-2} \, M = \bar{c}_B = \bar{c}_{BH} \gg \bar{c}_S$ then becomes 50 nanosec. The heating-time constant τ_0 should then be somewhat *below* this value. The aim would be $\tau_0 = 10$ nanosec. Monomolecular velocity constants can easily reach $10^4 \sec^{-1}$. One should therefore strive for at least $\tau_M = 100$ μsec. This value would also leave four orders of magnitude for the investigation of chemical relaxation. The velocity constant of particular concern for τ_M is that one which determines the turnover rate of an enzyme. Velocity constants such as k_3 in relation (18-28) are rarely above $10^4 \sec^{-1}$.

B1. The investigation of a system like that given in (18-10), where both steps proceed at about equal speed and which fulfills condition (18-12), is rather difficult. Under these conditions, the two different relaxation processes can only be evaluated by elaborate techniques, and even then only if they differ by a factor of about 2 (depending upon signal-to-noise ratios and repeatability). Computers would be needed for the full analysis of the data. Such a system cannot be applied to investigations by a combined apparatus, since relation (18-28) could not be established. The Fumarase-system (*10*) seems to offer these complications.

B2. The same considerations as for B1 are valid for a system with $k_4 \to 0$, except that only one relaxation process can be detected. This is also valid for the extreme case $k_2 = 0$ and $k_4 = 0$. The chemical relaxation of such a system would correspond to that illustrated in (18-31), but employing k_7 and k_8 only, *plus* the *very* fast interconversion between the two forms of the (free) enzyme.

C2. If the first step in system (18-10) is *slower* than the second, there are three possibilities for "irreversible" steps: (a) $k_2 = 0$; (b) $k_4 = 0$; (c) both k_2 and k_4 vanish. In all three cases, (18-23) should be replaced by

$$k_3 \gg \tau_M^{-1} \approx k_1(\bar{c}_E + \bar{c}_S) + k_2 \tag{18-33}$$

(a) $k_2 = 0$; the step containing k_3 and k_4 can be investigated *after* adequate amounts of $\tilde{c}_E$ and $\tilde{c}_P$ have been formed to allow the proper investigation of the fast step. It is then simply a question of re-indexing former equations.

(b) $k_4 = 0$; the intermediate ES is so small as to be effectively undetectable. All changes by temperature jumps would appear in ES. While a combination of a *flow* and a relaxation method is thus not possible, the over-all system could show chemical relaxation (see c). A bacterial catalase system (*11*) seems to belong to this particular type, if the methanol concentration is set at 1.0 M. In this system $k_1 = 3 \times 10^5 \ M^{-1} \ \text{sec}^{-1}$, $k_2 = 0.0075 \ \text{sec}^{-1}$, the pseudo-monomolecular constant $k_3 = 91 \ \text{sec}^{-1}$ and $k_4 = 0$.

(c) If

$$E + S \xrightarrow[\text{slow}]{k_1} \ ES \xrightarrow[\text{fast}]{k_3} E + P$$

there is again a very small but nevertheless detectable concentration of the intermediate ES: $\bar{c}_{ES}/\bar{c}_E = k_3/(k_1 \bar{c}_S)^{-1}$. Temperature jumps on the fast reaction step are possible; however, since microscopic reversibility no longer exists, the theoretical meaning of such a change is unclear. Chemical relaxation on the over-all system is possible in spite of $\Delta c_{ES} = - \Delta c_E$, if the optical signals from E and ES are quite different.

PROBLEMS

1. Derive L_3 and L_4 for a system, absorbing only 1 joule pulsed laser energy, but having $\pi r_0^2 = 2 \ \text{mm}^2$ and $\Delta T = 3°C$, $L_3 = 1$ cm. Compute u_0 for $k_{\text{slow}} = 10^3 \ \text{sec}^{-1}$. Then derive the conditions for as long as τ_{min} is possible.
2. Derive (18-20).
3. Derive (18-22).

REFERENCES

1. M. Eigen and L. DeMaeyer, *in* B. Chance, R. Eisenhardt, Q. Gibson, and K. Lonberg-Holm (eds.), *Rapid Mixing and Sampling Techniques in Biochemistry*, p. 175, Academic Press, New York, 1964.
2. G. Czerlinski, p. 183 of Ref. 1.
3. A. Kolin, *Rev. Sci. Instr.*, **16**, 109 (1945).
4. G. Czerlinski, p. 371 of Ref. *1*.
5. G. Czerlinski, p. 183 of Ref. *1*.
6. G. Czerlinski, p. 387 of Ref. *1*.
7. G. Czerlinski, *J. Theoret. Biol.*, **7**, 463 (1964).
8. H. Theorell and J. S. M. McKee, *Acta Chem. Scand.*, **15**, 1797, 1811, 1834 (1961).
9. G. Czerlinski and G. Schreck, *Biochemistry*, **3**, 89 (1964).
10. R. A. Alberty and W. H. Peirce, *J. Am. Chem. Soc.*, **79**, 1526 (1957).
11. B. Chance and G. R. Schonbaum, *J. Biol. Chem.*, **237**, 2391 (1964).

GLOSSARY OF TERMS

(Pertaining Mainly to Chapters 1 to 8)

SYMBOL	DEFINITION	EQUATION
A	dimensionless factor in front of exponential	(1-8) .
a_{ij}	negative coefficients of the Δc of (3-17) and (3-18), whereby i and j have no relation to isolated indices i and j (separated by a comma); here $i =$ row, $j =$ column (of a matrix)	(3-19) to (3-22)
b	dimensionless parameter, dependent upon the negative coefficients a_{ij}	(3-28)
c_i	instantaneous concentration of component Y_i	(1-2)
$\bar{c}_i$	equilibrium concentration (in general and before perturbation) of component Y_i	(1-4)
c_i^0	the *initial* concentration of the ith chemical component in *mixing* methods; the *analytical* concentration of the ith component in *relaxation* methods	(1-5)
$\bar{c}_i'$	equilibrium concentration *after* perturbation [distinction only until (2-22) and differently in Chapter 6]	(2-8)
$\bar{\bar{c}}_i$	equilibrium concentration of the ith component, *fixed* by buffering	(5-89)
$\bar{c}_{i,0}$	equilibrium concentration before perturbation, thus "practically" equal to $\bar{c}_i$	(6-34)
Δc_i	instantaneous concentration change	(2-9)
$\Delta \bar{c}_i$	equilibrium concentration change	(2-8)
$\Delta \bar{c}_{i,j}$	equilibrium concentration change of the ith component, belonging to the jth relaxation process	(6-34) to (6-36)
$\Delta H_{2,1}$	enthalpy of the reaction defined by $K_{2,1}$	(2-46)
i	index with rate constants k or chemical components Y	(1-1)
	index to differentiate among consecutive relaxation processes (and only used when differentiation becomes necessary)	(2-21)
k_i	velocity constant defined by the arrow in an equation; index unrelated to Y_i and c_i; odd indices generally refer to the "forward" reaction, even indices to the "backward" reaction	(1-1)
$K_{i,i-1}$	equilibrium constant, defined by the ratio of (singly indexed) velocity constants k_i and k_{i-1}	(1-4)
K_0	over-all dissociation constant, specifically defined within the context [such as (4-150)]	(4-150)
$\Delta K_{2,1}$	change of the equilibrium constant $K_{2,1}$ upon perturbation	(2-47)
l	length of light path in solution	(4-5)
ln	natural logarithm (base e)	(2-18)

R	gas constant ($2 \text{ cal deg}^{-1} M^{-1}$)	(2-46)
S_0	reference signal, the signal obtained without any indicating component Y_i	(4-3)
S_T	total signal measured (indicating components present)	(4-3)
ΔS_T	Over-all signal change (an observable)	(2-48)
$\Delta \bar{S}_T$	*total* equilibrium signal change obtained upon perturbation	(7-1)
$\Delta \bar{S}_j$	equilibrium signal change of the jth relaxation process	(7-5)
T	(absolute) temperature (in °Kelvin)	(2-46)
x	a reaction variable ($=$ concentration parameter) used operationally only	(1-6)
$\bar{x}$	equilibrium concentration variable of a system	(2-23)
X	external (perturbing) parameter	(2-45)
Y_i	the ith chemical component in a reaction	(1-1)
Δ	change of any parameter is indicated by Δ; see the individual parameter, carrying the sign in front	(2-8)
ε_i	(natural) molar extinction coefficient of the ith component (in $M^{-1} \text{ cm}^{-1}$)	(4-5)
η_i	characteristic signal of the ith component measured, for instance, in mvolts/μM [see also (7-16)]	(4-4)
η_i'	specific extinction, carrying a dimension of reciprocal micromolar [see also (7-16)]	(4-58)
$\prod_i$	product over the parameter, indexed with i within specified limits	(3-185)
$\sum_i$	summation over the index i from $i = 1$ to $i =$ total number of components present	(2-48)
τ	time constant, related to rate constants	(1-8)
τ_j	chemical relaxation time constant, which shows up in time at position j; thus $\tau_1 =$ time constant of fastest relaxation process	(2-21)

AUTHOR INDEX

Numbers in parentheses are reference numbers and indicate that an author's work is referred to although his name is not cited in the text. Numbers in italics give the page on which the complete reference is listed.

A

Alberty, R. A., 166(6), 177, *179*, 221, *227*, 303(10), *304*

B

Becker, M., 241, 263, 264, *268*
Behr, B., 267(9), *268*
Bell, D. A., 193(2), *212*
Benson, S. W., 7, *12*
Berger, R. L., 276, *281*, 286, *293*
Bergmann, K., 259, *261*
Berman, M., 3, *4*
Bjerrum, N., 245, *248*

C

Caldin, E. F., 2, *4*, 234, *234*
Castellan, G. W., 3, *4*
Chance, B., 166(5), *179*, 192(1), *212*, 272, 274, 275, 278, 279, 280, *281*, 283, 284, 286, 287, *293*, 303 (11), *304*
Clark, W. R., 192(1), *212*
Colen, A. H., 221(10), *227*
Crooks, J. E., 234, *234*
Czerlinski, G., 1(6), 2(7,8) *4*, 10, *12*, 18(1), 27(2), *29*, 38, 43(2), 62(3), *73*, 82(1), 83(2), 84(4), 93(5), 99(6), *100*, 106(1), 110(2), 112(2), 123(3), *128*, 130(1), 138(2), 144, 155(4), *158*, 160(1,2) 165(3,4) 166(5), *178*, *179*, 195(4), 197(6), 202(10), 203(11,12), 204(14,15), 206(16), *212*, *213*, 215(2,4,5), 216(6,7), 218(2,4), 220, 221, 222(5,12), *227*, 235(2), 241, 242(20–22), *247*, 269, 271(3), *274*,

Czerlinski, G.—*continued*
284, 286, 293, *293*, 294, 297(4), 298(5), 299(6), 300(7), 303(9), *304*

D

Davenport, G., 221(11), *227*
Debye, P., 243, *248*, 255(7), *261*
DeMaeyer, L., 1(5), *4*, 175(7), *179*, 191, *191*, 221, *227*, 236(3,6), 243(24), 244(24), *248*, 250, 259, *261*, *268* 294, *304*
Diven, W. F., 166(6), 177, *179*
Duffey, D., 166(5), *179*
Dulz, G., 291, *293*

E

Edlund, K. R., 275, *281*
Eicke, H. F., 236(4), *247*
Eigen, M., 1(3,5,6), 2(11), 3(17), *3*, *4*, 38, *73*, 160(2), 175, *178*, *179*, 191, *191*, 204(14), *213*, 215(2,3), 218(2), *227*, 236, 237(5), 240, 241, 243(24), 244(24), 245, 246, *247*, *248*, 250, 252, 259, *261*, *268*, 294, *304*
Einstein, A., 263, *268*
Engstron, R. W., 193(3), *212*
Ertl, G., 229, 233, *234*

F

Foerster, T., 238(8), *247*
Fry, T. C., 193(2), *212*

G

Gerischer, H., 229, 233, *234*

SUBJECT INDEX

A

Association. *See also* Dissociation-association
connected to two (or more) steps, 187–188
followed by monomolecular interconversion
  extended kinetics of, 109
  kinetics of, 36
  statics of, 81
  thermodynamics of, 140
from two sides
  extended kinetics of, 122
  kinetics of, 38
  statics of, 84
preceded by dimerization, 46
preceded by monomolecular interconversion
  extended kinetics of, 112
  kinetics of, 37
  statics of, 83
  thermodynamics of, 146
to monomer followed by dimerization, 48
toward two sides
  extended kinetics of, 122
  kinetics of, 39
Association step
with catalytic regeneration step, 51
connected to four-component step
  extended kinetics of, 122
  kinetics of, 40

B

Band width
  electronic, 199
  spectral, 198
Bi-cyclic system, with eight components, 172, 175

Brewster's law, 208–211
Buffering
and chemical relaxation (one step), 107–109
in complex systems, 166
definition of, 89

C

Catalyst
in four-component steps, 51, 53
interconversion between two forms connected to four-component step, 51
Cathode radiant sensitivity, 193
Cavitations, in rapid-flow experiments, 287, 290
Chemical relaxation
deduction from classical kinetics, 13–16
deduction from condition of small perturbations, 16–20
Classical kinetics, 5 ff.
  See also under individual systems
Competition methods, 1
Computer techniques, 3
for evaluation of relaxation curves, 18
Concentration-jump method, 269 ff.
Conical lenses, 215
Consecutive associations
  extended kinetics of, 119
  kinetics of, 39
  statics of, 90
Consecutive dissociations
  extended kinetics of, 119
  kinetics of, 39
  statics of, 90
Consecutive relaxation processes, 20
Constant-flow methods, 282 ff.
Coupled four-component steps, kinetics of, 42

311